All 5¢ o/w

D1488685

THIS IS

CHICAGO

Other Books by Albert Halper:

Union Square
The Foundry
The Chute
Sons of the Fathers
The Little People
On the Shore
Only an Inch from Glory

THIS IS
CHICAGO

An Anthology

EDITED BY

ALBERT HALPER

New York
Henry Holt and Company

FOREWORD

CHICAGO has never been, nor tried to be, a city like New York, London, or Paris. It has always been, loudly and vociferously, itself. Though it strikes out at the one-day or one-hour visitor bluntly, like a huge fist, it possesses a subtle inner complexity that almost always escapes even the most discerning out-of-town eye.

Its façade of jukeboxes, beer joints, and prancing, smiling women who parade on runways practicing the fine arts of syncopated bumps and grinds for conventioneers, coalesces into a gigantic paper billboard behind which the real city—Chicago—breathes and lives. Past the windswept glitter of Michigan Avenue, beyond slanting shadows thrown by the tall spires of the downtown section known as the Loop, four million people whose tragedies and comedies are bound up with this puzzling giant of the plains, work, sprinkle their lawns on summer dusks, bury their loved ones, worry over the price of meat, and adjust their television sets for laughs.

Because it is situated, geographically, at the crossroads of America, Chicago has played host to millions of transcontinental travelers, mostly for an hour or a night. Shunted past teeming, industrial smoke-stacked jungles, through slums of great magnitude, and along a shoreline of startling gray beauty, passengers stop over only long enough to board fresh planes or trains—then they're gone with the wind. The great metropolis of the prairie soon dwindles behind them.

Yet here and there, among the wan faces at the windows of the transports, one sees questioning looks, eyes that stare out at the city hungrily. "What kind of a place is this?" the glances ask. "What is this town—?"

It is the contention of this writer that most Chicago copy, written by non-Chicago writers, forms a woeful body of journalistic literature. I do not mean to say that one has to be born here in order to tell about this city. But one has to linger a while, to be open-eyed, open-hearted. In recent times, when Eastern editors have been starved for copy, they have sent knowing, clever people to the Windy City with the admonition, "Get the Chicago story," and the lads have come and gone, with flimsy essays to show for their junkets here.

Some of these visiting fire-eaters, sad to say, have been news-gatherers of dubious sincerity, cataloguing the city's off-color spots—as if other communities of the nation did not possess comparable shadings on their maps. Slapping their findings between book covers, they have labeled their warmed-over indexes as "confidential." Other out-of-town journalists have come to sit heavy and owlish in Chicago homes, smiling politely, accepting hospitality, and fronting with make-believe joviality, only to return to the editorial desks of Manhattan with copy that had already been "slanted" before their authors had dropped off the planes.

One feels these visiting reporters always carry their encrusted opinions with them, like patients traveling with hardened arteries. They have never probed Chicago's interior, never walked the grasses of Chicago's parks, never gone into the outlying homes, groceries, and playgrounds of Chicago's neighborhoods, never stood on street corners watching workers stream from the factories at dusk, never mingled with the youthful crowds jamming the great ballrooms, never sat in the big, air-conditioned bowling alleys listening to the crack of the pins as teams of men and girls, wearing sweaters with the names of their leagues stitched to their backs, send the heavy balls rolling along the smooth, smooth floors.

Sticking to their Loop hotels, or making the customary rounds of the city's newspaper morgues for dead "facts," the writers were never drawn to stand on the lake point at Fifty-fifth Street to watch the long ore-boats passing far out on the horizon, never walked up Plymouth Court listening to the symphony of giant printing presses inside the flanking buildings, never went out to Pullman to stare at the red glow of the mills against the prairie sky, never thought it worth while to walk along the lake north of the Drake where long gray rollers crash in spray upon the city as if in a dream.

No, these journalists never had the time, it seemed. In all their writings one never comes across descriptions of the city's haunting autumns, of its springs, or of a winter scene in Garfield or Humboldt Park, where, on a Sunday afternoon, thousands of skaters can be seen circling or mingling on the ice; one fails to read in their articles anything about the youth, or the scholarship, of the city, or about any municipal virtue the city may possess. Chicago is a city of crime, a desert. . . . True. It is as crime-ridden, as Sahara-like, as any other great American city. It admits it. Its inhabitants are the first to admit it. But no city can function if all its citizens traffic in crime. No metropolis can exist whose foundations are sunk in sand.

Ironically, while these Manhattan fact-finders were busy staying away from the interior of the city and, instead, were visiting night-spots and talking to bartenders, chambermaids, ward-heelers and police captains, a certain five-star New York public official was easing himself below the Mexican border, the Brooklyn waterfront was erupting with the worst large-scale hood violence in years, the financial machinery of big-time gambler Harry Gross was tangling the upper echelons of Manhattan's constabulary in its gears, and the "unsolved" case of Reles, who "jumped" from Coney Island's Half-Moon Hotel over ten years ago, was bobbing up in the press again, causing many of the city's highly placed functionaries to suddenly resign "because of illness." Even in its heyday, Chicago's big shots did not possess a Murder Incorporated, though they tried valiantly to erect an apparatus comparable in scope.

All this is a roundabout way of saying that Chicago does not own, exclusively, the corner sidewalk upon which American metropolitan crime rests its feet. It is always willing to share space, and honors. It still possesses a modicum of its old frontier spirit. "Help yourself to some of the same, pardners."

The thing that strikes visitors hardest is, I think, the almost abnormal braggadocio of the natives. It rivals that of Texans. Everything in Chicago is the biggest, the Chicagoans boast—the stockyards, the railroad terminals, the Merchandise Mart (the world's largest commercial building), the boulevard system, the hotels, the ballrooms, the mail-order houses, the farm machinery factories, and, yes, the town's gangland wars and political corruptions. This is no halfway town, they declare. And all this is true, true.

Yet behind this strident horn-blowing often lurk a feeling of deep inadequacy, a sensitivity to fine things, an aching for the sun. This confused, collective yearning is about the best thing in Chicago, when you get to recognize it, to feel it.

Chicago is not only a city, it is a city of cities—made up of great foreign blocs of population, impinging on one another. The Polish settlement here, next to Warsaw, is the largest Polish city in the world. There is also a sizable German city, and a big Czech city, and an Italian town, and a Jewish city, and a Scandinavian borough that stretches for miles, and an Irish town. And out of this sprawling mass of neighborhoods has come a literature that does not have to play second fiddle to any body of literature in the land.

The "Chicago School" of writers has gripped the public mind since 1900, and some of its names are major ones—Dreiser, Sherwood Anderson, Sandburg, Masters, Hecht, Richard Wright, Meyer Levin, James T. Farrell, Willard Motley, Algren—the list stretches on. And Ring Lardner, Hemingway, Willa Cather, Ferber, Frank Norris, and others, who sojourned here, did not escape the city's impact.

It's not a bad town for writers. It was never a bad town for writers. At this moment there must be a new young crop of them, totally unknown, writing painfully in family parlors and bedrooms on the North, South and West sides. It was always a good place for a writer to be born in, or to grow up in. And after a Chicago writer reaches adulthood it doesn't matter where he lives, in New York, Paris, or Rome. The silver cord is never cut, he never really gets away.

In offering this anthology to the public, the editor does not claim it to be a definitive one. No one can compile a definitive anthology on anything. But he does feel that the work of the authors gathered together between the covers of this volume—Chicagoans and non-Chicagoans alike—succeeds in painting an honest, sensitive, and extremely "viewable" portrait of a huge city that has always been exciting and newsworthy nationally and internationally.

In compiling this book, its editor came to feel, soon after he had begun to track down and sort out the pieces, that he was working with material that dealt not only with Chicago's past and present but also the past and present of the country as a whole. Chicago was indeed America—only more so.

To bolster this point of view, one had only to cast a cursory glance backward at the city's history. In its infancy, scholars tell us, Chicago was like most American frontier towns, only wilder, rawer. Its real estate booms were bigger, its collapses were greater; at times the values of its business property bounded upward so startlingly as to make the eyes of out-of-town realtors pop. On the other hand, the debacle of the Insull Empire, together with its three hundred holding companies which controlled one per cent of the nation's wealth, was of such depth as to shake the financial foundations of public utility companies throughout North America.

People remember that when the depression existed in the thirties, this city was the most depressed city in the nation. Schoolteachers were not paid for years. Banks closed and stayed closed; primitive currency exchanges opened up to keep the financial gears grinding.

Yet when the upsurge came in 1940 Chicago became the boomiest town on earth, its factories working around the clock, the red fires from the South Side steel mills lighting up the sky.

When culture hit this town in the 1920's, it hit like a tornado; Mencken called Chicago the literary capital of the continent. And when a new kind of excitement was called for, scientists, squatting under the gridiron stands of Stagg Field on the South Side, touched off the world's first controlled atomic chain reaction and launched the age of atomic jitters.

The list could be extended. Yes, everything seems to be in sharper relief here, good things and bad. It's a town that never wears a mask; it lives forthrightly, take it or leave it. Even its political corruption, one of its aldermen recently bragged, is more honest than that of most cities.

This forthrightness, this inner honesty, seems to be the hallmark of its indigenous writers. These attributes do not make for fine stylistic cachets. A finely mannered Chicago writer is almost unthinkable. Yet the individual styles of the Chicago writers whose pieces are included in this volume are as carefully wrought, as evocative, as those of any group of American artists today.

I have arranged the pieces in this volume in a way that I thought would make for good readability, for a wide audience. It was my plan to group the contents in a manner that would impart a change of pace to the eye, a welcome shift from mood to mood.

It is my contention that a good anthology should be entertaining, in the best sense of the word. It should be entertaining in the same way that a good novel should be thrilling to read. No one wants to nod over a book. That is a chore for dull radio broadcasts, poor television programs, and grade-B movies to perform.

I have had to omit various pieces I had hoped to include. The space was limited, or else there were copyright difficulties.

I have prefaced each contribution with a note, informative or biographical, which I hope the reader will not feel is a persuasive device. Its intent and function were merely meant to be that of a helpful prop or light, to set the stage for the next offering and author.

Albert Halper

CONTENTS

Contents

THIS IS

CHICAGO

THE GAY OLD DOG*

Edna Ferber

HERE is a story about a not uncommon figure in American life, a "mom's boy" (or "sisters' boy"), that tears at your heart. It is full of warm touches, deep insight, and drama. It is written by a writer who is the author of many best sellers, one of them, *So Big,* a Pulitzer Prize winner. Because novels are the big literary guns in the trade, Miss Ferber's reputation rests upon her full-length books. But it is my opinion that her early short stories, which are really entire novels crammed into five thousand words, comprise her best work. I submit as evidence, *One Basket,* her collection of stories.

Miss Ferber writes: "I've written a lot about Chicago, really. *So Big, The Girls,* about one third of *Show Boat;* many short stories. I'm practically never thought of as having written anything about Chicago. Strange." Strange indeed.

Miss Ferber was born in a Wisconsin town. She lived, worked and wrote in Chicago during the early part of her literary career.

THOSE of you who have dwelt—or even lingered—in Chicago, Illinois, are familiar with the region known as the Loop. For those others of you to whom Chicago is a transfer point between New York and California there is presented this brief explanation:

The Loop is a clamorous, smoke-infested district embraced by the iron arms of the elevated tracks. In a city boasting fewer millions, it would be known familiarly as downtown. From Congress to Lake Street, from Wabash almost to the river, those thunderous tracks make a complete circle, or loop. Within it lie the retail

* From *One Basket,* by Edna Ferber, Simon & Schuster, 1947. Reprinted with the permission of Edna Ferber.

shops, the commercial hotels, the theaters, the restaurants. It is the Fifth Avenue and the Broadway of Chicago. And he who frequents it by night in search of amusement and cheer is known, vulgarly, as a Loop-hound.

Jo Hertz was a Loop-hound. On the occasion of those sparse first nights granted the metropolis of the Middle West he was always present, third row, aisle, left. When a new Loop café was opened, Jo's table always commanded an unobstructed view of anything worth viewing. On entering he was wont to say, "Hello, Gus," with careless cordiality to the headwaiter, the while his eye roved expertly from table to table as he removed his gloves. He ordered things under glass, so that his table, at midnight or thereabouts, resembled a hotbed that favors the bell system. The waiters fought for him. He was the kind of man who mixes his own salad dressing. He liked to call for a bowl, some cracked ice, lemon, garlic, paprika, salt, pepper, vinegar, and oil and make a rite of it. People at nearby tables would lay down their knives and forks to watch, fascinated. The secret of it seemed to lie in using all the oil in sight and calling for more.

That was Jo—a plump and lonely bachelor of fifty. A plethoric, roving-eyed, and kindly man, clutching vainly at the garments of a youth that had long slipped past him. Jo Hertz, in one of those pinch-waist suits and a belted coat and a little green hat, walking up Michigan Avenue of a bright winter's afternoon, trying to take the curb with a jaunty youthfulness against which every one of his fat-encased muscles rebelled, was a sight for mirth or pity, depending on one's vision.

The gay-dog business was a late phase in the life of Jo Hertz. He had been a quite different sort of canine. The staid and harassed brother of three unwed and selfish sisters is an underdog.

At twenty-seven Jo had been the dutiful, hard-working son (in the wholesale harness business) of a widowed and gummidging mother, who called him Joey. Now and then a double wrinkle would appear between Jo's eyes—a wrinkle that had no business there at twenty-seven. Then Jo's mother died, leaving him handicapped by a deathbed promise, the three sisters, and a three-story-and-basement house on Calumet Avenue. Jo's wrinkle became a fixture.

"Joey," his mother had said, in her high, thin voice, "take care of the girls."

"I will, Ma," Jo had choked.

"Joey," and the voice was weaker, "promise me you won't marry till the girls are all provided for." Then as Jo had hesitated, appalled: "Joey, it's my dying wish. Promise!"

"I promise, Ma," he had said.

Whereupon his mother had died, comfortably, leaving him with a completely ruined life.

They were not bad-looking girls, and they had a certain style, too. That is, Stell and Eva had. Carrie, the middle one, taught school over on the West Side. In those days it took her almost two hours each way. She said the kind of costume she required should have been corrugated steel. But all three knew what was being worn, and they wore it—or fairly faithful copies of it. Eva, the housekeeping sister, had a needle knack. She could skim the State Street windows and come away with a mental photograph of every separate tuck, hem, yoke, and ribbon. Heads of departments showed her the things they kept in drawers, and she went home and reproduced them with the aid of a seamstress by the day. Stell, the youngest, was the beauty. They called her Babe.

Twenty-three years ago one's sisters did not strain at the household leash, nor crave a career. Carrie taught school, and hated it. Eva kept house expertly and complainingly. Babe's profession was being the family beauty, and it took all her spare time. Eva always let her sleep until ten.

This was Jo's household, and he was the nominal head of it. But it was an empty title. The three women dominated his life. They weren't consciously selfish. If you had called them cruel they would have put you down as mad. When you are the lone brother of three sisters, it means that you must constantly be calling for, escorting, or dropping one of them somewhere. Most men of Jo's age were standing before their mirror of a Saturday night, whistling blithely and abstractedly while they discarded a blue polka-dot for a maroon tie, whipped off the maroon for a shot-silk, and at the last moment decided against the shot-silk in favor of a plain black-and-white because she had once said she preferred quiet ties. Jo,

when he should have been preening his feathers for conquest, was
saying:

"Well, my God, I *am* hurrying! Give a man time, can't you? I
just got home. You girls been laying around the house all day. No
wonder you're ready."

He took a certain pride in seeing his sisters well dressed, at a
time when he should have been reveling in fancy waistcoats and
brilliant-hued socks, according to the style of that day and the inalienable right of any unwed male under thirty, in any day. On
those rare occasions when his business necessitated an out-of-town
trip, he would spend half a day floundering about the shops selecting handkerchiefs, or stockings, or feathers, or gloves for the girls.
They always turned out to be the wrong kind, judging by their
reception.

From Carrie, "What in the world do I want of long white
gloves!"

"I thought you didn't have any," Jo would say.

"I haven't. I never wear evening clothes."

Jo would pass a futile hand over the top of his head, as was
his way when disturbed. "I just thought you'd like them. I thought
every girl liked long white gloves. Just," feebly, "just to—to have."

"Oh, for pity's sake!"

And from Eva or Babe, "I've *got* silk stockings, Jo." Or, "You
brought me handkerchiefs the last time."

There was something selfish in his giving, as there always is in
any gift freely and joyfully made. They never suspected the exquisite pleasure it gave him to select these things, these fine, soft,
silken things. There were many things about this slow-going, amia-
ble brother of theirs that they never suspected. If you had told
them he was a dreamer of dreams, for example, they would have
been amused. Sometimes, dead-tired by nine o'clock after a hard
day downtown, he would doze over the evening paper. At intervals
he would wake, red-eyed, to a snatch of conversation such
as, "Yes, but if you get a blue you can wear it anywhere. It's
dressy, and at the same time it's quiet, too." Eva, the expert, wrestling with Carrie over the problem of the new spring dress. They
never guessed that the commonplace man in the frayed old smok-

ing jacket had banished them all from the room long ago; had banished himself, for that matter. In his place was a tall, debonair, and rather dangerously handsome man to whom six o'clock spelled evening clothes. The kind of man who can lean up against a mantel, or propose a toast, or give an order to a manservant, or whisper a gallant speech in a lady's ear with equal ease. The shabby old house on Calumet Avenue was transformed into a brocaded and chandeliered rendezvous for the brilliance of the city. Beauty was here, and wit. But none so beautiful and witty as She. Mrs.—er—Jo Hertz. There was wine, of course; but no vulgar display. There was music; the soft sheen of satin; laughter. And he, the gracious, tactful host, king of his own domain——

"Jo, for heaven's sake, if you're going to snore, go to bed!"

"Why—did I fall asleep?"

"You haven't been doing anything else all evening. A person would think you were fifty instead of thirty."

And Jo Hertz was again just the dull, gray, commonplace brother of three well-meaning sisters.

Babe used to say petulantly, "Jo, why don't you ever bring home any of your men friends? A girl might as well not have any brother, all the good you do."

Jo, conscience-stricken, did his best to make amends. But a man who has been petticoat-ridden for years loses the knack, somehow, of comradeship with men.

One Sunday in May Jo came home from a late-Sunday-afternoon walk to find company for supper. Carrie often had in one of her schoolteacher friends, or Babe one of her frivolous intimates, or even Eva a staid guest of the old-girl type. There was always a Sunday-night supper of potato salad, and cold meat, and coffee, and perhaps a fresh cake. Jo rather enjoyed it, being a hospitable soul. But he regarded the guests with the undazzled eyes of a man to whom they were just so many petticoats, timid of the night streets and requiring escort home. If you had suggested to him that some of his sisters' popularity was due to his own presence, or if you had hinted that the more kittenish of these visitors were probably making eyes at him, he would have stared in amazement and unbelief.

This Sunday night it turned out to be one of Carrie's friends.
"Emily," said Carrie, "this is my brother, Jo."

Jo had learned what to expect in Carrie's friends. Drab-looking
women in the late thirties, whose facial lines all slanted downward.

"Happy to meet you," said Jo, and looked down at a different
sort altogether. A most surprisingly different sort, for one of
Carrie's friends. This Emily person was very small, and fluffy, and
blue-eyed, and crinkly looking. The corners of her mouth when she
smiled, and her eyes when she looked up at you, and her hair,
which was brown, but had the miraculous effect, somehow, of looking golden.

Jo shook hands with her. Her hand was incredibly small, and
soft, so that you were afraid of crushing it, until you discovered she
had a firm little grip all her own. It surprised and amused you, that
grip, as does a baby's unexpected clutch on your patronizing forefinger. As Jo felt it in his own big clasp, the strangest thing happened
to him. Something inside Jo Hertz stopped working for a moment,
then lurched sickeningly, then thumped like mad. It was his heart.
He stood staring down at her, and she up at him, until the others
laughed. Then their hands fell apart, lingeringly.

"Are you a schoolteacher, Emily?" he said.

"Kindergarten. It's my first year. And don't call me Emily,
please."

"Why not? It's your name. I think it's the prettiest name in the
world." Which he hadn't meant to say at all. In fact, he was
perfectly aghast to find himself saying it. But he meant it.

At supper he passed her things, and stared, until everybody
laughed again, and Eva said acidly, "Why don't you feed her?"

It wasn't that Emily had an air of helplessness. She just made him
feel he wanted her to be helpless, so that he could help her.

Jo took her home, and from that Sunday night he began to strain
at the leash. He took his sisters out, dutifully, but he would suggest,
with a carelessness that deceived no one, "Don't you want one
of your girl friends to come along? That little What's-her-name—
Emily, or something. So long's I've got three of you, I might as
well have a full squad."

For a long time he didn't know what was the matter with

him. He only knew he was miserable, and yet happy. Sometimes his heart seemed to ache with an actual physical ache. He realized that he wanted to do things for Emily. He wanted to buy things for Emily—useless, pretty, expensive things that he couldn't afford. He wanted to buy everything that Emily needed, and everything that Emily desired. He wanted to marry Emily. That was it. He discovered that one day, with a shock, in the midst of a transaction in the harness business. He stared at the man with whom he was dealing until that startled person grew uncomfortable.

"What's the matter, Hertz?"

"Matter?"

"You look as if you'd seen a ghost or found a gold mine. I don't know which."

"Gold mine," said Jo. And then, "No. Ghost."

For he remembered that high, thin voice, and his promise. And the harness business was slithering downhill with dreadful rapidity, as the automobile business began its amazing climb. Jo tried to stop it. But he was not that kind of businessman. It never occurred to him to jump out of the down-going vehicle and catch the up-going one. He stayed on, vainly applying brakes that refused to work.

"You know, Emily, I couldn't support two households now. Not the way things are. But if you'll wait. If you'll only wait. The girls might—that is, Babe and Carrie——"

She was a sensible little thing, Emily. "Of course I'll wait. But we mustn't just sit back and let the years go by. We've got to help."

She went about it as if she were already a little matchmaking matron. She corralled all the men she had ever known and introduced them to Babe, Carrie, and Eva separately, in pairs, and en masse. She got up picnics. She stayed home while Jo took the three about. When she was present she tried to look as plain and obscure as possible, so that the sisters should show up to advantage. She schemed, and planned, and contrived, and hoped; and smiled into Jo's despairing eyes.

And three years went by. Three precious years. Carrie still taught school, and hated it. Eva kept house more and more complainingly

as prices advanced and allowance retreated. Stell was still Babe,
the family beauty. Emily's hair, somehow, lost its glint and began
to look just plain brown. Her crinkliness began to iron out.

"Now, look here!" Jo argued, desperately, one night. "We could
be happy, anyway. There's plenty of room at the house. Lots of
people begin that way. Of course, I couldn't give you all I'd like
to, at first. But maybe, after a while——"

No dreams of salons, and brocade, and velvet-footed servitors,
and satin damask now. Just two rooms, all their own, all alone,
and Emily to work for. That was his dream. But it seemed less
possible than that other absurd one had been.

Emily was as practical a little thing as she looked fluffy. She
knew women. Especially did she know Eva, and Carrie, and Babe.
She tried to imagine herself taking the household affairs and the
housekeeping pocketbook out of Eva's expert hands. So then she
tried to picture herself allowing the reins of Jo's house to remain
in Eva's hands. And everything feminine and normal in her rebelled. Emily knew she'd want to put away her own freshly laun-
dered linen, and smooth it, and pat it. She was that kind
of woman. She knew she'd want to do her own delightful haggling
with butcher and grocer. She knew she'd want to muss Jo's hair,
and sit on his knee, and even quarrel with him, if necessary, without the awareness of three ever-present pairs of maiden eyes and
ears.

"No! No! We'd only be miserable. I know. Even if they didn't
object. And they would, Jo. Wouldn't they?"

His silence was miserable assent. Then, "But you do love me,
don't you, Emily?"

"I do, Jo. I love you—and love you—and love you. But, Jo,
I—can't."

"I know it, dear. I knew it all the time, really. I just thought,
maybe, somehow——"

The two sat staring for a moment into space, their hands clasped.
Then they both shut their eyes with a little shudder, as though
what they saw was terrible to look upon. Emily's hand, the tiny
hand that was so unexpectedly firm, tightened its hold on his,

and his crushed the absurd fingers until she winced with pain. That was the beginning of the end, and they knew it.

Emily wasn't the kind of girl who would be left to pine. There are too many Jos in the world whose hearts are prone to lurch and then thump at the feel of a soft, fluttering, incredibly small hand in their grip. One year later Emily was married to a young man whose father owned a large, pie-shaped slice of the prosperous state of Michigan.

That being safely accomplished, there was something grimly humorous in the trend taken by affairs in the old house on Calumet. For Eva married. Married well, too, though he was a great deal older than she. She went off in a hat she had copied from a French model at Field's, and a suit she had contrived with a home dressmaker, aided by pressing on the part of the little tailor in the basement over on Thirty-first Street. It was the last of that, though. The next time they saw her, she had on a hat that even she would have despaired of copying, and a suit that sort of melted into your gaze. She moved to the North Side (trust Eva for that), and Babe assumed the management of the household on Calumet Avenue. It was rather a pinched little household now, for the harness business shrank and shrank.

"I don't see how you can expect me to keep house decently on this!" Babe would say contemptuously. Babe's nose, always a little inclined to sharpness, had whittled down to a point of late. "If you knew what Ben gives Eva."

"It's the best I can do, Sis. Business is something rotten."

"Ben says if you had the least bit of——" Ben was Eva's husband, and quotable, as are all successful men.

"I don't care what Ben says," shouted Jo, goaded into rage. "I'm sick of your everlasting Ben. Go and get a Ben of your own, why don't you, if you're so stuck on the way he does things."

And Babe did. She made a last desperate drive, aided by Eva, and she captured a rather surprised young man in the brokerage way, who had made up his mind not to marry for years and years. Eva wanted to give her her wedding things, but at that Jo broke into sudden rebellion.

"No, sir! No Ben is going to buy my sister's wedding clothes, understand? I guess I'm not broke—yet. I'll furnish the money for her things, and there'll be enough of them, too."

Babe had as useless a trousseau, and as filled with extravagant pink-and-blue and lacy and frilly things, as any daughter of doting parents. Jo seemed to find a grim pleasure in providing them. But it left him pretty well pinched. After Babe's marriage (she insisted that they call her Estelle now) Jo sold the house on Calumet. He and Carrie took one of those little flats that were springing up, seemingly overnight, all through Chicago's South Side.

There was nothing domestic about Carrie. She had given up teaching two years before, and had gone into social-service work on the West Side. She had what is known as a legal mind—hard, clear, orderly—and she made a great success of it. Her dream was to live at the Settlement House and give all her time to the work. Upon the little household she bestowed a certain amount of grim, capable attention. It was the same kind of attention she would have given a piece of machinery whose oiling and running had been entrusted to her care. She hated it, and didn't hesitate to say so.

Jo took to prowling about department-store basements, and household-goods sections. He was always sending home a bargain in a ham, or a sack of potatoes, or fifty pounds of sugar, or a window clamp, or a new kind of paring knife. He was forever doing odd jobs that the janitor should have done. It was the domestic in him claiming its own.

Then, one night, Carrie came home with a dull glow in her leathery cheeks, and her eyes alight with resolve. They had what she called a plain talk.

"Listen, Jo. They've offered me the job of first assistant resident worker. And I'm going to take it. Take it! I know fifty other girls who'd give their ears for it. I go in next month."

They were at dinner. Jo looked up from his plate, dully. Then he glanced around the little dining room, with its ugly tan walls and its heavy, dark furniture (the Calumet Avenue pieces fitted cumbersomely into the five-room flat).

"Away? Away from here, you mean—to live?"

Carrie laid down her fork. "Well, really, Jo! After all that explanation."

"But to go over there to live! Why, that neighborhood's full of dirt, and disease, and crime, and the Lord knows what all. I can't let you do that, Carrie."

Carrie's chin came up. She laughed a short little laugh. "Let me! That's eighteenth-century talk, Jo. My life's my own to live. I'm going."

And she went.

Jo stayed on in the apartment until the lease was up. Then he sold what furniture he could, stored or gave away the rest, and took a room on Michigan Avenue in one of the old stone mansions whose decayed splendor was being put to such purpose.

Jo Hertz was his own master. Free to marry. Free to come and go. And he found he didn't even think of marrying. He didn't even want to come or go, particularly. A rather frumpy old bachelor, with thinning hair and a thickening neck.

Every Thursday evening he took dinner at Eva's, and on Sunday noon at Stell's. He tucked his napkin under his chin and openly enjoyed the homemade soup and the well-cooked meats. After dinner he tried to talk business with Eva's husband, or Stell's. His business talks were the old-fashioned kind, beginning:

"Well, now, looka here. Take, f'rinstance, your raw hides and leathers."

But Ben and George didn't want to take, f'rinstance, your raw hides and leathers. They wanted, when they took anything at all, to take golf, or politics, or stocks. They were the modern type of businessman who prefers to leave his work out of his play. Business, with them, was a profession—a finely graded and balanced thing, differing from Jo's clumsy, downhill style as completely as does the method of a great criminal detective differ from that of a village constable. They would listen, restively, and say, "Uh-uh," at intervals, and at the first chance they would sort of fade out of the room, with a meaning glance at their wives. Eva had two children now. Girls. They treated Uncle Jo with good-natured tolerance. Stell had no children. Uncle Jo degenerated, by almost imperceptible degrees, from the position of honored guest, who is served with white meat, to that of one who is content with a leg and one of those obscure and bony sections which, after much turning with a bewildered and investigating knife and fork, leave one baffled and unsatisfied.

Eva and Stell got together and decided that Jo ought to marry. "It isn't natural," Eva told him. "I never saw a man who took so little interest in women."

"Me!" protested Jo, almost shyly. "Women!"

"Yes. Of course. You act like a frightened schoolboy."

So they had in for dinner certain friends and acquaintances of fitting age. They spoke of them as "splendid girls." Between thirty-six and forty. They talked awfully well, in a firm, clear way, about civics, and classes, and politics, and economics, and boards. They rather terrified Jo. He didn't understand much that they talked about, and he felt humbly inferior, and yet a little resentful, as if something had passed him by. He escorted them home, dutifully, though they told him not to bother, and they evidently meant it. They seemed capable not only of going home quite unattended but of delivering a pointed lecture to any highwayman or brawler who might molest them.

The following Thursday Eva would say, "How did you like her, Jo?"

"Like who?" Jo would spar feebly.

"Miss Matthews."

"Who's she?"

"Now, don't be funny, Jo. You know very well I mean the girl who was here for dinner. The one who talked so well on the emigration question."

"Oh, her! Why, I liked her all right. Seems to be a smart woman."

"Smart! She's a perfectly splendid girl."

"Sure," Jo would agree cheerfully.

"But didn't you like her?"

"I can't say I did, Eve. And I can't say I didn't. She made me think a lot of a teacher I had in the fifth reader. Name of Himes. As I recall her, she must have been a fine woman. But I never thought of Himes as a woman at all. She was just Teacher."

said it spoiled her evening. And the third time it was Ethel. S
was one of the guests at a theater party given by Nicky Ov
ton II. The North Shore Overtons. Lake Forest. They came in la
and occupied the entire third row at the opening performance
Believe Me! And Ethel was Nicky's partner. She was glowing like
ros. When the lights went up after the first act Ethel saw that h
Unle Jo was seated just ahead of her with what she afterward de
scred as a blonde. Then her uncle had turned around, and seein
he had been surprised into a smile that spread genially all ove
hi ump and rubicund face. Then he had turned to face forward
a quickly.

ho's the old bird?" Nicky had asked. Ethel had pretended not
t, so he had asked again.

uncle," Ethel answered, and flushed all over her delicate
d down to her throat. Nicky had looked at the blonde, and
rows had gone up ever so slightly.

iled Ethel's evening. More than that, as she told her
f it later, weeping, she declared it had spoiled her life.
lked it over with her husband in that intimate hour that
bedtime. She gesticulated heatedly with her hairbrush.
sgusting, that's what it is. Perfectly disgusting. There's no
n old fool. Imagine! A creature like that. At his time of

don't know," Ben said, and even grinned a little. "I
oy's got to sow his wild oats sometime."
e any more vulgar than you can help," Eva retorted.
nk you know, as well as I, what it means to have
n boy interested in Ethel."
terested in her," Ben blundered, "I guess the fact that
went to the theater with someone who isn't Ethel's
ause a shudder to run up and down his frail young
"

Eva had retorted. "If you're not man enough to stop
that's all. I'm going up there with Stell this week."
t notify Jo of their coming. Eva telephoned his apart-
e knew he would be out, and asked his man if he
aster home to dinner that evening. The man had

"You make me tired," snapped Eva impatiently. "A man of
your age. You don't expect to marry a girl, do you? A child!"

"I don't expect to marry anybody," Jo had answered.

And that was the truth, lonely though he often was.

The following spring Eva moved to Winnetka. Anyone who got
the meaning of the Loop knows the significance of a move to a
North Shore suburb, and a house. Eva's daughter, Ethel, was growing up, and her mother had an eye on society.

That did away with Jo's Thursday dinners. Then Stell's husband
bought a car. They went out into the country every Sunday. Stell
said it was getting so that maids objected to Sunday dinners, anyway. Besides, they were unhealthful, old-fashioned things. They always meant to ask Jo to come along, but by the time their friends
were placed, and the lunch, and the boxes, and sweaters, and
George's camera, and everything, there seemed to be no room for a
man of Jo's bulk. So that eliminated the Sunday dinners.

"Just drop in any time during the week," Stell said, "for dinner.
Except Wednesday—that's our bridge night—and Saturday. And,
of course, Thursday. Cook is out that night. Don't wait for me to
phone."

And so Jo drifted into that sad-eyed, dyspeptic family made up
of those you see dining in second-rate restaurants, their paper
propped up against the bowl of oyster crackers, munching solemnly
and with indifference to the stare of the passer-by surveying them
through the brazen plate-glass window.

And then came the war. The war that spelled death and destruction to millions. The war that brought a fortune to Jo Hertz, and
transformed him, overnight, from a baggy-kneed old bachelor whose
business was a failure to a prosperous manufacturer whose only
trouble was the shortage in hides for the making of his product.
Leather! The armies of Europe called for it. Harnesses! More harnesses! Straps! Millions of straps. More! More!

The musty old harness business over on Lake Street was magi-
cally changed from a dust-covered, dead-alive concern to an orderly hive that hummed and glittered with success. Orders poured
in. Jo Hertz had inside information on the war. He knew about
troops and horses. He talked with French and English and Italian

buyers commissioned by their countries to get American-made supplies. And now, when he said to Ben or George, "Take, f'rinstance, your raw hides and leathers," they listened with respectful attention.

And then began the gay-dog business in the life of Jo Hertz. He developed into a Loop-hound, ever keen on the scent of fresh pleasure. That side of Jo Hertz which had been repressed and crushed and ignored began to bloom, unhealthily. At first he spent money on his rather contemptuous nieces. He sent them gorgeous furs, and watch bracelets, and bags. He took two expensive rooms at a downtown hotel, and there was something more tear-compelling than grotesque about the way he gloated over the luxury of a separate ice-water tap in the bathroom. He explained it.

"Just turn it on. Any hour of the day or night. Ice water!"

He bought a car. Naturally. A glittering affair; in color a bright blue, with pale-blue leather straps and a great deal of gold fittings, and special tires. Eva said it was the kind of thing a chorus girl would use, rather than an elderly businessman. You saw him driving about in it, red-faced and rather awkward at the wheel. You saw him, too, in the Pompeian Room at the Congress Hotel of a Saturday afternoon when roving-eyed matrons in mink coats are wont to congregate to sip pale-amber drinks. Actors grew to recognize the semibald head and the shining, round, good-natured face looming out at them from the dim well of the theater, and sometimes, in a musical show, they directed a quip at him, and he liked it. He could pick out the critics as they came down the aisle, and even had a nodding acquaintance with two of them.

"Kelly, of the *Herald*," he would say carelessly. "Bean, of the *Trib*. They're all afraid of him."

So he frolicked, ponderously. In New York he might have been called a Man About Town.

And he was lonesome. He was very lonesome. So he searched about in his mind and brought from the dim past the memory of the luxuriously furnished establishment of which he used to dream in the evenings when he dozed over his paper in the old house on Calumet. So he rented an apartment, many-roomed and expensive, with a manservant in charge, and furnished it in styles and periods

ranging through all the Louis. The living room was
color. It was like an unhealthy and bloated boudoir. A
was nothing sybaritic or uncleanly in the sight of th
middle-aged man sinking into the rosy-cushioned luxur
ulous home. It was a frank and naïve indulgence of
senses, and there was in it a great resemblance to th
ecstasy of a schoolboy smacking his lips over an

The war went on, and on, and on. And the mon
roll in—a flood of it. Then, one afternoon, Eva, i
ping bent, entered a small, exclusive, and exp
Michigan Avenue. Eva's weakness was hats. She
now. She described what she sought with a langui
stood looking about her after the saleswoman ha
of it. The room was becomingly rose-illumined
so that some minutes had passed before she
seated on a raspberry brocade settee not five
with a walking stick, and yellow gloves, ar
check suit—was her brother Jo. From him E
leaped to the woman who was trying on h
many long mirrors. She was seated, and a sal
ing discreetly at her elbow.

Eva turned sharply and encountered h
turning, hat-laden. "Not today," she gasp
denly." And almost ran from the room.

That evening she told Stell, relating h
pidgin English devised by every family of
tion against the neighbors. Translated, it

"He looked straight at me. My dear
least he had sense enough not to sp
limp, willowy creatures with the gree
keep softened to a baby stare, and c
get her hands on those hats. I saw it
know the way I do. I suppose some
I don't. And her color. Well! And th
Not one of them under seventy-five
Suppose Ethel had been with me!"

The next time it was Stell who

said yes. Eva arranged to meet Stell in town. They would drive to Jo's apartment together, and wait for him there.

When she reached the city Eva found turmoil there. The first of the American troops to be sent to France were leaving. Michigan Boulevard was a billowing, surging mass: flags, pennants, banners, crowds. All the elements that make for demonstration. And over the whole—quiet. No holiday crowd, this. A solid, determined mass of people waiting patient hours to see the khaki-clads go by. Three years had brought them to a clear knowledge of what these boys were going to.

"Isn't it dreadful!" Stell gasped.

"Nicky Overton's too young, thank goodness."

Their car was caught in the jam. When they moved at all, it was by inches. When at last they reached Jo's apartment they were flushed, nervous, apprehensive. But he had not yet come in. So they waited.

No, they were not staying to dinner with their brother, they told the relieved houseman.

Stell and Eva, sunk in rose-colored cushions, viewed the place with disgust and some mirth. They rather avoided each other's eyes.

"Carrie ought to be here," Eva said. They both smiled at the thought of the austere Carrie in the midst of those rosy cushions, and hangings, and lamps. Stell rose and began to walk about restlessly. She picked up a vase and laid it down; straightened a picture. Eva got up, too, and wandered into the hall. She stood there a moment, listening. Then she turned and passed into Jo's bedroom, Stell following. And there you knew Jo for what he was.

This room was as bare as the other had been ornate. It was Jo, the clean-minded and simplehearted, in revolt against the cloying luxury with which he had surrounded himself. The bedroom, of all rooms in any house, reflects the personality of its occupant. True, the actual furniture was paneled, cupid-surmounted, and ridiculous. It had been the fruit of Jo's first orgy of the senses. But now it stood out in that stark little room with an air as incongruous and ashamed as that of a pink tarlatan danseuse who finds herself in a monk's cell. None of those wall pictures with which bachelor bedrooms are reputed to be hung. No satin slippers. No scented notes.

Two plain-backed military brushes on the chiffonier (and he so
nearly hairless!). A little orderly stack of books on the table near
the bed. Eva fingered their titles and gave a little gasp. One of
them was on gardening.

"Well, of all things!" exclaimed Stell. A book on the war, by an
Englishman. A detective story of the lurid type that lulls us
to sleep. His shoes ranged in a careful row in the closet, with a
shoe tree in every one of them. There was something speaking about them. They looked so human. Eva shut the door on
them quickly. Some bottles on the dresser. A jar of pomade. An
ointment such as a man uses who is growing bald and is panic-
stricken too late. An insurance calendar on the wall. Some rhubarb-
and-soda mixture on the shelf in the bathroom, and a little box of
pepsin tablets.

"Eats all kinds of things at all hours of the night," Eva said,
and wandered out into the rose-colored front room again with the
air of one who is chagrined at her failure to find what she has
sought. Stell followed her furtively.

"Where do you suppose he can be?" she demanded. "It's"—she
glanced at her wrist—"why, it's after six!"

And then there was a little click. The two women sat up, tense.
The door opened. Jo came in. He blinked a little. The two women
in the rosy room stood up.

"Why—Eve! Why, Babe! Well! Why didn't you let me know?"

"We were just about to leave. We thought you weren't coming
home."

Jo came in slowly.

"I was in the jam on Michigan, watching the boys go by." He
sat down, heavily. The light from the window fell on him. And
you saw that his eyes were red.

He had found himself one of the thousands in the jam on
Michigan Avenue, as he said. He had a place near the curb, where
his big frame shut off the view of the unfortunates behind him. He
waited with the placid interest of one who has subscribed to all
the funds and societies to which a prosperous, middle-aged businessman is called upon to subscribe in wartime. Then, just as he was
about to leave, impatient at the delay, the crowd had cried, with a

queer, dramatic, exultant note in its voice, "Here they come! Here come the boys!"

Just at that moment two little, futile, frenzied fists began to beat a mad tattoo on Jo Hertz's broad back. Jo tried to turn in the crowd, all indignant resentment. "Say, looka here!"

The little fists kept up their frantic beating and pushing. And a voice—a choked, high little voice—cried, "Let me by! I can't see! You *man,* you! You big fat man! My boy's going by—to war—and I can't see! Let me by!"

Jo scrooged around, still keeping his place. He looked down. And up-turned to him in agonized appeal was the face of Emily. They stared at each other for what seemed a long, long time. It was really only the fraction of a second. Then Jo put one great arm firmly around Emily's waist and swung her around in front of him. His great bulk protected her. Emily was clinging to his hand. She was breathing rapidly, as if she had been running. Her eyes were straining up the street.

"Why, Emily, how in the world——!"

"I ran away. Fred didn't want me to come. He said it would excite me too much."

"Fred?"

"My husband. He made me promise to say good-by to Jo at home."

"Jo?"

"Jo's my boy. And he's going to war. So I ran away. I had to see him. I had to see him go."

She was dry-eyed. Her gaze was straining up the street.

"Why, sure," said Jo. "Of course you want to see him." And then the crowd gave a great roar. There came over Jo a feeling of weakness. He was trembling. The boys went marching by.

"There he is," Emily shrilled, above the din. "There he is! There he is! There he——" And waved a futile little hand. It wasn't so much a wave as a clutching. A clutching after something beyond her reach.

"Which one? Which one, Emily?"

"The handsome one. The handsome one." Her voice quavered and died.

Jo put a steady hand on her shoulder. "Point him out," he commanded. "Show me." And the next instant, "Never mind. I see him."

Somehow, miraculously, he had picked him from among the hundreds. Had picked him as surely as his own father might have. It was Emily's boy. He was marching by, rather stiffly. He was nineteen, and fun-loving, and he had a girl, and he didn't particularly want to go to France and—to go to France. But more than he had hated going, he had hated not to go. So he marched by, looking straight ahead, his jaw set so that his chin stuck out just a little. Emily's boy.

Jo looked at him, and his face flushed purple. His eyes, the hard-boiled eyes of a Loop-hound, took on the look of a sad old man. And suddenly he was no longer Jo, the sport; old J. Hertz, the gay dog. He was Jo Hertz, thirty, in love with life, in love with Emily, and with the stinging blood of young manhood coursing through his veins.

Another minute and the boy had passed on up the broad street —the fine, flag-bedecked street—just one of a hundred service hats bobbing in rhythmic motion like sandy waves lapping a shore and flowing on.

Then he disappeared altogether.

Emily was clinging to Jo. She was mumbling something, over and over. "I can't. I can't. Don't ask me to. I can't let him go. Like that. I can't."

Jo said a queer thing.

"Why, Emily! We wouldn't have him stay home, would we? We wouldn't want him to do anything different, would we? Not our boy. I'm glad he enlisted. I'm proud of him. So are you glad."

Little by little he quieted her. He took her to the car that was waiting, a worried chauffeur in charge. They said good-by, awkwardly. Emily's face was a red, swollen mass.

So it was that when Jo entered his own hallway half an hour later he blinked, dazedly, and when the light from the window fell on him you saw that his eyes were red.

Eva was not one to beat about the bush. She sat forward in her chair, clutching her bag rather nervously.

"Now, look here, Jo. Stell and I are here for a reason. We're here to tell you that this thing's going to stop."

"Thing? Stop?"

"You know very well what I mean. You saw me at the milliner's that day. And night before last, Ethel. We're all disgusted. If you must go about with people like that, please have some sense of decency."

Something gathering in Jo's face should have warned her. But he was slumped down in his chair in such a huddle, and he looked so old and fat that she did not heed it. She went on. "You've got us to consider. Your sisters. And your nieces. Not to speak of your own——"

But he got to his feet then, shaking, and at what she saw in his face even Eva faltered and stopped. It wasn't at all the face of a fat, middle-aged sport. It was a face Jovian, terrible.

"You!" he began, low-voiced, ominous. "You!" He raised a great fist high. "You two murderers! You didn't consider me, twenty years ago. You come to me with talk like that. Where's my boy! You killed him, you two, twenty years ago. And now he belongs to somebody else. Where's my son that should have gone marching by today?" He flung his arms out in a great gesture of longing. The red veins stood out on his forehead. "Where's my son! Answer me that, you two selfish, miserable women. Where's my son!" Then, as they huddled together, frightened, wild-eyed. "Out of my house! Out of my house! Before I hurt you!"

They fled, terrified. The door banged behind them.

Jo stood, shaking, in the center of the room. Then he reached for a chair, gropingly, and sat down. He passed one moist, flabby hand over his forehead and it came away wet. The telephone rang. He sat still. It sounded far away and unimportant, like something forgotten. But it rang and rang insistently. Jo liked to answer his telephone when he was at home.

"Hello!" He knew instantly the voice at the other end.

"That you, Jo?" it said.

"Yes."

"How's my boy?"

"I'm—all right."

"Listen, Jo. The crowd's coming over tonight. I've fixed up a little poker game for you. Just eight of us."

"I can't come tonight, Gert."

"Can't! Why not?"

"I'm not feeling so good."

"You just said you were all right."

"I *am* all right. Just kind of tired."

The voice took on a cooing note. "Is my Joey tired? Then he shall be all comfy on the sofa, and he doesn't need to play if he don't want to. No, sir."

Jo stood staring at the black mouthpiece of the telephone. He was seeing a procession go marching by. Boys, hundreds of boys, in khaki.

"Hello! Hello!" The voice took on an anxious note. "Are you there?"

"Yes," wearily.

"Jo, there's something the matter. You're sick. I'm coming right over."

"No!"

"Why not? You sound as if you'd been sleeping. Look here——"

"Leave me alone!" cried Jo, suddenly, and the receiver clacked onto the hook. "Leave me alone. Leave me alone." Long after the connection had been broken.

He stood staring at the instrument with unseeing eyes. Then he turned and walked into the front room. All the light had gone out of it. Dusk had come on. All the light had gone out of everything. The zest had gone out of life. The game was over—the game he had been playing against loneliness and disappointment. And he was just a tired old man. A lonely, tired old man in a ridiculous rose-colored room that had grown, all of a sudden, drab.

HOW THE DEVIL CAME DOWN DIVISION STREET*

Nelson Algren

THERE are several large Polish settlements in Chicago, but the principal one is located along Chicago Avenue, Milwaukee Avenue, and Division Street, on the city's vast West Side. Lining these streets are Polish groceries, Polish bakeries, the offices of Polish newspapers, Polish banks and taverns catering to Chicago's Poles. Radiating from these arterial byways run the smaller residential streets, some of them sprinkled with low wooden houses almost old-world in appearance.

On holy days the ringing of Polish church bells tolls over Chicago's little Poland. The city boasts hundreds of Polish cultural and fraternal societies. More Polish men and women man Chicago's factory machines than do any other nationality. To watch the sturdy women climb into the overcrowded trolleys in the early morning clutching their lunches and with babushkas over their pale blonde hair makes one feel, almost, that one is standing on a curb in Warsaw or Lodz.

The taverns along Chicago Avenue, Milwaukee Avenue, and Division Street attract their coteries of "regulars." Many of the jukeboxes play Polish records. The crowded bars on Friday and Saturday nights are not quaint; most of them are bleak, filled with the smoky, sloppy, noisy, terrible sadness of the clientele.

"How the Devil Came Down Division Street" tells about one of these patrons. It is a poignant, rollicking tale, capturing the odd, old-world quality of its *mise en scéne*. Nelson Algren is the author of the novels *Somebody In Boots, Never Come Morning,* and *The Man With The*

Golden Arm. He has also published a volume of short
stories, *Neon Wilderness.* He is one of the few Chicago
writers who, after gaining a reputation, have remained in
Chicago.

LAST Saturday evening there was a great argument in the Polonia
Bar. All the biggest drunks on Division were there, trying to decide
who the biggest drunk of them was. Symanski said he was, and
Oljiec said he was, and Koncel said he was, and Czechowski said
he was.

Then Roman Orlov came in and the argument was decided. For
Poor Roman has been drunk so long, night and day, that when we
remember living men we almost forget Poor Roman, as though he
were no longer really among the living at all.

"The devil lives in a double-shot," Roman explains himself ob-
scurely. "I got a great worm inside. Gnaws and gnaws. Every day I
drown him and every day he gnaws. Help me drown the worm,
fellas."

So I bought Poor Roman a double-shot and asked him frankly
how, before he was thirty, he had become the biggest drunk on
Division.

It took a long time, and many double-shots, for him to tell. But
tell it he did, between curses and sobs, and I tell it now as closely
to what he told as I can. Without the sobs, of course. And of
course without any cursing.

When Roman was thirteen, it seems, the Orlovs moved into three
stove-heated rooms in the rear of a lopsided tenement on Noble
Street. Mama O. cooked in a Division Street restaurant by day and
cooked in her own home by night.

Papa O. played an accordion for pennies in Division Street taverns by night and slept alone in the rooms by day.

There were only two beds in the tiny flat, so nobody encouraged
Papa O. to come home at all.

Because he was the oldest, Roman slept between the twins, on
the bed set up in the front room, to keep the pair from fighting
during the night as they did during the day. Every day Teresa,
who was eleven and could not learn her lessons as well as some

of her classmates, slept with Mama O. in the windowless back bedroom, under a bleeding heart in a gilded oval frame.

If Papa O. got in before light, as happened occasionally early in the week, he crawled uncomplainingly under Roman's bed until Roman rose and got the twins, who were seven, up with him in time for Mass.

If Udo, who was something between a collie and a St. Bernard and as big as both together, was already curled up beneath the front-room bed, Papa O. slugged him with the accordion in friendly reproach—and went on into the back bedroom to crawl under Mama O.'s bed. In such an event he slept under a bed all day. For he never crawled, even with daylight, into Mama O.'s bed. Empty or not. As though he did not feel himself worthy to sleep there even when she was gone.

It was as though, having given himself all night to his accordion, he must remain true to it during the day.

For all manner of strange things went on in Papa O.'s head, as even the twins had become aware. Things so strange that Teresa was made ashamed of them by her schoolmates, whenever they wanted someone to tease.

This, too, was why no one, not even the twins, paid Papa O. any heed when the family returned from Mass one Sunday forenoon and he told them someone had been knocking while they were away.

"Some*body* was by door," he insisted. "I say 'Hallo.' Was no*body.*" He looked slyly about him at the children. "Who plays tricks by Papa?"

"Maybe was Zolewitzes," Mama O. suggested indifferently. "Mama Z. comes perhaps to borrow."

That Sunday night it was cold in all the corners. Papa O. was gone to play for pennies and drinks, Mama O. was frying *pierogi,* the twins were in bed, and Teresa was studying her catechism across the table from Roman, when someone knocked lightly twice.

To Roman it sounded like someone at the clothes-closet door; but that was foolish to think, since the twins were in bed. Yet, when he opened the hall door, only a cold wind came into the room from the long gaslit passage.

Roman, being only thirteen, did not dare look behind the door. Far less to speak of the clothes closet.

All that night a light snow fell, while Roman O. lay wakeful, fancying he saw it falling on darkened streets all over the mysterious earth, on the pointing roof tops of old-world cities, on mountain-high waves of the mid-Atlantic, and in the leaning eaves of Noble Street. He was just falling off to sleep when the knocking came again. Three times, like a measured warning.

The boy stiffened under the covers, listening with his fear. Heard the hall door squeak softly, as though Papa O. were sneaking in. But Papa O. never knocked, and Papa O. never sneaked. Papa O. came home with the accordion banging against buildings all down Noble Street, jingling his pennies proudly, singing off-key bravely, mumbling and laughing and stumbling. Papa O. never knocked. He kicked the door in happily and shouted cheerfully, "What you say, all peoples? How's t'ings, ever-body?" Papa O. pulled people out of bed and rattled pans and laughed at nothing and argued with unseen bartenders until somebody gave him sausage and eggs and coffee and bread and hung the accordion safely away.

Roman crept, barefooted, in the long underwear Mama O. had sewed on him in the early fall, to the hallway door.

The whole house slept. The windows were frosted and a thin line of ice had edged up under the front window and along the pane. The family slept. Roman shoved the door open gently. The tenement slept. Down the hall the single jet flickered feebly. No one. Nothing. The people slept.

Roman looked behind the door, shivering now with more than cold.

No one. Nothing. All night long.

He returned to bed and prayed quietly, until he heard Mama O. rise; waited till he knew she had the fire going in the big kitchen stove. Then, dressing with his back to the heat, he told Mama O. what he had heard. Mama O. said nothing.

Two mornings later, Papa O. came home without the accordion. It did not matter then to Mama O. whether he had sold it or lost it or loaned it; she knew it at last for a sign, she had felt the change coming, she said, in her blood. For she had dreamed a dream, all night, of a stranger waiting in the hall: a young man, drunken, leaning against the gaslit wall for support, with blood down the front of his shirt and drying on his hands. She knew, as all the Orlovs knew, that the unhappy dead return to warn or comfort, to plead or repent, to gain peace or to avenge.

That day, standing over steaming kettles, Mama O. went back in her mind to all those dear to her of earth who had died: the cousin drowned at sea, the brother returned from the war to die, the mother and father gone from their fields before she had married.

That night she knocked on Mama Zolewitz's door. Mama Z. sat silently, as though she had been expecting Mama O. for many evenings.

"Landlord doesn't like we should tell new tenants too soon," Mama Z. explained even before being told of the knocking, "so you shouldn't say it, I told. It was a young man lived in this place, in your very rooms. A strong young man, and good to look at. But sick, sick in the head from the drink. A sinner certainly. For here he lived with his lady without being wed, and she worked and he did not. That he did not work had little to do with what happened, and the drink had little to do. For it was being unwed that brought it on, at night, on the New Year. He returned from the taverns that night and beat her till her screams were a whimpering. Till her whimpering became nothing. A strong young man, like a bull, made violent by the drink. When the whimpering ceased, there was no sound at all. No sound until noon, when the police came with shouting.

"What was there to shout about? I could have told them before they came. The young man had hanged himself in the bedroom closet. Thus it is that one sin leads to another, and both were buried together. In unsanctified ground, with no priest near."

Mama O. grew pale. Her very clothes closet.

"It is nothing to worry," Mama Z. told her neighbor sagely. "He does not knock to do harm. He comes only to gain a little peace that good Christian prayer for him may give. Pray for the young man, Mama O. He wishes peace."

That night after supper the Orlovs gathered in prayer about the front-room stove, and Papa O. prayed also. For now that the accordion was gone, the taverns must do without him. When the prayer was done, he went to bed with Mama O. like a good husband, and the knocking did not come again.

Each night the Orlovs prayed for the poor young man. And each night Papa O. went to bed with Mama O. for lack of his accordion.

Mama O. knew then that the knocking had been a sign of good omen, and told the priest, and the priest blessed her for a Christian. He said it was the will of God that the Orlovs should redeem the young man by prayer and that Papa O. should have a wife instead of an accordion.

Papa O. stayed at home until, for lack of music, he became the best janitor on Noble Street. Mama Z. went to the priest and told of her part in the miracle of the poor young man, and the priest blessed Mama Z. also.

When the landlord learned that his house was no longer haunted he brought the Orlovs gifts; and when the rent was late he said nothing. So the priest blessed him equally, and in time the Orlovs paid no rent at all, but prayed for the landlord instead.

Teresa became the most important person in her class, for it became known that a miracle had been done in the Orlov home. Sister Mary Ursula said the child looked more like a little saint every day. And no other child in the room ever had her lessons as well as Teresa thereafter.

The twins sensed the miracle and grew up to be fast friends, doing all things together, even to wearing the same clothes and reading the same catechism. Udo, too, knew that the home was blessed. For he received no more blows from the accordion.

Only one sad aspect shadowed this great and happy change: Poor Roman was left bedless. For with Papa O. home every night like a good husband, Teresa must sleep between the twins.

Thus it came about that the nights of Roman Orlov became fitful and restless, first under the front-room bed and then under the back-room bed. With the springs overhead squeaking half the night as likely as not. The nights of Roman's boyhood were thereafter passed beneath one bed or the other, with no bed of his own at all. Until, attaining his young manhood and his seventeenth year, he took at last to sleeping during the day in order to have no need for sleep at night.

And at night, as everyone knows, there is no place to go but the taverns.

So it was, being abroad with no place to go and the whole night to kill, that Roman took his father's place. He had no accordion for excuse—only lack of a bed. He came to think of the dawn, when the taverns closed and he must go home, as the bitterest hour of the day.

This is why he still calls the dawn the bitterest hour: he must go home though he has no home.

Is this a drunkard's tale or sober truth? I can only say he told it like the truth, drinking double-shots all the while. I only know that no one argues about who the biggest drunk on Division is if Roman O. is around.

I only know what Mama O. now tells, after many years and Papa O. in his grave and the twins scattered: that the young man who knocked was in truth the devil. For did she not give him, without knowing what she did, a good son in return for a worthless husband?

"I'm drownin' the worm t'night," Poor Roman explains, talking to his double-shot. "Help me drown the worm t'night, fellas."

Does the devil live in a double-shot? Is he the one who gnaws, all night, within?

Or is he the one who knocks, on winter nights, with blood drying on his knuckles, in the gaslit passages of our dreams?

HEEL, TOE, AND A 1, 2, 3, 4*

George Milburn

DESPITE claims made by publishers, really good short-story writers in America are not common. One can count them on the fingers of three hands. Every recognized short-story writer has written one or two first-rate pieces. But very, very few can lay claim to having authored a full dozen stories of a high order. Most of O. Henry's tales are tricky and mediocre; a few are superb. Stephen Crane possesses a far better record. So do Hemingway, of course, and Sherwood Anderson, and the early Caldwell, and Katherine Anne Porter, and William March, and John O'Hara, and William Saroyan, and a few others, including George Milburn.

George Milburn was born in Oklahoma. For two years he lived in a basement on the Near North Side in Chicago, writing Haldeman-Julius Blue Books, to eat. He was in his early twenties at the time and the experience didn't seem to harm him. I first heard about him in those days from a fellow postal clerk when I was working on the night shift in the Chicago Post Office. My informant, a big, tobacco-chewing Oklahoman, used to bend my ear almost every night at the mail-cases, talking about a friend who he claimed would some day become one of America's best short-story writers.

Soon after, Milburn's work began appearing in Mencken's *American Mercury* and other magazines. His first book, *Oklahoma Town,* is a sort of *Winesburg,* dealing with a small Southern community. His second collection, *No More Trumpets,* is, I believe, one of the best volumes of short stories published in America.

ONE night Joe had been staring at the white paper in his typewriter so long that he thought he would go snow-blind. Finally he let his tilted chair down and began writing.

The types did a tap dance on the platen and words marched across the page: "*Wife:* Henry, have you got everything shut up for the night?"

Joe double-spaced and wrote "Hubby"; but, before he could finish the line with the good one he had thought up for *Hubby* to say back to *Wife,* he heard a scratching on the iron grille of the basement window. He turned around in his chair and saw two hands gripping the bars and a twisted monkey-face squeezed between them.

"What do you want?" he asked.

"Say, buddy, how do you get down to the Lake from here?" the monkey-face said without moving its lips.

Joe got up and went over to the open window to see how anyone could talk without moving his lips. He said, "You follow this street right on, and it'll take you to the Lake. It's only three blocks on over."

"What street is this, buddy?"

"This is Superior Street—East Superior Street," Joe said.

The stranger took his hands away from the window bars and sat down on the basement steps so that his head was level with the sidewalk and the window. Joe could see now that when he talked his lips did move a little. They jerked down on one side like those of a man rolling a cigar in the corner of his mouth.

He didn't make any move to go. Instead, he began explaining, apologetically. "Well, I know Chi' pretty good, but I ain't never been down to the Lake. I thought I would go down to the Lake tonight. Reckon is there any benches a man could sleep on down there at the beach?"

"Sure, you can find plenty of benches if you'll walk on up the shore a ways, up about Oak Street."

Joe turned around and went back over to his typewriter again. But the bum kept on sitting there, hunched up on the basement steps. It annoyed Joe to have him sitting there looking in, and he was about to tell him to move on, when the bum said, "What're you doing, buddy? You writing a story book?"

"No, I'm writing two-line jokes," Joe said. "I make my living writing two-line jokes." Joe was proud of making his living by writing jokes.

The bum commenced talking again without paying any attention to what Joe had said. "Listen, buddy, you let me come in there, and I'll tell you some good stories you can write."

"What kind of stories?"

"Oh, all kinds of stories. Any kind of story you want to hear."

Joe got up and walked out into the hall and turned back the snap-lock on the basement door. The bum had moved quickly, because he was there at the bottom of the steps waiting when Joe opened the door. When he stepped inside he put his foot down on some plaster that had fallen and it made a loud gritting noise on the concrete floor.

"Sh-h-h!" Joe said. "Don't make so much noise. The landlady lives right back there, and if she caught me letting you in she'd throw me and you both out in the street."

The visitor, stepping high, walked on past quickly and stood in Joe's room under the electric light, blinking. When Joe saw him in the light he knew that there wasn't any danger. The bum was a kid about sixteen years old. He looked tough, but not hard to handle. His back was twisted and he held his elbows out from his sides as if he had boils in both his armpits. His marmoset's face was broad and pleasant, but one of his eyelids drooped halfway shut. His other eye was as black and lively as a beetle.

"Start in," said Joe, sitting down in his chair.

"Well, what kind of a story would you want to hear?" the little bum asked, seating himself nervously on the edge of the cot.

"Just use your own judgment," Joe said. "You were the one that suggested this."

"Well, I can tell you about when I was handling greyhounds for the races out in Tia Juana and one day Roman Queen broke her leg and they give her to me to shoot. So I took her and set her leg and fixed it up and cured her. That dog sure did love me and I sure did love that dog. So one day Mr. Rambo, that was my boss, seen that Queenie was up and getting around again without much of a limp, and nothing would do him but he should run her. Well, she wasn't much account for running, the bone in her leg wasn't good and knit yet, but Mr. Rambo took Queen and shot her full of dope, and that day she run and win the race and Old Man Rambo win six grand. I sure did love that dog. But that last race tore her leg loose again and the dope and all was too much for her and I had to shoot her after all. How is that for a story? Is that the kind you like?"

"That's all right," Joe said. "Go slower and talk so as I can understand what you're saying."

"Well, I've been all around. All over this country, Canada, and Mexico. I've been to Havana and Bonus Airs. I've just got out of a turpentine camp down in Florida. When the boom bust down there me and another kid was riding out in a Studie that was hot— that we had stole. We was almost to the line when the law caught us, and the judge shipped us off to this turpentine camp. They used to whup us regular, whether we'd done anything or not. But that turpentine gets into your hide and it gets so they can't hurt you so much when they cut you up with a cat-tail whip. I've got a back like a washboard. Here, let me show you something."

The little bum unbuttoned his coat and slipped his arms out of it gingerly. He bent his naked back over under the light bulb. The close, narrow welts on his back made it look like a piece of tan corduroy.

"Just feel that," the kid said. "Go on, just feel it."

Joe ran his fingertips along the leather-colored welts.

"That's what them cat-tail whips they use on you in a turpentine camp does to you," the boy said proudly.

"Well, me and this other kid was in there, and this kid was a wop kid from Chi'. He said that if ever he could get back to Chi' ever'thing would be jake for him and me both, because he could get me a job driving a beer truck for fifty bucks a week. He was a good kid all right. I sure did like him. So after a while he gets

out and comes back to Chi' and before long he sends the money
to get me out and sends me an address to come to here in Chi'. I
didn't lose no time.

"I was riding the blinds out of Atlanta when a railroad dick
come climbing down over the tender. She was hitting around seventy. I steps around on that little ledge out of sight, and when
this yard dick sticks his beezer around trying to see where I had
went, I lets him have it, and he goes over, squealing like a stuck
pig.

"I got into Chi' this afternoon late, and I went around to this
tobacco store on North Clark Street, this address this buddy of
mine had give me. When I got there they told me that this dago
buddy of mine had been put on the spot day before yesterday and
they had a big funeral for him yesterday. I sure liked that kid. Kid
by the name of Liberatore. Old Vic Liberatore.

"Well, here I am now. That's the breaks. The next time you see
me I might be wearing a silk shirt and smoking a two-bit cigar.
That's the breaks. That's what they call the lawr of averages. I've
had it to work out for me before. I've had the bucks before this,
plenty, and I spent 'em, too. Say, buddy, you ain't got another
Lucky there, have you?"

Joe pulled a package of cigarettes out of his shirt pocket and
handed them over to the little bum. The kid took one, lighted it,
and sent a blue veil eddying up around the electric light. He stood
there, naked to the waist. Joe was looking at the bum's arms.
From wrist to elbow they were splotched with livid scars. Some of
the places were unhealed and they were open wounds.

"How did you burn your arms like that?" Joe asked.

"Them blisters? Buddy, if I told you how I got them, I'd have to
tell you about Heavy Henderson. I don't know if I can tell you
about Heavy, exactly. I ain't right in my head yet about Heavy.
You see how I walk? Sort of on my heels? Some thinks I'm punch-
drunk, but I ain't punch-drunk. I never have talked to anybody
about this before, but I'll try and tell you about it.

"I wasn't more'n ten years old when I first started on the road.
My old folks used to live in a little town in Missouri. I guess they

still do if they ain't dead. That's been six or seven years ago. My old man always said that if ever I run off, I could just keep on a-running, because he never would send after me. So I run off.

"Well, I hadn't been out long before I met up with Heavy Henderson. It was in the jungles near Boise, Idaho. I had been having a pretty tough time of it, and I sure was needing somebody who was big enough to stand up for me.

"Heavy was a big, fine-looking man, and he was looking to get a good punk to do his moochin' for him. So when I come along Heavy and me joined up. Heavy was a good guy at heart; they don't make them no better than Heavy was. He'd 'a' done anything in the world for me, but I have to admit that Heavy did have a mean temper. Part of it was my fault, though. I was always kind of headstrong, and that made it hard for him to keep me in line. So Heavy used to have to put the bug on me pretty often. That's what made them burns."

Joe said, "Oh, I see!"

"You know what the bug is, don't you?"

"Well, it seems to me like I do, but I'm not quite sure," Joe said. "What is it?"

"The bug is what they call blister beetle, a sort of a little bug. The juice of it on you blisters to beat hell. Heavy nearly always used some kind of acid on me, but he called it the bug just the same. Ever'time I got so I wouldn't do like he said, or when I helt out something on him, Heavy would catch me and take and blister my arms. That worked two ways. For one thing, it hurt me a whole lot more than a whupping, and for another thing, the next day when I went into town to batter backdoors, why I could show the woman that opened the door the sores on my arms and tell her I had got scalded in an accident and that I was trying to get back to my folks. That always worked, and sometimes it paid off in money, too.

"I used to try to fight Heavy off, but that didn't do no good. That was one strong man. He had a big heart, and I bet that he'd 'a' gone through hell for me, but, like I say, he did have a quick temper. When he got mad, he'd just burn the hell out of my arms.

I guess I needed it sometimes. But Heavy sort of overdone it. Some of them sores ain't never healed up yet, and that turpentine I been working in is a quick healer.

"But I never could find it in my heart to anything else but respect Heavy. I sure did like him. He was as good a jocker as any kid could want. Wasn't scared of nobody, and I seen him mash a bird's face in for just grabbing me by the neck. I sure did like Heavy, but I never did know how much I liked him until after it was too late.

"The way it was, one night Heavy tanked up on white mule out in a place in Dakota. Man, talk about your raw liquor, that stuff was *raw*. I seen one guy take a snort of it, and an hour later he was having a hem'rage. But stuff like that didn't bother Heavy. He was a *man*. He had a set of cast-iron guts. We was waiting for a train, and Heavy was feeling good.

"I remember just as well. It was moonlight, and we was laying around a watertank waiting for the flier. The drip from the tank made a funny sound where it splashed in the white chat down below. The moon made ever'thing look kind of like silver, except in the shadows. Old Heavy was propped up again' one of them watertank posts singing just as loud as he could sing. He was singing a song he knew about a bum that was one hell of a liar, and one day while he was setting there telling these lies a fly crawls up him and tickles him to death. It's a kind of a dirty song in places.

"Pretty soon we could hear a train working steam away off down the track. I don't know if you know how it is out there on the prairies, but the first thing you see is this long white light come shaking down the rails. It don't make no noise at all, just white and still. It sure is pretty. It puts me in the mind of one of them stories my old woman used to read out of the Bible. Then after a while you begin to hear the drivers, away off acrost the plains. Pretty soon, when it gets nearer, it seems like the dark is just alive and beating with that sound.

"Well, this here was a manifest coming, a hot-shot freight. Heavy and me was passenger stiffs and we never did ride nothing slower than a fruit express. It was two hours yet before the flier was due, but Heavy took it into his head that he was going to ride this rattler. Nothing would do him but we had to ride that manifest freight out. He got stubborn spells like that when he had been drinking.

"I thought he was too lousy drunk to even get on, and I tried to talk him out of it. But he slapped my jaws, and nothing else would do him, so we walked on down the track a ways, and when she stopped for water, I got Heavy on.

"After we was on, Heavy took a notion that he would ride the bumpers. You know how the bumpers is on a box car: there's a block where the coupling pin is fastened on, and it sticks out far enough for you to sit on it. Heavy was riding down there between two cars, sitting on the bumpers with his feet propped up over the coupling pins.

"I was riding the tops right above him, where I could keep my eye on him, like I aimed to do. I guess I must of drowsed off, though. I never will get through blaming myself for what happened anyway. Pretty soon something woke me up. It was old Heavy screaming. I climbed down to where he was. He had went to sleep and let his foot slip down between the coupling pins. The cars had jostled and the coupling pins had jammed together and it had smashed Heavy's heel off. I felt of it, and it was all bloody and mushy there in his shoe.

"God, I was scared! I knew that I had to get that train stopped. Old Heavy was just like a daddy to me. I was so scared that I didn't want to think about what had happened.

"I climbed back up on top, and I begin to run over the tops toward the engine. It was funny, but you know something popped into my head about that time, and I can't get shut of it yet.

"How I happened to run off from home: the spring I run off they was learning us kids at school a dance for some kind of a doings they was having. I mean they *tried* to make me learn it along with the others, but I never did like any sissy business like that, and I wouldn't learn it. So they whupped me. My old man always said that if ever I got a whupping at school I'd get one twicest as hard when I got home. And when my old man set out to whup me, he would just about half kill me. So I just didn't go home that night. I left out of there. Well, of all the crazy things, this tune they tried to learn me to dance to back in the fourth grade at school popped into my head, and it kept running in my head all the time I was high-tailing it down toward the engine acrost them box cars.

" 'Heel, toe, and a one-two-three-four,' it went. 'Heel, toe, and a one-two-three-four!' I got so I could make it come out even, and when I got to the 'four' I would be at the end of a car and I would have to jump acrost to the next one and begin all over again, 'Heel, toe, and a one-two-three-four!'

"That seemed to me like the longest rattler ever I rode, and I thought I never was going to reach that engine cab. Finally I did, and I crawled up over the coal and jumped down into the cab, screaming and bawling and carrying on. They couldn't make out what I was saying, but they stopped the train. The head-end shack got off and run down the track with me, and finally we found the car where Heavy was, cussing and groaning. Ever'time old Heavy groaned, it was just like someone had slit me with a shiv. We got him off of there, and they carried him back to the caboose. I plugged along behind the con and the shack that was carrying him, and ever'time I took a step one of them words—heel, toe, and a one-two-three-four—would snap into my head. It just kept running through my head.

"And when the train started up again, it seemed like the wheels was clicking, 'Heel, toe, and a one-two-three-four!'

"They put us off at a little town about fifteen miles up the line so as I could get Heavy to a doc. I don't know how I ever did get that croaker out of bed that night, because I must have been crazy in my mind. Anyhow, the one I got must of been a horse doc, because he just looked at Heavy's smashed heel once and says, 'Um-mmm. Iron rust in it. I'll have to cut it off.' He fixed up a little frame over Heavy's face, and he showed me how to drop the ether. I let the drops fall, and as they dropped this 'Heel, toe, and a one-two-three-four' jerked through my head in time to the drops.

"After a while the croaker started sawing. I could see the bone show white through the raw meat. Zup! that saw would go acrost, and I would think, 'Heel!' and Zup! it would come back, and I

would think, 'Toe!'; and then it would go zup-zup-zup-zup, and I would count, one-two-three-four.

"Pretty soon I passed out myself. I was awful sick that night, but I went to sleep there in the croaker's office on a couch he had there, and when I woke up the next day the doc told me that Heavy was dead. They claimed he died of lockjaw. I don't know. I didn't cry or anything. All I done was lay there with that crazy dance tune running through my head.

"They buried Heavy that same day. They had him a coffin made out of a goods-box and they loaded that in an old wagon and hauled him out to the graveyard. I walked along behind the wagon. I remember how the dust let my feet go down in it easy like I was walking on clouds. And the wagon wheels was warped and they clocked back and forth, making a kind of a hollow sound in a regular beat, and that 'Heel, toe, and a one-two-three-four' kept time to that beat the wheel hubs made.

"I sure did hate to see old Heavy go. Nothing never has meant anything to me since then. I didn't take on or nothing, but I don't have no memory of what happened at the grave or how I ever got away from there. I get that way ever' onct in a while now. I'll be walking along and that 'Heel, toe, and a one-two-three-four' will start up in my head and I take to walking in time to it. Some thinks I'm punch-drunk, walking like that, but I ain't punch-drunk.

"And sometimes I have dreams at night. I drempt that I was running along the tops of a long string of box cars that seems like it hasn't got no end, and the cars is swinging and swaying and I'm screaming and screaming, but the engine whistle up ahead is blowing so loud I can't hear what I'm screaming. Only I know what I'm screaming. It's that 'Heel, toe, and a one-two-three-four!' "

The little bum stopped talking and peered at Joe with one bright black eye. "You think I'm as full of nuts as a peach-orchard boar, don't you? Crazy as hell, ain't I?"

He stood up. "Well, I guess I'll try and see if I can't get on down to the Lake," he said briskly.

Joe said, "No, you don't need to do that. You can sleep here to-

night if you want to. I've got me a shower bath fixed up back there. You go in and take a good bath, and you can sleep here."

The little bum said, "No, I'll find me a bench down on the beach somewheres. You don't want me sleeping here. I'm crazy in the head."

Joe stood watching him get into his coat. The kid slipped his arms tenderly into the sleeves. When he had reached the door, Joe called, "Well, so long, then!"

"So long, buddy. Did I give you any ideas you could use for stories?"

"Sure, you gave me some swell ideas," Joe said. "I can get a whole batch of stories out of what you told me. Much obliged!"

"Well, so long then, buddy. You're O.K."

The basement door slammed. Joe heard a footstep on the bottom step. There was a pause. One on the second. Another pause. Then, in quick succession, four that brought his departing visitor to the sidewalk level.

Joe walked over to the typewriter and ripped out the sheet that had his half-finished married-life joke on it. He crumpled the paper and threw the wad on the floor. Then he sat down, fed in a fresh sheet, and tapped the space bar nervously.

He started writing rapidly, *"Kind Old Lady:* My poor man, what brought you to this miserable state?"

Joe double-spaced and wrote "Hobo." He paused to phrase a snappy comeback for *Hobo.* Off down the silent, lamp-lit street he could hear the footclicks growing faint.

POEMS

George Dillon

George Dillon is not a prolific writer. But his two slim
volumes of poems, *Boy in the Wind* and *The Flowering
Stone,* disclose a talent of the first rank. His poems are
clear-cut in style and intagliolike in their imagery. *The
Flowering Stone* was awarded a Pulitzer Prize.

The two poems published here indicate the scope and
intensity of his writing.

LATE AUTUMN *

Sparrows flock into a tree out of the gutter
As if last summer's leaves were blowing somehow
On to the branches again with a quick flutter.
They will be here all winter now,
Swarming from tree to gutter, from gutter to bough.

They are most meager of the meagerless we have kept,
After the loud leaves going in hurried herds,
After the rain has washed, and the wind has swept.

Earth's clear incredible music dies in a rush
Of red on the wind. Out of a furious hush
I hear the cold calm voices of these birds.
They are more real than butterfly or thrush.

Indurate brood, who endlessly chatter and cheep,
You are the fragments of a night no sun
Can scatter. You are less birds than shadows spun
Out of a tired brain in a troubled sleep.
And it is shadows I keep.

TWILIGHT IN A TOWER *

Finding the city below me like a flame
In the last sunshine, I said to autumn, "Blow on!
We are building a beautiful spring you cannot claim
In this country of stone."

And seeing so many men march in a thousand ways
The old way of hunger and thirst, I thought,
They are going somewhere, somewhere their dream is waiting,
Whether they know it or not.

But night came, smelling of far fields, and even
That brave procession moving with purpose and pride
Became like shadows wandering or driven,
And the wind cried,

And the world seemed a world of autumn and wind,
And the city but a frail rustling by the sea
Of men like leaves blown blindly without end
From life's flowering tree.

* From *Boy in the Wind.*

THE STRANGEST PLACE
IN CHICAGO*

John Bartlow Martin

CHICAGO is divided into three sections, the North Side, the South Side, and the West Side. Each is a subcity containing a semi-insulated segment of population, and each subcity is vast in area. On the South Side is the Negro belt which, after Harlem, is the largest Negro community in the world. To pass through this Black Metropolis (as sociologists St. Clair Drake and Horace R. Cayton call it) is an experience an out-of-town white person does not soon forget. The topography of the streets is different from that of Harlem, where the main thoroughfares are lined with tall tenements or apartment houses which at two points crouch at the bases of Morningside Heights and Sugar Hill. Here in Chicago the streets of the South Side Negro community are, for the most part, flatly bleak; small, low houses of brick and wood stretch away for miles. Their back porches and back yards give one, free of charge, the kind of shock one receives upon viewing a cluster of municipal dumping grounds. A few streets lined with dilapidated mansions whose rooms have been turned into "kitchenette apartments" relieve the flatness somewhat. For over sixty years the Mecca reared itself like a Roman colosseum above this area.

By the time this volume is published, however, the Mecca will have ceased to exist. A short while ago I was riding around the South Side with my brother when he suddenly stopped his car at the sight of huge mounds of debris and long rows of half-demolished walls and shattered doorways. A large house-wrecking crew was in action. Accompanied by the crunches of the crowbars, bricks, window sashes, and ledges were diving to the ground, creating slow, atomiclike dust clouds. We sat in the car for a half-hour, watching the great building going through its death throes, then drove away.

I have included John Bartlow Martin's fine article in this volume, even though the Mecca itself will be gone, because I think it is a piece of enduring Chicago memorabilia.

FROM the Chicago Loop, where sunlight off the lakefront strikes the shining towers, State Street runs straight south, wide, busy with streetcars and heavy trucks. Quickly the buildings get shabby—little stores selling auto parts, a junkyard crammed with rusting wreckage. The city is harsh: concrete streets, brick building walls, black steel viaducts. Beyond Twenty-second Street the faces of the people are black. This is the South Side Negro section. Here the street is quieter, the sun is hazy and dirty and pale, the sky is a network of trolley wires. Across an expanse of new-turned earth stretches a new public housing project, with a playyard for the children, and at Thirty-second Street begins the new campus of the Illinois Institute of Technology, sleek brick-and-glass buildings surrounded by new trees and new grass. And just beyond the Institute rises a great gray hulk of brick, four stories high, topped by an ungainly smokestack, ancient and enormous, filling half the block north of Thirty-fourth Street between State and Dearborn. It is the Mecca Building.

Let us note its setting. Across State Street are a cleaning shop, a barber shop, a grocery, the Railroad Men's Social Club, McClain's Hair Goods, a Bar-B-Q, the office of H. Young the Icer, the Church of God & Saints of Christ in an old store front. An old man pulls a handcart filled with junk across an empty lot. From a deep hole tunneled under the sidewalk emerges the head of a little Negro boy, playing. The sidewalk is cracked and broken. Nearby are rickety wooden tenements.

The Mecca Building is U-shaped. The dirt courtyard is littered with newspapers and tin cans, milk cartons and broken glass. Pigeons roost on a car on blocks. A skinny white dog huddles in a doorway. Iron fire escapes run up the building's face and ladders reach from them to the roof. There are four main entrances, two on Dearborn and two on State Street. At each is a gray stone threshold and over each is carved "The Mecca." The Mecca was constructed as an apartment building in 1891, a splendid palace, a showplace of Chicago. Today it is still an apartment building and a showplace but of a very different sort. It has become one of the most remarkable Negro slum exhibits in the world. Let us pass through the arched doorway of the Mecca; let us see what the Mecca looks like inside, see who the people in it are and how they live, whence they came and why they stay.

Inside, a powerful odor assails the visitor at once, musty, heavy, a smell compounded of urine and stale cooking and of age, not necessarily an unpleasant odor but a close powerful one, which, like that of marijuana, once smelled is never forgotten. The stone slab step is hollowed. The lower part of the walls of the vestibule once was covered with marble but now the marble has been stripped away in ragged patches, revealing naked brick and mortar. It is dark here. Ahead stretches a corridor; it is like a tunnel, it seems endless and it is indeed a block long, running all the way to the Dearborn Street entrance; down its whole length hang only five light-bulbs, glowing feebly in the gloom. Tan paint is peeling from the wall, the doors of apartments open into the corridor. This is the base of the U in the U-shaped building.

The arms of the U are identical. They are great halls, each lit by a skylight four stories overhead which, because of the dirt that has accumulated on the glass through years of neglect, admits the kind of unreal light found underseas. This light slants down in great long angling shafts filled with floating dust, shifting as the sun moves across the sky, falling in fitful patches on the floor. Around the walls run three balconies guarded by ornate wrought-iron grill-work, and off these balconies open the doors to the apartments, like tiers of cells in a prison cellblock. The floor in the center of the well is of hardwood, splintered now, and beneath the balconies it is of tile, broken in many places. A janitor with a wheelbarrow is slowly patching the tile with concrete; his shovel makes a rasping, scraping sound. From somewhere in the building comes always the sound of distant human voices—women talking, a baby squalling, children screaming, men muttering, no words distinguishable. Spittle splats flatly on the tile floor, falling from a great height, spat by a man or a woman standing on an upper balcony. All day long people stand at the balconies, leaning on the wrought-iron railings with hands clasped out over them, gazing out at other people facing them across the well in silence, gazing down at the floor far below, spitting, small human figures in a vast place, two or three on each of the four floors, occasionally calling back and forth to one another but most of the time just standing silent. The building is never entirely quiet, not even very late at night, since so many people live here; but it is so vast that it seems quiet, even amid uproar.

In the center on the ground floor is a long narrow bank of mailboxes, tarnished brass, 176 of them. One has thirteen names on it, including seven different family names, indicating that thirteen adults expecting mail occupy that particular apartment. Late in the morning the postman comes, a man in blue. Three tenants wait respectfully at the side while he distributes the mail. On the balcony above, two men leaning on the railing watch him critically: "He'll never get it all done doing it one at a time," and, "He's a new man." At last he finishes, and tenants emerge from their apartments to get their mail. From a high balcony a toddler throws a chunk of broken tile; it bounces on the floor by the mailboxes. A stooped old woman wearing a black sweater and black shawl, only her hair and eyeballs white, moves slowly and painfully in the shadows beneath the balcony, keeping close to the wall as long as possible, touching it with bony fingers, and only leaving it when she must to venture across the open floor to the mailbox; gets her mail, then retreats along the wall to the stairs, where a man steps aside, saying kindly, "You come down to see what you got, didn't you?" and she says, in a gasping voice, "I'm going take my good time," then begins to ascend, pulling herself up by the railing, first her right foot up one step, then the left slowly after it, her body bent so low that her face almost touches the next step, stopping at the landing to rest and stare at the peeling walls with watery, halfblind eyes. Near the mailboxes three children are jumping rope, us-

ing a doubled rope, two boys swinging the two long strands in
sweeping arcs while a girl rocks to and fro at one side to get
into the rhythm before jumping in. Children ride battered tricycles
across the floor, safe here from the traffic of the streets. On a balcony children are playing store, using a cardboard box. One of
them throws a fistful of paper over the railing and it flutters down:
policy slips, there must be a policy station here.

The wind blows in off Dearborn Street and a young woman neat
in black enters, walking a leashed dog and humming a hymn. Somewhere a child is crying over and over, "Mummy, Mummy." In the
long dark corridor a dog is nosing at garbage from an upset garbage can. From somewhere comes a clatter, perhaps of a falling
garbage-can lid, and the high mad cackling laughter of an old
man. A very young child standing on the third floor balcony urin-
ates through the ornate iron grillwork and the urine falls to the
ground floor far below and a woman calls to him, "Don't you do
that, you got no right to do that, I'm going to tell your mother."
The iceman comes wearing a leather protector on his shoulder
and back, carrying a cake of ice that gleams whitely against his
black face and hat. A woman calls from the third floor, "Bring
fifty pounds to 304½," and he plods to the stairs.

In the shadows against a pillar marked with match-strikes leans a
man, his shirt-collar buttoned but without a necktie, his hat-brim
slanting low over his scarred face, a cigarette slanting from
his mouth; he is just standing there watching. How many people
live here? He laughs. "I don't know." Two thousand? "Oh, more
than that. There's 176 apartments and some of 'em's got seven
rooms and they're all full." A heavy round-faced man in a long
white apron holding a ball-peen hammer approaches: "You are
visiting some of the historic sites of the city? You found one all
right. If it don't fall in on you while you're lookin'." How many
people live here? "That," he says, "is a mystery. You'll find them
sleeping in bathtubs, sleeping in the kitchen under the sink, anywhere they can sleep." Nobody, in truth, knows how many people
inhabit the Mecca Building. The janitor, Jimmy Sanders, estimates
2,300; the Democratic precinct captain, William Patrick Fitzgerald,
who has lived here eighteen years, estimates 1,400; the owner

doesn't know. All the inhabitants except one woman are Negroes. The Mecca Building contains more people than most Chicago precincts; indeed, it constitutes a precinct in itself, the Twenty-seventh Precinct of the Second Ward.

On the third floor an old woman stands by the railing, a towel wound round her head, a big gold ring on her finger. Watching dispassionately as children run in from school for lunch, their screams ringing piercingly through the building, she says judiciously, "That size runs to roller skates," and then, "When I first came here they used to control the children. White people hadn't been gone so long, 1917 it was. They used to have a policeman here nights, you could hear a needle drop. Now they's shooting here five times a night. Them young men and the young girls is the worst. I'd move out tonight if they'd find me a house. I moved out for a while once but I came back to have company, my daughter lives here and my granddaughter was born here," and she turns and shuffles into her flat.

In the flat, wallpaper hangs from the walls in great sheets. Clean newspapers are spread on the floor. Over the dresser are some arti-ficial flowers, and a transparent plastic wrapper covers the bed. The sideboard, radio, and table are cluttered with family photographs. Mottoes and pictures hang on the walls, a picture of Jesus Christ and a crucifix put out by a liquor store, a plaque, "My Help cometh from the Lord," and also secular shrines: a large frame holding the pictures of Abraham Lincoln and Frederick Douglass flanked by Booker T. Washington, Paul Laurence Dunbar, W. E. B. DuBois, and other race leaders. And a framed faded campaign picture of Franklin D. Roosevelt. She calls Lincoln "Abraham." She was born in Alabama. She is bent and stooped, aged. She says, "I live here all by myself, me and my Lord," and then, as her visitor departs, she touches his arm and says gently, "Do you know anything about that man we call Jesus, do you know him personally, you ought to get in touch with him." Outside her door a teen-age boy is standing at the balcony railing, trying to spit clear across to the other side.

In the long first-floor corridor the janitor passes, Jimmy, a short squat man in a leather cap and jacket, ambling along with a

Yankee drill in his hand. "I'm the maintenance man," he says.
"I do a little of everything—work a little, fight a little, sleep a
little, play a little." Right now he is accompanying the rent collector, a white man, a wiry Scot named John. "I go around with
him," Jimmy says, shifting the stub of his dead cigar to the other
corner of his mouth, "because the young fellas in the building
think he's got money with him." About a year ago the young
fellows robbed an insurance collector of $17. The rent collector,
John, says, "I lost all my hair fighting with these people,"
and laughs. Actually, he has little trouble collecting rents, which
are cheap. His troubles are of a different sort: he and Jimmy fight
a hopeless rearguard action against decay and vandalism. "Last
night they shot out the light-bulbs," says Jimmy. "And the windows
—in the last year I bet I put in over two hundred windows. They
break 'em fast as you put 'em in." Who does it? "Outsiders, most
of it. And the kids here. The kids get to playin' and throwin' at one
another and first thing you know they break the glass. There's
nothin' you can do about it. You can't kill one 'cause he broke the
glass."

As the rent collector walks along, a woman calls from the third-
floor balcony, "Hold your head up, John, John, hold your head up,
I want to talk to you," but John plods on, grinning secretly. A sign
by the basement stairs reads, "Put All Complaints in Mail Box."
Near the State Street entrance another janitor has temporarily left
his job of cementing a broken place in the floor and is stooping
over at an apartment door, digging with a knife at something in
the door. He gets it out: a bullet. "That's a .38," he says, turning
it over in his hand, shiny and twisted. Then, to a woman who has
come to the door, "They try to shoot you out last night?" She
laughs. "Yeh, try to kill me. Like shootin' rabbits in a swamp down
yonder." He says, "They was really shootin' here last night. Some
of 'em shootin' for fun, some of 'em fightin'. That's every night
around here. Couple of 'em got shot the other night." Any ever
killed? "Oh, yes, one got killed summer before last up there in that
corner," pointing upward. Why? "I don't know."

Down the stairs comes a man on crutches, his left leg off above
the knee, his pants leg pinned up, coming down the steps, the

crutch and his good leg visible first, then the man, thin, wearing white pants and a brown coat and hat; he walks diagonally past the mailboxes to the grocery, pausing to adjust his pipe.

High on the fourth west gallery, close up under the skylight, the balcony seems narrow. Two boys wrestle on it, and one falls heavily against the iron railing, which trembles but holds firm. It is four stories down to the ground floor; nobody ever heard of a child falling. An old woman is sweeping the floor. High up here at the north end a dozen young men and women are congregated, well-dressed, two of the men off to one side leaning idle on the railing and peering sullenly down, the others close together, laughing, fooling around with each other, the girls in tight white sweaters, the young men in snap-brim hats and suitcoats over sweaters.

At the south end in the corner, as in all the corners, a dark narrow passageway angles back from the balcony, and at its end is apartment 417½, the three-room apartment of Mrs. Corene Laur Griffin. It is one of the neatest in the building. Christmas cards dangle from a string looped along one wall. Mrs. Griffin, a small woman with a wrinkled forehead that makes her look always worried, is at home today and so is her mother, as usual. Mr. Griffin, a construction worker, is out hunting a job.

Mrs. Griffin, who wears her hair drawn tightly back and who speaks in a soft fluent voice, laughing often and rather loudly, was born May 5, 1900, in Edward, Mississippi, where her parents "had their own place." She was the youngest of six children. Her father sold the farm at Edward and died on a rented farm at Shelby and her mother took the children to Pine Bluff, Arkansas —"We thought we'd move away, after people die, you know, you want to go some place." The other children left or died; Corene stayed with her mother in Pine Bluff. "They had berry farms there, we used to pick cotton, we had all kinds of different work, my mother and I did laundry work for people." Her mother's parents had been slaves in Virginia. "Yeah, we have done some kind of work, me and her," and she nods toward her mother, a large woman of eighty-nine now rocking in the sunlight by the window, a shawl around her shoulders, a white lace cap on her head. "I been working since my father died when I was fourteen. Work all that time, taking care of my mother. Till 1929, when the work went down, I did day work all over Chicago since 1920."

In 1924 she and her mother moved into this apartment, No. 417½, and they have been here ever since. At first they paid $42.50 a month; they pay only $20 now; "but at that time it was kep' up, it was decorated every year, the halls was decorated too, it was beautiful, it had the fishpond downstairs and everything, and the stores were lovely. Since then it's just gone down and down, that's what makes you so tired, you don't have nothin'. The building isn't in such bad condition. Only they haven't done anything to it in twenty years. People came in and carried the marble off the walls and carried it out and sold it." Her cheekbones are high, her face a little pinched. "We did everything to keep it together 'cause we had to have some place to live. There isn't no place else. Once I put up a five-dollar deposit on a place, didn't get the place, like to never got the deposit back. *Some* people. I got tired of going out lookin' for places, spend all that carfare, couldn't find nothin', I just settled down here and try to fix this up to be comfortable. I've got my mother here, she's sick, she's old, can't walk up and down stairs, she can't hardly walk at all, only creep around the house."

Mrs. Griffin is sitting in an upholstered chair. The Mecca Building noise—squalling babies, fighting children, unidentified crashes—is but dimly audible. "I don't know what we're gonna do. What I just can't stand is the big boys that come here shooting, terrorize the place. We don't even have the landlord's telephone where he lives. When we call the police station they tell us, 'We're not the people to see, you want to get your landlord.' How'm I going to get the landlord, I don't have his telephone?"

She straightened a doily on a chair. "Yeh, we livin' in a dangerous condition but still we have to stay here. We get out and scrub the hall, they get back and tear it right back up, tear out the walls, everything. I've always lived decent—*till now.* I don't know why people don't be decent, if people can't be decent the world can't run. It's pitiful. But they just want you to go along, don't have nothin', don't do nothin', don't be nothin', don't know nothin', just be here, then they satisfied at you. I think that's a terrible world." Why has she stayed here so long? "At first, it was good heat. And when I went out to work, she," nodding toward her mother, "she was surrounded with people, I wasn't afraid to leave her, everything'd be all right when I come home. I stayed till the Depression—and then I wasn't able to move. And after the Depression, I couldn't find no place. Wasn't able to buy nothin'. I wanted to get a flat with a back porch so she could sit out in the sun."

Outside, an old woman leaning over the railing muses, "Alabama —the best place in the world. Ain't nobody gonna bother you if you don't go messin' 'round with white folks." She is watching for the rat man; he is in the building on his regular visit. Somewhere a telephone is ringing. The day must be ending; the skylight darkens.

High on the fourth floor dwells George Kinchlow, an old man. He is seventy-seven. He is sitting on a daybed in the dark. Saving electricity. He rises, a frail white-haired little man in cracked cheap slippers, and turns on a small dangling light for his visitor. The living room is nine feet by six. Against faded wallpaper hang publicity photographs of Irene Castle and of Veloz and Yolanda and an old gold-framed photograph of a little boy in a sailor suit, his son. Clothing, rumpled and dirty, hangs on the chairbacks. Kinchlow apologizes for the way things look. "I been sick with high blood pressure, can't do much. That's why I got this towel around my neck to keep warmed up. Sometimes I sit in front by the window." The window is in the bedroom; it offers a view of the trolley wires on State Street and, in the distance, a dim grayness, perhaps Lake Michigan, far away. On the walls are more fan pictures and also pictures of the Pope and Franklin D. Roosevelt. On a dresser stand family photos and over the bed is a figure of Christ on a crucifix beneath a picture of the Boswell sisters.

Kinchlow was a porter all his working days. He left Indianapolis because "my hopes died out." He married, moved into this flat in 1915, and stayed. They raised their son here. The son has proved a disappointment to Kinchlow. "He does very little work of no kind." Mrs. Kinchlow died, "different ailments, locked bowels, the

doctor said can't do nothin', they took her to county hospital and
that night they called me up and told me she had died."

On the wall above the daybed are a picture of an Indian on a
horse, and a cloth motto, "Father and Son." The steam in the
radiator hisses; the apartment is hot but Kinchlow wraps the
towel more closely about his thin throat. His fingers are long and
skinny. Does he like living in the Mecca Building now? "God no!
There ain't nothing here to like. But it's been awful hard to get a
flat. Even hard to find a room. So, I just stuck on anyhow. It gets
worse all the time. And for one thing, if there was flats to rent,
my money's too thin. I only get the old-age assistance and that was
cut last month—they chopped $4 off of that, I was getting $62.
I was already livin' from hand to mouth, I didn't dare to buy myself a pair of pants or I'd be good and hungry for a few days before that next month come around. When they cut that, they said
the cost of living come down. I wonder O my God, on what?
'Cause all kinds of staple foods that you've got to have, they've got
me so I'm scared to go into a butcher shop and order a decent
piece of meat, oh my, it's terrible high." He gets his check monthly.
"My check day is for tomorrow, get my little $58, go pay $20
rent right away, I wouldn't take no chances on getting held up
or being wild or nothing, I take it right over. Or send my son over
with it. Then starts my hustling and scrabbling for another
month. I have to be awful careful how I buy. I used to go downtown to Goldblatt's and Hillman's, buy my stuff on Saturday, I
could get it so much cheaper, halfway decent roast of beef. Then
the carfare went up to fifteen cents and I walked. I enjoyed it,
too. But since I gotten old it look like walkin' is mean to me."

Presently he shuffles out to the tiny kitchen. "Supper last night,"
and he touches a pot of spareribs and lima beans on the stove,
"it won't be throwed out, warm it up, *eat it,* all I can do is just
look at those nice chops and roasts."

Now near dusk, the fourth-floor balcony is wrapped in gloom,
and young men congregate, lounging, smoking cigarettes, they are
not talking; and down on the ground floor beneath the balcony a
wiry girl of twelve wrestles with a smaller, prettier girl in a new

blue snowsuit, throwing her to the floor, rolling over and over with her in the dirt by the fresh cement the janitor poured. And whooping from the darkness in the far recess of the well comes a rushing crowd of boys and girls, flowing past the iceman, who is still at work, and the din grows louder, screams and cries, loud thumps and thunderous footsteps as the crowd swirls on around the corner into the dark then back, ten children, perhaps ten or twelve years old, armed with spears and bows and arrows, running, screaming, whooping. A man says, "That's all day. And all night too." They are dark leaning shadows racing around a pillar; they have upset and plundered a garbage can and now they throw applecores and onions at each other across the well, the air is filled with flying applecores and onions, and a boy of sixteen armed with a whiskey bottle chases a girl on roller skates, at whom another boy shoots an arrow.

In a corner a small child sits on the floor, playing a mouth organ, and a boy about ten with a long-bladed knife lurks behind a post. Near the doorway two boys of nine or ten detach themselves from the rest and fight, fight in earnest, biting, kicking, hitting, swearing, then silently fighting, not talking, just breathing heavily, until a man comes in off the street and stops them, a tenant with a brief case home from the office, taking one boy with him as he ascends into the upper reaches of the building.

When the Mecca Building was constructed it was considered one of the largest and finest apartment buildings in Chicago if not in America. It catered (almost needless to say) to a white clientele. But after 1900 the Negro migration to Chicago forced the black belt to expand, and by 1912 the Mecca Building was the home of the Negro elite—doctors, lawyers, businessmen.

A woman who lives there still, Mrs. Florence Clayton, arrived in 1916, and she remembers, "There were carpets on the stairs and halls. There were goldfish in the fountain. On the first floor there were lounge chairs and outdoors we had a flower garden and beautiful trees and green grass, you could go out there, oh, it was lovely. The courtyard was all fenced in and there was a lovely walk through the flowers."

The building started to deteriorate during the 1917–18 war. So did the whole neighborhood. Booming war industries pulled thousands of Negroes to Chicago. The luckier ones abandoned the region of Thirty-fifth and State to the poor and the wicked. The black-and-tans where Chicago jazz flowered were right here. Jimmy, the janitor, recalls, "There were lots of fights and cuttings. Building was full of prostitutes. I saw a man throw a prostitute over the third floor railing—from the third floor to the first floor. Didn't hurt her much. She only weighed ninety pounds, kind of light. Finally one of the pimps killed the building watchman. Did it over a woman. And she wasn't even living with him." Jimmy pushes his leather cap back off his forehead. "That about ended it, though. They got a new watchman and he was a killer. He was just a little man but he had great big eyes and he'd shoot you with either hand. He had a cemetery of his own before he died. He only killed nine people—between the basement here and that wire fence. The building got kind of decent after that—families, working people."

And then the Depression came along, and the wicked left, and almost none but the poor remained. The Depression was awful in the black belt. About 1932 the bottom fell out. One woman who lived here then recalls, "The building was partly empty. Onc lady told me she was sitting down on the curb and the police passed and it was cold and they asked her what was the matter and she said she'd been set out and they told her to come on in here and the first flat she'd find, sit down. They carried her to court later but they didn't make her get out, they couldn't, people had no work to do then. It was always warm and nice in here during the Depression."

The Depression accounts for the presence today of the building's only white tenant, a heavy, soft-faced, white-haired woman of sixty-six. "I'd been a housekeeper at a hotel and one of my maids, a colored girl, she was married to a white doctor and they lived here in the Mecca Building. I couldn't find a job, I just got stuck, I couldn't make it, and they took me in." Some of the Mecca inhabitants who moved in while they were on relief are now earning good money in the steel mills or on Pullman cars and one or two earn upward of $5,000 a year, but they are imprisoned here by the scarcity of dwellings for Negroes. A few of the long-time ten-

ants remain by choice, oddly proud of the building. A few earn
money by living there—they sublet rooms in their apartments for
as much as $12 a week. The janitor Jimmy says, "Every day peo-
ple come in, many as ten or twelve a day, lookin' for a place,
they been walkin' the street, lookin' for some place to go, say,
'Janitor, if you can get me an apartment in here I'll give you
$100, but there ain't none."

There are several women's clubs in the building, such as the Old-
Age Pensioners Club and the Twelve Tribes. Fitzgerald, the Democratic precinct captain, has been elected sweetheart of these. Fitzgerald, a neat, well-dressed, youngish man, has said, "If there's a
weddin' I'm there, if there's a death I'm there, if there's a birth
I'm there. I had a baby born in my car a while back, trying to
get the mother to the hospital." Fitzgerald is a court bailiff by
day. The Mecca precinct has voted Democratic since 1932. Like the
other tenants, Fitzgerald worries about the children. "In summertime the police chase them off the street. One day I come home
and the police had backed up a wagon ready to take a whole
load to the station for standing in front of the building. I had to
put a stop to it. I had three ball clubs last summer and got uniforms for 'em all."

In a vacant store on the ground floor is the Mecca Center, for
children. Nobody knows how many children are being raised in the
Mecca Building but most people guess five hundred, and now at
4:30 P.M. on a Thursday fifteen of the five hundred are in the
Mecca Center. The Center is a big square bare room, a dais at
one side, a great clutter of dusty newspapers behind a desk, a piano
and a windup Victrola against one wall, a tom-tom and Indian
heads in the display window. Two older boys are playing Ping-pong
and at a small table two younger ones are playing checkers; but
the rest of the younger ones, probably from nine to twelve years
old, are chasing each other around the room, snapping cap-guns
at each other, and soon the checker game stops and all thirteen
of the younger ones are chasing each other, climbing over tables
and chairs, leaping through the air onto each others' backs, screaming wildly; the Ping-pong players, older, proceed with their game,
each with an arm outstretched to fend off the littler kids, occasion-

ally pausing to take a cut at a near one's head; a dozen chairs stacked against a wall collapse as a boy's body crashes into them. A man in a hat is standing in a corner watching, saying vaguely, "She was supposed to come and be a musical program but I ain't seen her come in."

On the wall is a program schedule allotting various hours of the week to such activities as "Teen-Age Club," "Children's Story-Telling Hour," "Parents' Club Meeting." Right now, it is "Children's Game Period." The man watching says sharply, "You—let that victrola alone," to a boy climbing onto it in order to leap onto another boy's back. A woman arrives bustling in. "I teach music and dramatics and folk dancing. I have about sixty enrolled. From six to eight we have singing and at nine physical culture and clubs." She is taking off her gloves, as unmindful of the children as they are of her; the children are growing more serious in their play, the temper has changed, ugliness has crept in. they battle silently, not laughing or screaming, only panting hard. The man is making plans to take some of them to the circus.

In one apartment in the building a woman and her husband are raising nine children, raising them in one room. This summer afternoon she is sitting in a chair by the door of the one room, her baby on the bed, evidently asleep but looking dead it is so thin and still, and the mother is saying, "It is hot at night, at night you burn up. My husband and I sleep in the bed. The kids sleep on the cot." The nine kids. They are from nine months to fifteen years in age. The room is eight feet by eleven. In it are one bed, one davenport, one radio, one light-bulb, one picture, two straight wood chairs, one wicker table (on which stand a seashell, a jar of deodorant, and a can of face powder), one calendar. Back of the bed is a closet curtained with a rag. One necktie hangs on a nail in the wall. The plaster is broken. Her husband earns $45 a week as a machine operator. They pay $6 a week for this room. They have lived in this room four years.

The mother is twenty-nine years old. When she and her husband first came to Chicago they lived in one room on Wentworth Avenue, then in three rooms on Prairie Avenue until "the lady sold the building," then in five rooms elsewhere on Prairie Avenue again "till the lady sold the building," then in four rooms elsewhere on Prairie "till the man sold the building," then here. They came here on August 6, 1946. "My husband knew the man that had this apartment so he let us have a place in it that same evening. We were out on the street." They can find no other place to live. "I looked so much that I'm just disgusted about it. They say you're a citizen of Chicago and on votin' day they're right up to your door to vote. My husband, he wrote to the Mayor of Chicago and everyone else and I don't see no results," and she rises and fumbles behind a curtain on the window ledge and finds two letters. She is young, quick-moving, pretty; her teeth flash and she wears big gold earrings and she appears about the age of her oldest daughter, fifteen, who now comes in and stands in the doorway looking reproachful. One letter is a long form letter from the Chicago Housing Authority:

"Dear Friend,

". . . The housing projects now in operation have such lengthy waiting lists that no additional applications are being taken at this time. . . ." The other is a personal letter from a Housing Authority official: "Mayor Kennelly has referred to us for reply your letter of March 2, concerning your need for adequate housing. We are very sorry."

"All this stuff's just a racket," says the mother of nine. "They ain't doing nothing about it. Makes me sick." She hitches her chair around to face the wall. "After all, my husband works and makes an honest livin' and he do support his family the best that a workin' man can. His children do get clothes, the onliest kick that they can have is that they don't have no place to live. And that's not his fault." The baby on the bed stirs a little, then lies still again.

Until 1941 the Mecca Building was owned by a New York estate. The janitor Jimmy only once saw a representative of the estate. In 1941 the estate sold the Mecca to its next-door neighbor, the Illinois Institute of Technology. The Institute bought the building for only one purpose: to tear it down. The Institute was expanding its campus in accordance with a neat plan integrated with the neat plans of numerous other agencies for clearing the South Side slums. It wanted to replace the Mecca Building with a laboratory.

But its plans ran head-on into an important need of the people who dwelt in the Mecca Building, the need for a place to live.

For nine years it has tried to evict them, taking them to court and warning them the Mecca is a firetrap. Thus far the tenants have managed to generate enough political pressure to stay. Recently, when the Institute again started eviction proceedings, State Senator C. C. Wimbish, a lawyer who has represented the tenants in court, said, "If they try to put these people out, they'll have a race riot down there on State Street and I intend to make it as tense as possible. Any roof is better than no roof."

It is quiet in the building on a summer morning, quiet as a tomb. Spit falls flatly on the ground floor, spat by a silent watcher high on the balcony, and in a dark corner recess on the topmost floor a young girl, pretty, wearing a tight white sweater, strains against a young man leaning on the wall. An old man in blue pajamas, his eyes wild and staring, his body very thin, totters along, clutching at the railing, saying in a high, cracked voice to a visitor, "Call me a telephone number please, mister, will you call me a telephone number," but a large woman steps from a doorway and shakes her head at the visitor, making circling motions beside her temple, and moves to take the old man's arm, and seeing her he starts, as though to run, then weeps, and she leads him away. A puff of blue smoke hangs in the dead air on the second balcony where a man is leaning on the railing, smoking. A janitor collects garbage in a cart that rumbles on the broken tile like a tumbril. Everything echoes in the halls, voices are hard to comprehend, are confused with distant sounds.

A visitor twists the bell on Mrs. Griffin's apartment and she calls, "Who is it?" then unfastens the chain. Her mother is sitting by the window in the sun, as always. Mrs. Griffin says that when she got the most recent notice to vacate, she went house-hunting: "I found a place to buy at a real estate office way up on the North Side but no other colored people live right there, and I don't want to get bombed on," as indeed many Chicago Negroes have been when they tried to leave the black belt. She goes over beside her mother, who is rocking. "I think this housing situation is terrible, it's all politics, that's all. I'm not mad at the school. It's their property, we know that. I'm mad 'cause all this politics. Put 'em in office and they didn't did nothin'. They build streets and superhighways and recreation—not houses. They should turn that money loose and stop it—people has got to have some place to live. They gonna do *anything* if they don't."

She laughs, but does not sound amused: "They say they gonna place us somewhere. *Place* us! I don't wanta be placed anywhere myself. They might place me in some mudhole somewhere and I never did live in that," and she laughs again. Her mother mutters something. "I don't know what they going to do with us. After all, there's no use in pushing us around from one place to another, that's no way to live." And then, after a pause, "It's all so mean."

Her mother, rocking, has started muttering steadily; she is looking out the window, her head in its white lace cap bobbing gently up and down. What is Mrs. Griffin going to do?

"I don't know. I'll have to have a place for my mother. I couldn't tell you what I'm going to do, to save my neck." Her mother, rocking, begins to mutter louder, but her words are not intelligible, it is just a human voice, muttering, and it is impossible to tell whether in anger or in joy, it is only sound.

THE PEACOCK CASE*

LeRoy F. McHugh

THE Peacock Murder Case was spread across the front pages of the newspapers from the day of Dr. Peacock's murder until the case was closed. It possessed all the ingredients for which a morbid, mystery-loving public hungered—mysterious phone calls; a principal with a past that struck the avid as too spotless; possible women in the victim's life. . . .

I include it here not only because Mr. McHugh has written an expertly put-together, exciting story, but also because the case itself possesses peculiar qualities often found in Chicago crime: inventiveness, daring, and crass and brutal stupidity.

IF THERE'S a monstrous secret in your private life, an embarrassing chapter in your past, or a single peccadillo you are striving to forget, try to arrange things so that your demise will not be conducted under homicidal auspices. If you are a beautiful character and your life is an open book, the advice is still good.

They were phrasing it a little differently, but on this general theme the students of philosophy were agreed. The class was in session, as usual, around the pinochle table in the press room at the Chicago Detective Bureau. I was listening with desultory interest—until a familiar name was mentioned.

Tough questions were being propounded. What man's career can emerge unscathed from under the microscope of a murder probe? Who can explain the touch of mob psychology that sways public thinking as to a crime mystery? What perverse streak leads one

* From *Chicago Murders,* edited by Sewell Peaslee Wright, 1947. Reprinted by permission of the publishers, Duell, Sloan and Pearce, Inc.

individual to embrace, eagerly, a rumor with scandalous implica-
tions, reflecting on a hapless neighbor's integrity?

"Take the case of Doc Peacock," said a student as he prepared
to meld. "They really took that fellow apart, didn't they?"

"They sure did," nodded a cub, trying to talk like a veteran.
"And as I understand it the police were to blame. They messed
that one up, but good."

"Junior, you're wet again," I said, for the crime in question had
been one of my babies. "The police work was marvelous. Half
a dozen motives, one 'obvious.' So they had to follow them all,
and maybe it seemed ruthless. But the last trail led to pay dirt. It
was a masterpiece, lads; I can prove it."

I did so, and I can do it again.

The story started with a "missing person" report to the Summerdale police on the morning of January 3, 1936. Dr. Silber C. Peacock, successful and wealthy pediatrician, had failed to return to
his home on Sheridan Road the night before. The report was routine except in the manner of its filing. It was relayed to the station
on the North Side by State's Attorney Thomas J. Courtney, a close
personal friend of Dr. Peacock's, to whom a mildly disturbed Mrs.
Peacock had telephoned these facts:

She and her daughter, Ruth, eight years old, had returned on
the previous evening from her family home at Bowen, Illinois. Dr.
Peacock had met them at the Union Station; they dined leisurely at
a North Side restaurant and then went home. The doctor had gone
to bed when the telephone rang.

Mrs. Peacock answered the phone. A man was calling. Refusing
to disclose his name, his address, or the nature of his business, the
caller insisted on talking to Dr. Peacock. Reluctantly Mrs. Peacock
summoned her husband. She heard him say: "What is it? . . . Oh,
a child is ill."

There was a pause. The doctor began scribbling on a pad. He
inquired for a telephone number, evidently was told that the caller
had no telephone. He replaced the receiver, sighed deeply, walked
to his bedroom, and began to dress. Meanwhile Mrs. Peacock
strolled to the telephone stand and examined a sheet on which the
doctor had scrawled: "G. Smale. 6438 North Whipple Street."

In an effort to be helpful, Mrs. Peacock wrote the name and address on a loose slip of paper and handed it to her husband at the door. He kissed her, picked up his instrument case, and departed. She glanced at the clock in the hall. The time was 10:05.

At 1:30 A.M., she awoke from fitful slumber. The doctor had not returned. She was vaguely disturbed. Not often, nowadays, with his excellent practice established and thoroughly organized, was he asked to leave his home on a night call; even less frequently would he consent to respond, as he had tonight, to a summons from one who was not a regular patient. With these thoughts in mind, Mrs. Peacock reached for the bed phone and called the building manager. Had the doctor's car returned to the garage? It had not.

There was no more sleep that night for Mrs. Peacock. At the break of dawn she ventured to call Mr. Courtney. He attempted to quiet her mounting fear, assured her that he would notify the police at once, and made good his promise. Whereupon the search for the missing pediatrician was under way.

I recall very well the casual manner in which the Peacock missing report was received that day at the Detective Bureau, high in the Police Building at Eleventh and State Streets. This skeleton report merely sketched the bare details of the man's departure from his home and appended this paragraph:

"Dr. Peacock is forty years old and a member of the staff of Children's Memorial Hospital. He was driving his 1931 black sedan, bearing 1936 license 25-682, when he left. He wore a gray suit, gray overcoat, and gray felt hat. He is five feet seven inches tall, weighs 150 pounds, and wears glasses."

Up in the bureau's press room, the boys around the pinochle table heard an outline of the missing report from one of the smaller fry and favored it with brief and completely objective consideration. After all, it was one of a dozen such doubtful leads reaching the bureau daily, and the weeding-out process, which to a veteran reporter becomes instinctive, is an important part of the reportorial routine. Most of the newsmen elected to give the Peacock yarn a complete pass.

"It looks to me like the good doctor has had himself a large evening," commented one of the younger pinochle players, amiably and utterly without rancor. "He'll show up, all right, when the old head stops throbbing. But he'd better warn that babe to stop phoning him at his home. I could never get by with one of those 'night call' excuses. My weaver's too smart."

"Hope we're not passing up a good kidnaping," said Ed Kennedy, case-hardened representative of the *Tribune,* settling down comfortably to his game. He had expressed a thought dawning in my mind. I glanced over the daily schedule; things looked unusually dull. I determined to learn a little more about this North Side doctor's disappearance, in preparation for a remotely possible newsworthy development. I studied the known facts, as revealed in the report, and picked up a telephone directory.

No "G. Smale" was listed at 6438 North Whipple Street. This was not unexpected since the report mentioned that Dr. Peacock's caller had claimed to have no telephone. What was surprising, however, was the fact that a "G. W. Smale" was listed at 6438 South Washtenaw Avenue. The names and the house numbers tallied, but addresses were separated virtually by the length of the city. And herein lay one of several fantastic, confusing coincidences which defied analysis, misled investigators, and made of the Peacock case one of the most baffling puzzles in Chicago's crime history.

"I do not know a Dr. Peacock," said G. W. Smale of 6438 South Washtenaw Avenue, in response to my telephoned inquiry. "I never called the man in my life. I have no need of a child specialist. I am not a father." His statement was convincing, and, in later conversations with police, was satisfactorily corroborated.

I got my car and drove northward. This much was clear: the call that inveigled Dr. Peacock from his bed and home on the previous night was phony. Either it was prearranged to supply an excuse for a tryst he wanted to keep, or it was a lure, planted by someone with an ulterior motive. In either event, my interest was definitely aroused. At the end of the trail, I was now convinced, lay a news story.

My destination was 4753 Broadway, Dr. Peacock's office address. Here I learned that he shared sumptuous quarters with Drs. George Edwin Baxter, Walter C. McKee, and F. J. Corper, medical specialists of uniformly high repute. Soon I was in conference with

Miss Kathryn Maloney, Dr. Peacock's attractive but agitated office secretary.

"I know your first question," she burst forth after I had identified myself. "No, the doctor had no patient named Smale. What's even stranger, he almost never answered night calls. His regular patients seldom asked him to do so, and his practice has become so large that he wasn't accepting any new cases. It is unbelievable to me that he would have got out of bed. . . . Oh, please!" she exclaimed, possibly noting a significant look in my eyes. "Please don't leap to horrid conclusions. Dr. Peacock was a man of impeccable character. He loved his family and his home passionately. He was the antithesis of a playboy. He loathed night clubs and all they stand for. He didn't even drink. That he might have been involved in an affair with a woman other than his wife is unthinkable. And that's why I am convinced something terrible has happened. Won't you please believe me?"

I soothed the troubled secretary as well as I could, and presently she had given me, with justifiable pride, these facts about the missing doctor:

He was born near Beverly, in Adams County, Illinois, in 1896. He received his early education in that community. Son of sturdy farm folk, he enlisted early in World War I and served both in the United States Army Intelligence Unit and in the British Naval Intelligence Department.

Discharged with honor, young Peacock matriculated at Knox College in Galesburg, Illinois. There he met Miss Ruth Pearce, a popular and beautiful coed of Bowen, Illinois, and a romance developed. In 1922 Peacock enrolled at Rush Medical College in Chicago, was graduated in 1925, and immediately married Miss Pearce. After internship at Presbyterian Hospital, Dr. Peacock entered private practice in Chicago.

Specializing in pediatrics, he soon became respected among professional men as one of the city's most skillful young doctors in that field. His practice flourished, particularly along the fashionable Gold Coast, and became extremely lucrative. No breath of scandal ever touched either his professional or his private life.

"As to his orderly way of living," Kathryn Maloney concluded, though I had not even hinted a doubt on that point, "consider the manner in which he spent New Year's Eve. Knowing that his family was out of town, several of Dr. Peacock's professional associates had invited him to join them at a rather gay holiday celebration at a reputable downtown night club. The doctor appreciated the invitation, but rejected it. He preferred to spend the evening alone in his home, reading and studying."

I asked Miss Maloney one more question. Had the parents of any patient, however unjustly, blamed him for failure in treatment of their child, perhaps threatened him with reprisals? The secretary denied it. Later events disclosed that on this point she was holding out on me, but I never resented her subterfuge. A loyal employee, that girl, protecting her boss's interests in every possible way.

In the Peacock home, high in the Edgewater Beach Apartments, the missing doctor's wife greeted me politely, but with an obvious weariness born of tension. I didn't keep her long. She repeated the story she had told the police, without discrepancies. The doctor was a perfect husband and father. His habits were regular and beyond reproach. He had no known enemies. She believed he had been lured by robbers, possibly that he had been made the victim of some terrible mistake in identity.

In spite of an honest desire to be fair, my thoughts as I left the Peacock home were these: "So many wives know so little about their husbands. So many cheaters convince their mates that they are paragons. How many times, McHugh, has a gangland hooligan's little woman told you that her man, freshly mowed down by a tommy-gun, was a noble character, an ideal provider, a quiet citizen dabbling in real estate or dry goods or the oil business?"

My doubt, so far unfounded on fact, was given something to rest upon as I paused in the lobby of the apartment house and discussed the disappearance with an attendant. I learned that Dr. Peacock, rushing through the lobby to his waiting car on the previous night, had suddenly turned and spent five minutes in a telephone booth!

Yes, it was true. I checked at the desk, at the switchboard, and verified the story. Dr. Peacock had paused in his abrupt departure, rushed to the desk, tossed down a coin, and demanded a phone slug. He had been seen in earnest conversation in the booth.

Now, there was a reasonable explanation for this procedure. The doctor, stepping off the elevator, might have recalled an urgent business call which he had meant to make before leaving his apartment. Still, he had retired only an hour previously, with no indication of pending business on his mind. And the thought persisted —indeed, it was patently uppermost among those who discussed it in the excitement-charged lobby—that Dr. Peacock used the lobby phone because he didn't care to have Mrs. Peacock overhear his conversation. This explanation was the more readily accepted, I'm afraid, because it dovetailed beautifully with theory, already taking shape, that the "mercy call" had been a frame-up: that the baby specialist had been on his way to a rendezvous.

I returned to the bureau press room as shadows began to mark the close of the bitterly cold afternoon. I called my office and reported my findings. Already the city desk was alert, obsessed with the hopeful notion that a kidnaping was under way and that an epic story was in the making.

It was, indeed, though kidnapping was not the angle. At 7 P.M., twenty-one hours after "G. Smale" had summoned Dr. Peacock from the comfort of his bed on the pretext of ministering to an ailing child, they found the doctor's body.

Police squads assigned by Supervising Captain Martin Mullen to seek the missing doctor had performed their obvious duty, but perfunctorily. They had canvassed the apartment building at 6438 North Whipple Street and established that "G. Smale" was not a resident. Nor had any tenant there observed the doctor's large limousine on the previous night. Officers had checked on "G. W. Smale" on South Washtenaw Avenue, just as I had done, and had returned empty-handed and mystified at the coincidence of the house numbers.

They had looked for the Peacock automobile in the vicinity of the North Whipple Street address, but they hadn't looked far enough. Had they ventured three blocks west, to the 6000 block in North Francisco Avenue, they would have come upon the Cadillac car—and in it the gruesome evidence of a particularly vicious murder.

The machine, parked opposite a vacant lot, had been there since shortly after 11 P.M., on January second, the evening of the doctor's disappearance. This was one of the first facts established by Patrolmen Hugo Olsen and James Sullivan, early arrivals after the alarm went out on the evening of the third.

A resident of 6326 North Whipple said that he had looked out the front window of his home at midnight and had seen the machine standing there, its lights burning and at least two men inside. A maid employed at No. 6322 had seen the same thing at 1:30 A.M. She was positive that one occupant of the big car was a man, surmised that a second might have been a woman.

Still another neighbor, leaving for work on the morning of the third, noted that the car's lights were burning. On his return in the evening, he dispatched his son to see whether the car was locked, and, if not, to turn out the lights. That was how the battered figure in the tonneau was discovered.

Dr. Peacock's body was in a kneeling position on the floor of the tonneau, facing the rear and bent over the seat. His overcoat had been tossed over the body, shielding it from the view of passers-by and of children who played nearby throughout the day. His glasses, which he habitually wore, were folded and tucked carefully, as if for protection, between the seat and one side of the car. His professional case lay open, and its ordinarily gleaming instruments were strewn on the seat and floor, spotted by blood which had stained the upholstery, the floor, and the rear windows. His crumpled hat, also flecked with scarlet, rested on the seat. A small street guide lay on one running board, as though discarded after the driver had sought the unfamiliar address of his destination.

A .45-caliber revolver bullet had entered the right temple and emerged behind the left ear. The bullet itself was never found, though a newspaper reporter later picked up a .45-caliber revolver shell from the snow a short distance north of the car. The victim had been slashed seven times on the top of the head, and his skull had been crushed by innumerable terrible blows with a heavy club. His right hand was gloved, but his bare left hand had been caught and smashed in the door as it closed. The left glove was near the body.

I noted all these details and tried to catalogue them in my mind for future reference. Like other early arrivals, including police officers who had viewed the revolting handiwork of many a calloused gangster with a gun for hire, I was appalled and shaken by the savagery of this attack. I can remember now that my first conclusion, which I believe the veteran police shared, was that only a bitter personal hatred would impel a murderer to such extreme, fanatical, pointless violence. Such hatred is seldom aroused save by a single emotion—jealousy. A bandit would go to these lengths only if demented.

This was rank prejudgment, I must confess, but in our defense I hasten to point out that all available evidence veering toward a simple, unvarnished robbery motive was speedily sought and fairly weighed. It weighed little.

It is true that the doctor's wallet was missing. Mrs. Peacock later insisted that it had contained no more than $20, her husband having invariably refused to carry more than that amount on his person since an occasion some two years before, when thugs had set upon him on a dark street and had been beaten off by the doctor, but only after a terrific struggle.

Balanced against the significance of the missing wallet, as well as against the absence of two small vials from the doctor's medical kit, was the puzzling circumstance that considerable silver in a trousers pocket and personal jewelry of great value remained untouched. Indicative of the careful consideration given the robbery theory by police before it was reluctantly abandoned, or at least shunted into the background, was the logic of Detective Chief John L. Sullivan, in general charge of the case.

"Grant that Mrs. Peacock is correct and that the doctor habitually carried no more than about $20," the chief told me in an interview. "It is entirely probable that bandits, seeking a victim, would expect to find a far richer haul in the pockets of this successful specialist. I will concede the doctor was a likely subject for professional gunmen's attention. It is even conceivable that the killers were frightened away so suddenly that they neglected to strip the victim of his jewelry and change.

"Also supporting this theory is the known fact of Dr. Peacock's personal bravery. Once previously he was attacked by thieves, and he did not hesitate to fight them off, though the risk must have been great. If bandits killed the doctor, obviously it was because he resisted their assault in the face of overwhelming odds."

"Then you lean to the robbery theory?" I ventured.

"No," he sighed, "and I'll tell you why. First, men in the robbery business seldom lure their victims into their clutches through any such elaborate, melodramatic plot as is here presented. Too many potentially treasure-yielding victims are available anywhere, any time.

"Second, if a seasoned gunman had to dispose of a battling victim, he would shoot him swiftly and mortally, and that would be that. Instead, Dr. Peacock was not only shot, but was subjected to a terrific slugging, topped by several slashes with a weapon I believe to have been his own scalpel.

"No," Chief Sullivan concluded a bit ruefully, for by this process of elimination he was posing for himself a deeper problem, "fury like that visited on poor Dr. Peacock is rarely displayed by a common garden variety of bandit. We are not shelving the robbery theory, mind you, but we must use our best judgment and depend on our experience. We must look elsewhere—probably somewhere deep in the slain man's life we will find a key."

"What do you make of the two vials missing from the medical kit?" I asked, and the veteran criminologist's eyes lighted.

"Ah, there you have a live lead," he exclaimed. "You and I know, or think we know, that those vials did not contain narcotics. A baby specialist isn't likely to be toting dope around on his calls. But did his assailant consider this angle? Isn't it possible that an addict chose Dr. Peacock's name at random, unaware of his specialized field, and lured him to a lonely spot to seize his supply of narcotics? Couldn't the maniacal rage of an addict, when denied his dope ration, explain the killer's savagery?"

I leaped to my feet excitedly, but the chief laughed and restrained me.

"That's theory, not fact," he pointed out. "Don't go to press with it. As a matter of fact, I expect romance to rear its seductive head at any moment. Dr. Peacock was rich, handsome, personable. He had, I understand, upwards of five hundred patients—children whose mothers, of course, visited the doctor with them. And it looks as though my men may have to interview every confounded one of them!"

It was the theory involving narcotics, nevertheless, which yielded the first "outside" or volunteered clue in the case, as a result of its presentation in my newspaper, the *Evening American*, in speculative form. The clue set forth a possibility even more sinister than that suggested by Chief Sullivan.

Dr. Morris Fishbein, editor of the *Journal of the American Medical Association,* made the disclosure. His memory jogged by reading that a crazed narcotics addict was a possible suspect, he recalled that Dr. Peacock had confided to him that he was engaged in highly secret investigations for the United States Bureau of Narcotics.

Substantiation, plus elaboration, was forthcoming from Dr. Fishbein's assistant, Dr. Johnson F. Hammond, an old army physician, who had met Dr. Peacock when the latter was doing histological work in the medical corps at Fort Sheridan in 1920. He said, "Dr. Peacock called recently at the A.M.A. offices to inquire about a cure for asthma. On that occasion, speaking rather mysteriously, I thought, he told me that he was conducting some sort of undercover investigation involving narcotics. It was not clear, however, whether he referred to a city or a federal inquiry."

It wasn't much, but it created a sensation. Rumors budded and blossomed out of all proportion to the published facts. Dr. Peacock, a secret federal agent, had incurred powerful underworld enemies and had been murdered by hired killers of the dope ring! Dr. Peacock had set a clever trap for the dope peddlers and had attempted, bravely but foolishly, to round them up singlehanded! Most poisonous poppycock of all—Dr. Peacock, himself deep in the narcotics traffic, had been instigator or victim of a double cross, and you know what happens when thieves fall out!

The unimpeachable testimony of Drs. Fishbein and Hammond opened a perfectly legitimate field for police investigation. Detectives, joined by reporters, began a determined effort to crystallize the clue into something tangible. At the offices of the Narcotics Bureau's Chicago division we were informed, coolly and firmly, that Dr. Peacock was unknown and had never had dealings with the staff. It was not conclusive. The ways of federal investigations are devious, and the possibility remained that the doctor was acting on behalf of agents not connected with the Chicago office.

Meanwhile other new clues were turned up. A pinkish blotch and deep tire tracks were discovered in the snow in front of the apartment building at 6438 North Whipple Street, the address to which Dr. Peacock had been summoned. Numerous cigarette butts were taken from the snow at this spot and were studied minutely.

Considered as a unit, these discoveries appeared to establish beyond doubt that the person or persons who enticed the doctor from his bed and home had, indeed, awaited his arrival at the given address; that either the wait was an extended one or that a lengthy discussion had followed his arrival; and that the violence and bloodshed had begun at this point before the scene of action shifted three blocks west to North Francisco Avenue.

A man's felt hat, of high quality, but battered and soiled, was found a half block north of the position in which the car and body had been left. Since Dr. Peacock's hat lay at his side in the automobile, it was assumed one of his assailants' hats had been lost en route. Detectives were assigned to the routine chore of tracing its ownership, with no more light than that supplied by the label of a large men's store in the Loop.

Re-examination of the death car had been under way in an atmosphere of secrecy, for great developments were expected. I sought out Supervising Captain John Prendergast, an old and trusted friend, under whose direction the examination was being made. He spoke guardedly.

"We have learned some things and we expect to learn more," he told me. "I can say now that Dr. Peacock drove directly from his home to the North Whipple Street address, where he presumably expected to minister to a sick child. The gas tank of his car was filled at the garage just before his departure. And the tank is still almost filled to its nineteen-gallon capacity. Undoubtedly he was unfamiliar with the district, as attested by the street guide which he produced and examined. Nevertheless, he used the most direct course to his destination and his tragic fate."

Captain Prendergast, a shrewd criminologist, who has mastered many a crime puzzle, paused and shrugged.

"There is another clue in that car," he muttered, "but just now it isn't clear enough to talk about."

"Fingerprints?" I asked hopefully, and he nodded.

"But they are somewhat smudged," he said, "and they may be of no value whatever. And they may turn out to be nobody's but Dr. Peacock's. A good, clear set of the murderer's prints would be just too, too pat!"

The episode of the "Man In The White Muffler" next intrigued the press, the public, and in lesser degree, the police. A woman who lived close to the spot where the body was found, brought this story to Captain Prendergast:

"On Thursday afternoon [the day of the murder] I was walking on Devon Avenue, a half block from Whipple Street. It was four o'clock when a taxicab, a Yellow, stopped near me, and the passenger inquired the way to 6436 North Whipple Street. That, as you know, is in the same building as Number 6438.

"I supplied the information, then watched as the cab drove to the front of the Whipple Street building. The man got out, paid his fare, and started walking slowly north. The man wore a black derby, a black overcoat, and a white muffler."

Others in the neighborhood also saw the stranger, investigation disclosed, but none could offer a better description. Captain Martin McCormick, pointing out that the mufflered "phantom" might well have been the killer himself, engaged in "casing" the lonely neighborhood before setting his plot in operation, enlisted the aid of Yellow Cab Company officials. There began, and continued for days, a tedious check-up of all drivers and records in a desperate effort to trace the reported trip to 6436 North Whipple Street.

Days were passing and clue upon clue was failing. The public outcry for a solution was increasing, and the tension was becoming unbearable. A bit of comic relief was definitely in order—and this need was adequately filled in the unfolding of what was termed at its outset "the most important break in the case to date." An actual, physical key, it seemed, was to unlock the now-famous Peacock murder mystery.

The incident developed during one of a series of inquest hearings, during the run of which all the actual evidence and a plethora of aimless theorizing were paraded before an increasingly bewildered coroner's jury. At one stage of the questioning of Mrs. Peacock, who throughout conducted herself with amazing fortitude, Deputy Coroner Edward Edlestein thrust a hand into a trousers pocket. With a dramatic flourish he drew forth a key and stated, "This key was one of the objects found in Dr. Peacock's possession. Can you identify it?"

Mrs. Peacock couldn't. She examined the key closely. It was one stamped out of a blank slug, obviously the duplicate of an original, and it bore only the number 428. Mrs. Peacock said she had never seen it before.

Intensified police activity ensued. A special detail was assigned to locate the door which held the lock which the key would open. For a reason never explained, this detail established special headquarters in a Webster Hotel suite and operated exclusively from this base, its every movement shrouded in secrecy.

Rumor-lovers had a field day. So Mrs. Peacock had never seen the key? Well, that was the way with "model husbands." Didn't the key make it clear the good doctor was up to his neck in some extra-marital hanky-panky? Chances were, many an I-told-you-so observer leered, police would find the key provided open sesame to a swank love-nest, and the whole sordid story would be out.

The police traced the key, all right. They traced it to Suite 428 in the 5200 Sheridan Road Apartments (by coincidence, not far from the home of the Peacocks). They learned that the occupants of this apartment were Mr. and Mrs. Isadore Lidschin—and that the Lidschins were the parents-in-law of Deputy Coroner Edward Edlestein.

The conclusion, painful as it was to the deputy, was inescapable. Edlestein had somehow mixed a key of his own among the exhibits taken from the pockets of Dr. Peacock. We all dropped the widely heralded "key clue" as gently and as swiftly as possible. After all, it was an entirely unpremeditated blunder and, in a way, a very human one.

In the midst of this unfortunate affair, and before the real identity of the key had destroyed the love-nest theory, another attack on the Peacock integrity occurred—a sensation-studded series of developments which most of us viewed, candidly, as the coup de grâce to the specialist's tottering reputation.

The chapter began on a note of simple, absolute finality. It seemed to make everything crystal clear. It appeared—for a few breathless hours—to be a signpost bearing the legend: "This Way to a Complete, Logical Solution to the Peacock Murder Mystery." And then—well, after those first few exhilarating hours the confounded "break" developed so many ramifications that it seemed to defy all common sense, and to point to two motives simultaneously.

Earlier that day I had been sitting with Captain McCormick in his office at Summerdale Station. Also in the conference were Chief Sullivan, Captain Daniel Gilbert, head of State's Attorney's investigators; Supervising Captain Prendergast, Assistant State's Attorney Marshall V. Kearney, and, I believe, Lieutenant Otto Erlanson of the homicide squad. Everybody was dead tired. Swirling about the officials' heads and lashing them on to ceaseless activity was a storm of public criticism, an insistent and unreasoning demand that, with or without evidence, a solution be obtained and guilt be established.

"Gentlemen, our clues are fading," Prendergast was wearily saying. "The hat found near the scene is like a thousand others. We can't establish who bought it, nor when or where. The fingerprints inside Dr. Peacock's car were smudged and are useless. Our 'witnesses,' such as they are, cannot even agree whether two men were arguing in the death car that night, or a man and a woman. The boys tracing the narcotics angle have found themselves in a cul-de-sac.

"We know the doctor drove directly from home to the Whipple Street address, met his slayers outside, had trouble with them there —for blood was spilled—and showed up three blocks away in his own car, very dead. That's all we really know, and where does that leave us?"

"Exactly nowhere," Kearney commented unhappily. "Personally

I can't accept a conclusion that bandits killed this man for $20 in loot and left gems worth many times that amount. If a kidnaping was intended and the doctor proved too hot to handle, we may never solve the case."

Chief Sullivan nervously tapped the desk with a pencil.

"Keep in mind the fury of the attack," he advised, but his voice carried no conviction. "I am unshaken in my belief that a brain fired by jealousy, or by a real or fancied wrong, conceived this crime. I admit freely that little has turned up as yet to bear me out.

"My detectives have checked the parents of more than five hundred Peacock patients. We haven't found a disgruntled person, or a situation involving the suspicion of heart interest. Dr. Peacock's private life has withstood our scrutiny—despite what people are saying.

"I had hoped the telephone call made in the lobby by the doctor would open the way. Instead, we have now learned Dr. Peacock merely called his secretary on business. That leaves the so-called 'mystery key,' stamped '428,' as the only lead that's still alive—and somehow I'm desperately afraid that, too, will fail." (Prophetic fear!) "Nevertheless, gentlemen, a powerful emotion—perhaps a twisted brain—is involved here. A break will come. . . ."

A door swung open and the chief paused. The newcomer, a mild little man, announced himself as the Reverend Kenneth A. Hurst, a Lutheran minister.

"I am unversed in police affairs," he said timidly, after a couple of false starts which I attributed to extreme nervousness. "I feel strongly, however, that you men should know of a conversation which occurred last New Year's Day during a chance meeting between myself and my great and good friend, Dr. Peacock, God rest his soul."

He was being eyed with varying degrees of disinterest, but the pastor plunged ahead.

"On that occasion the doctor confided that a strange man, a fellow who claimed to be a chiropodist, had come bursting into his Broadway office and had made vile accusations. He quoted this caller as crying, 'You, sir, performed an abortion on my wife!' "

Now there was tense, restrained excitement in Captain McCormick's office. Half of those in the room were on their feet.

"Go on," commanded Chief Sullivan impatiently. "What happened then?"

"Why," said the Reverend Hurst, slightly taken aback, "Dr. Peacock said it flashed through his mind that the man was a crank. He had never set eyes on him before. And he had never performed an abortion in his life. I remember just what the doctor told me. He said, 'I was suddenly very angry at this absurd charge. I yelled, "I think you are a little crazy." Whereupon I threw him bodily out of my office.' "

"When did this occur?" snapped Prosecutor Kearney. "Did Dr. Peacock say whether his caller mentioned his name?"

"He said it occurred last October," said the minister, after some thought. "And he understood the caller to say he was Thompson, the chiropodist."

The Reverend Hurst was questioned further but knew no more. He was thanked abruptly and dismissed. There was work to do. The doctor's brush with his irate visitor seemed to crystallize a suspicion that long had been in the mind of every investigator on the case. Through just such a revelation, timidly volunteered, "inscrutable" mysteries often are made clear.

No shrewd deduction or tedious police work was required to locate Arthur St. George Thompson at his Wilson Avenue address. He was one of the few Chicago chiropodists with that surname. He was found to be a slim man, forty-one years old, with graying hair, and a disconcertingly lackadaisical air. He was seedy; it was presently established that he was a foot doctor with virtually no practice.

He accompanied officers without protest to Chief Sullivan's office in the detective bureau. He faced the same group which had gathered earlier at Summerdale, with two or three additions. His first statement was an admission that he had "known" Dr. Silber C. Peacock. His second was to the effect that he remembered very well his visit to the Peacock office in October. His third was so unexpected and puzzling that we who heard it could scarcely credit our ears.

"Certainly I disliked the doctor," the enigmatic Thompson blandly stated. "But I never accused him of performing an abortion on my wife. That is ridiculous. I was angry and jealous because I

thought Dr. Peacock was paying attention to my wife, Arlene Johnson Thompson—and I blamed this association for the fact that my
wife left me."

His listeners stared in silence. Here was another of those incredible twists that had marked the case from its outset. We had pictured Thompson as the outraged husband of a Peacock patient. Now
he was telling us, quite calmly, that he was the outraged husband of
a Peacock paramour. It was positively baffling; why had Dr. Peacock told his friend the story of the abortion charge? But it was also
enlightening; it supplied a jealousy motive, and it offered support, at
last, to the cynical suspicion that the pediatrician had stooped to
philandering.

"I'll tell you, before you ask me, how I got hep to Dr. Peacock
and my wife," Thompson was saying easily. "On the night of June
29, 1935, Arlene and her sister-in-law, Ann Johnson, wife of Arlene's brother Carl, came home from one of their parties. Both had
been drinking and I was angry; I was sure they'd been out with
men. I accused them, and they admitted it.

"Arlene explained they had been to the Subway Café on North
Wabash Avenue. She said, brazenly, that her escort had been Doc
Peacock. That was enough for me. I looked in the classified directory; Dr. Silber C. Peacock was the only physician of that name
listed, so I knew he must be the man.

"I mulled it all over for many weeks. Arlene was very cold to
me. I decided at last to see this Doc Peacock, who was destroying
the happiness of my married life. I went to his office with the sole
idea of having it out with him, man to man. I accused him only of
having been out with my wife. That made him very angry. He
jumped up and yelled, 'Get out of here right now. I never heard of
you or your wife either. I don't wish to hear any more.'

"When I mentioned the Subway Café he said he had never heard
of that place either and had never been there. He kept shoving me
until we were in the corridor, so I went away. . . . Well, that's
all."

But it wasn't all, and suddenly the indigent foot doctor, whose
mind was patently none too sharp, seemed to realize it. His role as

suspect No. 1 in a murder mystery didn't disturb him outwardly, though he went swiftly on the defensive.

"I was angry at Doc Peacock, but I didn't kill him," he said, before an accusation had been voiced. "I had nothing whatever to do with his death. I have an alibi. I can prove I couldn't have committed the murder."

He explained that in the absence of clients he had taken menial work at the Medinah Club; that he had worked there throughout the day of the murder and had returned home by bus, arriving at 9:30 P.M. He had been asked by the building manager, he recalled, to attend a patient in the neighborhood, after which he had spent the night in his room.

Things were getting chaotic. Every reporter's office, alert to the tremendous possibilities of the new break, was noisily demanding action. I chose to let others check Thompson's alibi. As quietly as possible, I set out to locate Arlene Johnson Thompson.

I found her in the home of her brother, Carl Johnson. Carl's wife, Ann, was standing by. Arlene turned out to be a plump, attractive redhead, about twenty-five, and imbued with an effervescent quality that used to be called "ginger." She volunteered that after leaving her husband, whom she termed "erratic," she had gone to her former home in Cumberland, Wisconsin, and then to Minneapolis, where she had been employed as a domestic. She had returned to Chicago recently with the intention of returning to Thompson—for, as she explained with simple expressiveness, "I still love the lug."

I explained my mission briefly. I mentioned the night of June 29, 1935, in the Subway Café. The Subway, incidentally, was a gay and robust honkytonk whose atmosphere became so free and easy that its license was revoked on July 3, 1936. I mentioned "Doc Peacock." Arlene and Ann exchanged wide-eyed glances—and began to laugh heartily. It was as unseemly a reaction as I could have imagined. I experienced an uneasy, sickish feeling. Was this "solution," like so many others, to end on a ludicrous note?

"That poor man!" cried Arlene, and it speedily became evident that she was referring, not to the slain Dr. Peacock, but to

the "erratic" Arthur St. George Thompson. "Has that streak of insane jealousy got him into trouble again? Well, let me tell you, mister, there's nothing to it, nothing to it at all. Here's how it happened. Draw up a chair."

While Arlene talked, Ann listened and occasionally giggled. The
two young women had gone unescorted to the Subway on that
June twenty-ninth, Arlene related, and not surprisingly had met two
men. They were blithe blades and ready spenders. They set out to
show the girls a good time. There were no objections.

"Well," said young Mrs. Thompson, and her demeanor lacked the
seriousness the occasion seemed to demand, "one of these fellows
was introduced to me as Doc Peacock. He was a very tall man,
with a head of wavy hair, and the nicest manners you could ask.
He danced with me. The other fellow danced with Ann. It was
about dusk when we went home.

"Outside our home my husband met us. He knew we had been
drinking and he got stormy. He's a little narrow that way, Arthur is.
He talked about men who would take married women out to parties.
He demanded to know whom we had been with.

"I didn't have anything to hide," she went on, reasonably, "so I
didn't hide anything. I told him my friend was named Doc Peacock.
That's all, brother—but it seems to have been more than enough. I
don't even think the fellow in the Subway was named Peacock at
all; it was probably just a name he picked out of a hat. But Arthur
went and got all excited and kept talking about Doc Peacock—
though I never knew until now that he actually went to this doctor's office and tried to raise hell. Poor Arthur!"

While I covered up my gnawing disappointment at the collapse
of this latest and spiciest "solution" of the Peacock murder, the girls
gaily completed its demolition. They had seen the slain pediatrician's picture in the papers, they said, and he didn't even remotely
resemble Arlene's "nice-mannered" Casanova of the honkytonk.

"What's more," Ann interposed with merry sarcasm, "Arthur
Thompson is not exactly the killer type. He was always a poor,
weak thing. He cried over a Christmas card that Arlene sent him.
But he never had enough pep to hurt a fly."

I reached dejectedly for a telephone. I had a story, of course, but it was definitely anticlimactic. And when my city editor informed me that Arthur Thompson's alibi had been checked, and proved iron-clad, I was not surprised. I thanked my carefree hostesses and drove back to the detective bureau. The air down there was fairly blue with frustration.

For a time, words failed all of us. Two weeks had flashed past and a half-dozen "solutions" had served only to confuse the issue, supply innumerable newspaper headlines, and inflict untold damage on the reputation of the luckless specialist who fared forth one cold night on a mission of mercy. Hot clues were lacking, now, but the cruel, irresponsible gossip went on. I felt the injustice of this keenly, and I called on Mrs. Peacock, seeking her reaction. As I had feared, she was morose and caustic in her grief.

"Now that they have pictured my husband as an abortionist, a dope peddler, and a honkytonk philanderer," she said dully, and her voice was hard, "perhaps they will agree at last that his personal life was blameless. In that event the police may conclude, as I did at the outset, that Dr. Peacock was the quite innocent victim of robbers and that his sole offense was in displaying his personal courage in the face of hopeless odds."

There was no disposition on my part to censure the overwrought woman, though I knew her criticism of the police was unfair. Investigators had been fully justified in every move, however futile each had been. For the known facts inexorably pointed away from the robbery theory and to an explanation less favorable to the victim. But Mrs. Peacock's loyalty was admirable, it was superb—and in her surmise as to the police's next activity she was entirely right.

Rumor and innuendo and fanciful theorizing had led us all up many a blind alley. A lone fact had emerged: Silber Peacock's armor of integrity remained undented. The man apparently had had no personal enemies. By unspoken, but mutual, agreement, the murder victim was accorded a clean bill of health, and automatically the theory of a bandit plot grew in relative importance.

This tacit decision was reached January 16. That night a seemingly remote and irrelevant episode began to form a pattern which eventually—and oh, so slowly—spelled out the solution of the celebrated Peacock case.

Dr. Joseph Soldinger, 1016 North Oakley Boulevard, was robbed of $37 and his car. Five days later Dr. A. L. Abrahams, 1600 Milwaukee Avenue, lost $56 to gunmen. On February 14, Dr. L. A. Garness, 2542 Mozart Avenue, was waylaid and robbed of $6. Each of these routine crimes made a little entry on a police blotter and a brief flash over the police radio system.

Captain Harry O'Connell, who had been advanced to command of the West North Avenue Station on the day Dr. Peacock was slain, first recognized these isolated incidents as a connected series. His attention was focused on the problem on the night his own brother, Dr. John P. O'Connell, experienced a brush with four men who forced him from his car at Surf Street and Sheridan Road. The doctor gave battle and escaped—but not before he noted that three assailants were tall and husky, the fourth noticeably shorter.

Reports of these affairs were similar in details. Each featured a call to hurry to a bedside, an address in a lonely neighborhood, an ambush. In each case the take was small. The hour never varied more than a few minutes from 10 P.M.

Chief Sullivan, alive to the significance of the several attacks on doctors, made certain assignments and enlisted the aid of organized medicine. In the *Medical Journal* appeared definite instructions to be followed by any physician receiving a "suspicious" summons after nightfall. Police in general, then, settled down to a policy of alert waiting.

Not so Captain Harry O'Connell, in whose district the latest robberies had been staged. He devised a plan and set it in motion. To follow his line of reasoning, you must study this background:

In 1935, the West North Avenue police had assembled evidence against a flat at 1336 North Maplewood Avenue, which they branded a "school for crime," operated by Rose Kasallis, a flabby, unkempt woman of thirty-eight. Her place was revealed as a sort of underground way-station for girl runaways and boy fugitives from the reformatory at St. Charles. Among youngsters corrupted by this unspeakable female Fagin with booze and other fleshly inducements was her own son, whose name was Robert Goethe. He was then eighteen, offspring of one of Mrs. Kasallis' four marriages.

Rose Kasallis was sent to prison for contributing to the delinquency of minors. Her son and another eighteen-year-old lad, Durland Nash, were convicted of strong-arming a pedestrian and entered the Bridewell. During their confinement the district enjoyed a period of serenity; soon after their release in December, a fresh outbreak of robberies occurred. Now guns were being used.

Peter Payer, sixty-four, a tailor, picked up a hammer when three young ruffians entered his shop on December 11. The gesture saved him $3.50, the amount in his pockets, but cost him his life. The youngsters shot him down and fled.

Less than a month later Chicago was rocked by the Peacock outrage. It was outside the West North Avenue district, of course, but Captain O'Connell, confiding in no one, grimly marked it down as a possible item in the pattern that was forming in his mind. And the crime wave continued.

Two days after Dr. Garness was victimized, Frank Chleblak was shot in the back by three or four youthful bandits in his grocery on Augusta Boulevard. He lost $50 but survived. On March 7, Matthew Holstein, eighty-three, was subjected to a terrific beating by hoodlums who entered his home at 2038 Emerson Avenue and ransacked it in the belief that Holstein was a miser with hidden gold. The old man died a month later in a hospital.

Shortly thereafter Irving Schrankel, a laundry driver, accosted in an alley near Damen and Chicago Avenues, sought to run from his gun-toting assailants. A shot in the back stopped him for good. Like the earlier instances of violence the case was marked by a ruthlessness and an eagerness to kill which for a time led Captain O'Connell and the other investigators to believe experienced criminals were at work.

A series of petty holdups right in his district, involving the theft and juggling of numerous automobiles, next engaged Captain O'Connell's attention. On nine successive nights these minor irritations were endured whereupon the captain's thoughts turned to young Robert Goethe and his pal, Durland Nash, graduates of Rose Kasallis' school of crime and themselves not long out of the Bridewell.

An order went out. Patrolman Fred Susebach was approaching Goethe's home when he saw the youth in company with another nineteen-year-old toughie named Emil Reck and nicknamed, aptly enough as it turned out, Emil the Terrible. Both boys were arrested. Durland Nash was seized shortly thereafter.

Sergeant Andrew Aitken, "just sitting" at the West North Avenue Station, watched with unusual interest as the three tall, husky boys were brought in. With three others, he had been "just sitting" for five weeks, waiting for some physician to telephone Wabash 4747 and tell the operator, "I'm calling in accordance with the instruction in the *Medical Journal* that any doctor receiving a suspicious call should telephone this number."

No such call had arrived, but during his waiting Andy Aitken had studied every known angle of the murder of Dr. Peacock. In his fertile mind he had formed a picture of the slayers—and, whether right or wrong, it was clear and sharply etched. This picture flashed back to him now as Goethe and Reck and Nash strode past the sergeant. He rushed into the captain's office, and an animated, whispered conference ensued.

Captain O'Connell raised his eyebrows. He had judged the boys from Rose Kasallis' "school" as bothersome vandals and petty thieves, hardly as vicious gunmen willing to kill. Now, with the pattern of recent events in his mind and Andy Aitken's shrewd suggestions in his ears, the captain swiftly revised his judgment. He nodded and turned to the prisoners. He had reached a decision.

Preliminaries were speedily dispatched. The physicians who had been robbed—and had survived—viewed the three boys and identified them unhesitatingly. Captain O'Connell, adopting a venerable and proved technique, ordered the trio separated. Facing Robert Goethe alone, he said, "You killed Doc Peacock!"

Eyes wide, Goethe sullenly denied it. The captain waved him away and presently was closeted with Durland Nash. He told the boy that Goethe had been explaining how he, Nash, had slain the doctor. Durland blurted out, "He can't get away with that. He's the guy that shot Peacock."

The three boys were brought together. Quarreling, accusing each other, competing for the "honor" of revealing truths, they laid bare in its terrifying details the repulsive history of their crimes.

Suddenly Captain O'Connell remembered his brother's description of a fourth member of the gang, a little fellow who merely watched. He asked about this.

"That's Mickey Livingston," said Nash in a casual tone. And presently the police had in custody diminutive, seventeen-year-old Michael Livingston, brightest of the dull quartet, who acted only as "the two-block jiggers guy," but shared equally in the gang's meager profits.

In short, pungent phrases the murder of Silber Peacock was swiftly depicted. The four boys, cruising in a stolen car, pausing in a candy store, picking their victim's name at random from a directory, picking another name and address, then altering it, to lure the doctor to a spot chosen for its isolation. Emil the Terrible, cradling a heavy club in his hand, crouching in the shadows across the street from 6438 North Whipple Street; Nash loitering at the entrance; Goethe, with a gun provided by Reck, hiding behind a nearby tree; Little Livingston at the wheel of the car parked a half block north.

Dr. Peacock drives up, steps out with kit in hand. Goethe closes in, prods the doctor with his revolver, mutters, "Don't move." The victim is marched a block north after Reck "hits him a lick for luck," and the robbery is staged in a dark spot with prairies on both sides.

Suddenly the brave doctor wheels and grapples with Goethe, who fires at Peacock's head. The victim falls, and, wild-eyed, moronic Emil Reck is upon him with his club, raining blows. Goethe adds more needless blows with the butt of the weapon. The two stand over their murdered victim.

Nash drives up with the doctor's car, Livingston following in the other. The body is thrust in the tonneau of the Cadillac, which is then driven three blocks and abandoned. The evil deed is done— and the total loot is $20!

The age and mental state of the criminals explained many discrepancies in the crime that had bothered the police—the smallness of the loot, the viciousness of the attack, and the whole "unprofessional" air of the crime.

The trials of the Peacock killers were sensational. The death penalty, demanded by the state for the three older boys, was withheld.

Emil Reck, Bob Goethe, and Durland Nash were given identical terms of 199 years, plus consecutive terms of one year to life on four robbery counts—and these seemed a trifle superfluous. Little Mickey Livingston escaped with a thirty-year sentence, and he alone may reasonably look forward to a period of freedom. Already he has sought parole, though futilely.

That hope is not dead in the hearts of Goethe and Nash was attested in April, 1944, when both filed parole applications. The pleas were rejected by the Illinois Board of Pardons and Paroles, but not through any persuasion on the part of the tragedy's most pitiful victim, Ruth Pearce Peacock.

Shortly before beginning this narrative, I telephoned Mrs. Peacock at the home she has occupied in Quincy, Illinois, since the agonizing events of 1936. She mentioned the parole petitions of her husband's slayers and added, "They asked my opinion as to the proper course. I declined to make any recommendation. The law took its just course. In my belief the boys had a fair trial before an excellent judge, with capable defense lawyers. It is up to the authorities, and not to me, to decide their release or further punishment. Except for the safety of society, I am not personally concerned."

Mrs. Peacock has found a degree of happiness in social service, in church and Red Cross work, as president of the American Association of University Women and of a Parent-Teacher Association unit. In a large measure her life revolves around her two lovely daughters, Betty Lou, now sixteen, and Nancy, eight, who never saw her father. Best of all, Mrs. Peacock has attained inner serenity through the healing qualities of forgiveness.

"You remember my bitterness and resentment," she told me in our latest conversation, and her gentle voice reflected her deep sincerity. "It was you, Mr. McHugh, who were sometimes called upon to bring me details of the public's heedless, brutal attacks on Dr. Peacock's reputation. You know how this procedure tortured me, how I even grew to feel that the police were against me.

"Now I am reconciled to my loss, and I can see more clearly. It was the police, of course, who in the end revealed the truth, and it was the truth that vindicated my husband. Since his name is fully cleared and justice has prevailed, I find it helpful, and not at all difficult, to forgive all those thoughtless persons who once maligned the doctor so dreadfully."

Now you'll see what I meant when I pinned back the ears of the Cub-Who-Talked-Like-A-Veteran. The police work on the case *was* excellent. What made it seem fruitless for so long was the almost unbelievable series of red herrings—and the tendency, so deeply rooted in almost all of us, to believe the worst about the other fellow.

I wouldn't call myself a moralist; few newspaper men who have covered homicides as long as I have fit into that classification. Yet I would like to put down in this record, in most unmistakable language, that few men in private life have ever been more traduced than was Dr. Silber C. Peacock—and no man could have emerged from such an experience with a more completely unblemished reputation. There simply was no chink in his armor.

That Dr. Peacock could not answer the attacks, that the plain facts had to speak for themselves, makes this all the more remarkable. All of us who were close to this case, I feel sure, learned, or relearned, one vital fact about the not-so-gentle art of detection: the obvious trail is *usually* the right one to follow, but not *always*. It certainly was not the right trail in the case of Dr. Peacock.

WITH "KING" OLIVER
ON THE SOUTH SIDE *

Louis Armstrong

FROM 1916 to about 1928, the South Side rocked with the best indigenous music in the country. The ripples these musical notes created spread throughout the nation and the world. Jazz did not originate in Chicago, of course, but the Windy City gave it one of the greatest shoves forward of its career, thanks to the great South Side bandsmen who played their hearts out in the smoke-filled cabarets, as they were then called, of that exciting era.

In that era, also, the great "white" dance halls of Chicago were built, and flourished. As a boy I used to travel to all the ballrooms of the city, lured by the new "name" bands that were attracting the young people to the polished floors. These white bands had come under the influence of the South Side's rocking, tumultuous style of playing. As musicians, the members of these aggregations could not touch the South Side bandsmen with a six-foot pole, but they were very good. I remember that before the entrances of the dance halls there were displays of blown-up photographs of the jazz bands, as they were called. The lads of these ensembles never stared quietly at the lenses of the cameras; they struck frenzied poses, their horns tilted, their eyeballs rolling, the pianist in an attitude suggestive of St. Vitus' dance; the drummer always crouched low over his equipment like a maniac, and the leader always grinned like a manikin. The inscriptions read, "West Side Wildcats," "The Windy City Aristocrats," "The Wolverines," etc.

We were all conscious of jazz; and Louis Armstrong already was a legend. In the following excerpt from his

autobiography, *Swing That Music,* you will find, simply
stated without any of the convoluted phraseology employed
by many "historians" of jazz, a description of swing, what
it is and what it means, told by one of the great creative
musicians of our time.

THAT winter passed the same as the winter before, playing in
Marable's orchestra and running excursions out from Canal Street.
Then April came around and I decided to go north with the *Dixie
Belle* for another summer. For several weeks after I had come
home, Daisy and I were happy together and then our troubles began all over again the way they were before. We just couldn't
seem to keep things quiet and smooth between us—there was always something coming up to spoil it. It was a shame.

The trip upriver that second summer, the summer of 1921, was
like the first, except that we played at a few new towns and skipped
some we had visited before. I was sorry Quincy was one of those
we skipped. I guess the captain didn't feel any too good about that
place. We had another long stay at St. Louis where I saw the
friends I had made the year before, and then we went up and
caught St. Paul in good time for Labor Day.

Getting home the second time wasn't as big a kick as the first
time, of course, but I am always glad to be back in New Orleans,
at any time.

I had played on the boat for two full years by then, and traveled
about five thousand miles in all. Playing and practicing day and
night, and the experience of playing to hundreds of crowds, had
done a lot for me. I could read music very well by now and was
getting hotter and hotter on my trumpet. My chest had filled out
deeper and my lips and jaws had got stronger, so I could blow much
harder and longer than before without getting tired. I had made
a special point of the high register, and was beginning to make my
high-C notes more and more often. That is the greatest strain on
the lips. Even today I am very careful about my lips, because if a
trumpeter's lips go back on him, he's just done.

But I was getting tired of the routine on the boat and ready for
a change, so I decided to join the orchestra at Tom Anderson's

cabaret. They featured me in trumpet solos. On the side, I joined up with the Tuxedo marching brass band.

Daisy and I couldn't get along any better than before. We were running into our fourth year of marriage, so we decided to get a divorce.

Winter and spring of 1922 went by. I was doing very well with my music. Along in July, just after my twenty-second birthday, the Tuxedo Band was called out one day to march in a fraternal funeral. It was terribly hot out on the street and I remember my uniform almost choked me. After the lodge member was buried, we marched back to the lodge house. As we were disbanding somebody came up with a telegram. It was for me. I couldn't imagine what it could be. I opened it and found it was from "King" Oliver. It said he had a place for me in his band and wanted me to come at once to Chicago. "Papa Joe" had meant what he said.

A few days later, my mother and her husband, my stepdaddy, and "Mama Lucy" and some of my best friends went down to the train to see me go. It was the last time I was to see New Orleans again for nine years, and the last time I was ever to see my mother until I saw her on her deathbed, for she died very young—in her early forties.

Well, we pulled into the old LaSalle Street station in Chicago about ten o'clock at night. I went right over with my bag to the Lincoln Gardens, which was at Thirty-first and Gordon Streets. When I walked in the door, King Oliver was standing out there in front of his orchestra, swinging away. It was a big place, with a big balcony all around, and I felt a little frightened, and wondered how I was going to make out. I knew it was a big chance for me. I went up to the bandstand and there were some of the boys I had known back home. They were glad to see me and I was tickled to death to see them all. The band was the hit of Chicago at that time, but as you know that was a good many years ago. It was made up as follows: King Oliver, ace trumpet; "Baby" Dodds, drums; Honoré Dutrey, trombone; Johnny Dodds, clarinet; Bill Johnson, bass violin; a piano; and a second trumpet, the place I had come to take. Bill Johnson had gone north some years before with the old pioneer Creole Jazz Band.

Of course I couldn't start in playing with them that night—I needed to rehearse with them a little and get onto their ways. I went in the next week. That first night Papa Joe was very kind to me. He said he was going to take me home with him and that I should live with him for a while until I got more used to Chicago. His wife Stella was a very fine lady and they had a daughter named Ruby who is married now. "Mama Stella" was a good cook and used to feed me up. That is when I began to take on weight, trying to keep up with Papa Joe in eating.

One night soon after I started in, and after our show was over Papa Joe said to me, "Louis, do you want to go over and meet Lil? She's playing at the Dreamland now." I knew what he meant. The winter before King Oliver had sent a picture of his band down to New Orleans and the pianist in the band was an attractive-looking, brown-skinned girl named Lillian Hardin. I had said in my next letter to him, "Tell Miss Lil I like her." I certainly never thought anything would come of it. So I was a little bit embarrassed when Papa Joe mentioned it, but I said I didn't care if I went with him.

The Dreamland was a very popular night club. They had a fine band, too, headed by Ollie Powers, a great entertainer and singer. He used to be a partner of Sheldon Brooks. Ollie was a good friend to me later. When we got there Lillian Hardin was at the piano. She was, and is, one of the best woman jazz pianists in the country. King Oliver introduced us. He didn't know, or maybe he *did* have an idea, that he was introducing me to my second wife.

After that first night I didn't see much of Lil for two or three months, until she came back to join our band at the Lincoln Gardens. Pretty soon we got to going around more and more together. Lil believed in me from the first. Being new in a big town and not sure I could make good, her believing in me meant a great deal and helped me a lot. She told me one night she thought I could swing trumpet better than King Oliver and said I should have a chance to be first trumpet myself, and would never get it as long as I stayed with Papa Joe's band, because, naturally, he was first trumpet with his own band. I knew she was talking big, and just laughed at her. But I could see, too, that she was serious and thinking of me. Lil had been born in Memphis, but she had lived in Chicago a long time where she had studied music. She was always going to music school to learn more about it, and she studies that way still. We used to practice together, "woodshed" as we say (from the old-time way of going out into the woodshed to practice a new song). She would play on the piano and I, of course, on my trumpet. I had learned how to transpose from a piano part. We used to play classical music together sometimes. We bought classical trumpet music. Through this, later on, we played in churches once in a while. All of this was giving me more and more knowledge of my music.

Right here I want to say something more about swing music, because this isn't supposed to be so much about me as about swing; where it came from, how it grew and what it is. It is just an accident that swing and I were born and brought up side by side in New Orleans, traveled up the Mississippi together, and, in 1922, the year I am writing about now, were there in Chicago getting acquainted with the North—and the North getting acquainted with us.

When you're brought up with something and it has been natural to you, you may love it, but you don't ever appreciate it—you can't, because you haven't measured it against anything else. Maybe it's good, and maybe it's bad, but you'll never really know until you put it against something else like it. Well, as I began to see soon after I got around a little in Chicago, I had been swimming all my life in a pond with a lot of real big fish. I had been brought up with a group of great musicians. They didn't know Bach from Beethoven, or Mozart from Mendelssohn, and maybe hadn't even heard of them, and, strange as it may sound, I think that is exactly why they became great musicians. Not knowing much classical music, and not many of them having proper education in reading music of any kind, they just went ahead and made up their own music. Before long, and without really knowing it themselves, they had created a brand-new music, they created swing. They made a music for themselves which truly expressed what they felt. They were composers *and* players, all in one, and they composed as they played and held what they had done only in their musical memory. They didn't write much of it down—swing *can* be written down by someone listening to it, but if the players continue to follow it the way it is written down, very soon swing becomes set and regular and then it is not swing any more and that is what almost happened later when jazz tunes became so popular. People began writing them down and publishing them and wanted to have them played the way they were written. Swing music, as it started in New Orleans, was almost wiped out. Only because a few men really loved it and held onto it, it came through, and only in the last few years has the true swing come back to its own, the way it started out. The very soul and spirit of swing music is free improvisation, or "swinging" by the player.

If those early swing musicians had gone to music schools and been taught to know and worship the great masters of classical music and been told it was sacrilegious to change a single note of what was put before them to play, swing music would never have been born at all. They would have got the idea that written music, whether it is a great classic or just a popular air, is something sacred that must never be touched, especially by a beginner. That was the way music was taught in the schools, and nobody ever questioned it. Every piece of music, good or bad or indifferent, as soon as it was published was supposed to have sort of a life of its own, apart from who played it or what the player felt in playing it—and nobody could meddle with it in the least. It makes me think of the people who collect books, as against the people who write them. The book collector gets to feel that a book has a life of its own and is sacred, apart from what's in it, and just because it is written down and bound up in covers.

Now I do not believe that books or music, or any other kind of art, are sacred, or even important to us, apart from what they truly express. What makes a composer or author or artist a real master is that his work so wonderfully expressed what he felt that nobody but a clumsy fool would *want* to change it. As likely as not he didn't follow after anybody else's way of doing, but went on his own way, as he himself felt and thought, and that is the way new and younger people should do, too, because that is the way music and art grow and the only way they can keep growing. Now I think that there are two kinds of men chiefly who *can* break loose like that. One is the kind of man who learns everything about his art and what has been done before him so he can go on beyond it, and the other is the kind who doesn't know *anything* about it—who is just plain ignorant, but has a great deal of feeling he's got to express in some way, and has to find that way out for himself. Swing came mostly from the last kind of men. That is why, during those early years, people noticed two things about it, that it was very strong and vital, and also that it was crude and not "finished." And it is very true that the swing music we have today is far more refined and subtle and more highly developed as an art because the swing men who learned to read and understand classical music have brought classical influences into it. I think that may be said to be the real difference between the original New Orleans "jazz" and the swing music of today. And in taking in the classical influence, real jazz has gained a very great deal and not lost—it is growing into a finer and broader and richer music, a music that is truly American, that will surely take its place, in time, alongside of the great and permanent music of other countries. Until swing music came, America had no music it could really call its own. If you will look at the European music journals, you will see what their critics think of our own swing music. You will see that they already think of it as a new and permanent music. Some of them even write that the swing principle of free improvisation by the player will affect all of music—and at last make the player, the instrumentalist, as important as the composer, because he, too, in swing, becomes a composer—a player-composer. I don't know about that, but it is funny that swing music got its first serious recognition, not at home, but in Europe. During my own three years playing in England and on the Continent, the very finest music critics would come back to my dressing room, or call upon me at my hotel, and talk with me for hours about the "significance" of our music and what they thought it meant. That had never happened to me before, in America, although since I have been home this

last time I notice that our own critics and journals are beginning to
have the same kind of serious interest. I don't believe that I, myself, ever realized swing music was really important until I went to
Europe and saw what they thought of it. I had just been playing it
and growing with it since I was a kid.

Well, to go back to the winter of 1922–1923, the first winter
I was in Chicago when swing was hot as fire but still pretty crude
in form. I had only been there a little while, as I said, before I began to see how much I had learned in the South. There were only
a very few bands that played the way we did, and most of the
good players, though not all of them, had come North from the
lower Mississippi country, from Memphis down to the Delta. Another thing I noticed quickly was that the people who liked those
bands best at that time, and followed them, were the people who
didn't know much about the older music, mostly the young people
in high schools and colleges. They loved to hear us swing, and to
dance to it. Then there were a few real musicians, classical musicians, who liked us. There was a professor of music in one of the
big Chicago colleges who used to come down to the Lincoln
Gardens and sit there night after night, taking notes. The waiters
didn't like him much because he never ordered a drink and never
brought anybody with him, but just sat there and listened. I didn't
understand it then, but I do now. As I say, it is the very learned
man or the very ignorant one who can break loose, and I say,
too, about most of the musical people of that day, and a lot of
them still today, "There's none so blind as he who will not see."
But swing has gone on anyway, and will go on. The men who play
it and make it put their music ahead of everything in their lives.

Take the "jam sessions" for instance. I am sure you have heard
about them. Where do you find anything like that among "regular"
or "sweet" musicians? A group of swing players, tired out after
their pay performances, getting together alone in the early morning
hours to swing together just for the fun of it. "Swing it, Gate," one
of them will sing out and that will be a "sender" to them and
they'll all go into their music, swinging hot, only because they love
it. That "sender," "Swing it, Gate," by the way, came from me.

When I was a kid, you remember, they started calling me "Gate-mouth," and then "Satchel-mouth." Well, I started calling the other boys "Gate," too, to sort of throw it back at them, so it wouldn't stick too close to me, I guess. Then I got used to saying it and when I got into Kid Ory's band when the boys were all swinging good and hot, I would sing out, "Swing it, Gate." That has stuck to me ever since, like "Satchmo," and now "Gate" is a word swing players use when they call out to one another in their own language, but most of them, I guess, don't know how it started. I have heard some of them explain that it came from the word "alligator"—that is the word we use for a person who is not a player himself but who loves to sit and listen to swing music. We will say about some new number we plan to play, "The 'alligators' will like that." I may mention here that there are more than four hundred words used among swing musicians that no one else would understand. They have a language of their own, and I don't think anything could show better how closely they have worked together and how much they feel that they are apart from "regular" musicians and have a world of their own that they believe in and that most people have not understood. I hope this will help to explain it a little—it is the real reason I have tried to write it and kept on after I found what hard going writing was for a man who has lived all of his life mostly with a trumpet, not a pencil, in his hand.

CHICAGO, JAZZ, BIX
AND THE BOYS*

Eddie Condon

HERE is another piece on Chicago jazz, written by one of the first disciples of South Side music. You will not only find it interesting but, if you are "in the know," you will experience the shock of recognition as Condon reels off the then-unknown names.

Condon, saxophonist Bud Freeman once told me, knows more people in the United States than any other living person. This has always made him a valuable outrider for the cause.

Besides functioning as a bandsman, Eddie Condon operates a successful night club in Greenwich Village, New York.

MY UNION card was being transferred; ninety days had to pass before I could take a steady job in town. Husk O'Hare's office sent me on high school and college party dates, and to dances in different parts of the city.

One night I went to a part-time cabaret on the far North Side called the Cascades. It was run by Palmer Katy, a well-dressed ragtime guy, slightly on the promotional side. "Katy likes your kind of music," I was told. "You'll get $5 if there's a crowd." The Cascades was a moderate-sized upstairs place, bring your own bottles and buy setups. When I got there the other musicians had arrived. One of them, Squeak Buhl, was setting up drums. A good-looking kid was trying to get notes from a tenor saxophone which was green with corrosion. It sounded the way it looked. A blond, solidly built boy was watching him; he had a cornet. I introduced myself; the saxophone player shook hands with me. "My name is Bud Freeman," he said. "This is Jimmy MacPartland." We sat down and began to play. Freeman seemed to know only one tune; everything sounded vaguely like "China Boy." MacPartland had a strong, rugged tone; he knew where he was going and enjoyed the journey. Buhl set a good beat and we all pushed it a little. Now and then Freeman hit a note that sounded like music.

Between sets we gabbed and I discovered that MacPartland and Freeman were from the West Side. They were about my age; they had been in Austin High School together and with some other students had formed a band. They talked about jazz as if it were a new religion just come from Jerusalem. When MacPartland mentioned King Oliver smoke come out of his eyes. "He's playing a fraternity dance at the Chez Paree tonight," Freeman said. "Let's go down there after we finish."

We arrived in time for the last set; the musicians were reassembling as we pushed our way to the stand. "That's Oliver," MacPartland said, pointing to a big, amiable-looking Negro with a scar over one eye who stood in front of the band holding a cornet. Near him was a slightly smaller and much younger man, also holding a cornet. "That's Louis Armstrong," MacPartland said. He pointed to the others: Johnny Dodds on clarinet and his brother Baby on drums, Honoré Dutrey at the trombone, Johnnie St. Cyr playing banjo, and Lillian Hardin at the piano. Oliver lifted his horn and the first blast of "Canal Street Blues" hit me. It was hypnosis at first hearing. Everyone was playing what he wanted to play and it was all mixed together as if someone had planned it with a set of micrometer calipers; notes I had never heard were peeling off the edges and dropping through the middle; there was a tone from the trumpets like warm rain on a cold day. Freeman and MacPartland and I were immobilized; the music poured into us like daylight running down a dark hole. The choruses rolled on like high tide, getting wilder and more wonderful. Armstrong seemed able to hear what Oliver was improvising and reproduce it himself at the same time. It seemed impossible, so I dismissed it; but it was true. Then the two wove around each other like suspicious women talking about the same man. When they finally finished MacPartland said, "How do you like it?" There was only one thing to say: "It doesn't bother me."

We listened until the last note; Armstrong was reaching, showing his high shoes and his white socks; Oliver was looking at him with a fatherly smile. We hit the cold air outside and Freeman said, "Let's go down to the Friars' Inn." It was a late place, open until the customers stopped buying or went home. I spotted a few changes when I got to the bandstand; Schoebel wasn't at the piano and Ben Pollack was playing drums. Rappolo, Mares, Brunies, Pettis, and the others, including Lew Black, were still setting fire to "Shimmy Shawabble," "Angry," "Sobbin' Blues," "Sugarfoot Stomp," and "Everybody Loves Somebody Blues." What was left of our capacity for enjoyment we turned over to Rappolo. He played clarinet the way Shakespeare played English. It was afternoon when I got back to Chicago Heights.

At O'Hare's booking office I ran into a character who operated under the name of Murphy Podolsky; he played piano and had an inside track on school dance dates. He played a good opinion of himself straight for the amusement of his friends; he pretended to believe in his own greatness. But he pretended to nothing else; he would crawl on his hands and knees through a moving field of wild cats to needle a phony. Often we went window-shopping together; I was saving my dough for some of the haberdashery in Dockstader-Sandberg's on Michigan Avenue, a store so high-class it eventually soared out of business. One day I spotted a new-style hat, with a high crown. That's for me, I thought, when I get enough paper. The next night I worked on a date at Northwestern University in Evanston, just over the line from Chicago. A gaunt, hollow-looking kid came in, dragging drums. Something about him seemed familiar. Then I spotted his hat—he had the pilgrim's model. Damn him, I thought, he got it before I did. He said his name was Dave Tough; he set up the drums and I wondered where he would find the strength to hit them. He was behind me when we started our first number; what he did to the drums nearly drove me through the opposite wall. I turned around and looked at him. He was possessed.

While we were having a drink between sets I said to him, "You sort of like this music, don't you?" He nodded gloomily. "I guess I do," he said. "My family doesn't understand what I'm doing. I can't get a job with a big band because they don't play this kind of stuff. I must be crazy to keep on playing it, but I do."

"Where do you live?" I asked.

"Oak Park," he said.

I knew he wasn't kidding about bucking his family; Oak Park, a suburb of Chicago, was credited with being the richest village in the world.

"Do you go to school?" I asked. I had a feeling he ought to be at Harvard; maybe he was being kept at Northwestern so his drumming could be watched for symptoms of violence.

"I go to Lewis Institute," he said. "It's a prep school for two kinds of people—those who can't go to the best schools and those who get thrown out of them. We have a dance there once a week, with a pickup band—this kind of music. Why don't you come and sit in?"

"Who plays?" I asked.

"Almost anybody. Some weeks we have all saxophones, some weeks we have all cornets, some weeks we have three sets of drums. Only two of us are regular, myself and a kid named Benny Goodman."

I knew Benny; we had met at union headquarters and played pool together until we discovered both of us were after the same thing, carfare and walk-around money. After that we took on separate opponents. I had been to Benny's home for dinner—a widowed mother, lots of kids, big bowls of good food, pitch until you win.

"So you know Benny," Tough said. "He and I joined the American Musicians Union the same day. We were both in short pants; I was thirteen, Benny was twelve. He's going to Lewis Institute now. I hope the education won't ruin his clarinet playing. We jazz players are supposed to be vulgarians beyond the moral as well as the musical pale; I guess we might as well live up to what is expected of us."

He looked at me.

"Do you expect to go on playing jazz?" he asked.

"While I'm eating meat*," I said.

"Then you are a no-good drunken tramp and you'll never get anywhere," he said. "Come over to the Institute and play with us. Last week we had twelve trombones and a rhythm section."

When we finished and I was about to leave he said, "If you want to go to Lincoln Gardens ask Voltaire Defoe. He took me when I was small. He's a friend of mine."

"Thanks," I said. "I can usually get in by myself."

"Come to the Institute," Tough said. "We have never had twelve banjos."

A lot of older white kids had been enlisted from time to time to take youngsters to the Lincoln Gardens, the South Side cabaret where King Oliver played. It was by and for Negroes, and the white kids in short pants who went there—some of them on bicycles—to hear the music had good reason to feel slightly uncomfortable until they had pushed their way close to the bandstand and been recognized by Oliver. A nod or a wave of his hand was all that was necessary; then the customers knew that the kids were all right. Night after night we made the trip.

In the cubicle outside where we paid admission the sound was loud; it came like a muscle flexing regularly, four to the bar. As the door opened the trumpets, King and Louis, one or both, soared above everything else. The whole joint was rocking. Tables, chairs, walls, people, moved with the rhythm. It was dark, smoky, gin-smelling. People in the balcony leaned over and their drinks spilled on the customers below. There was a false ceiling made of chicken wire covered with phony maple leaves; the real roof was twenty-five feet up. A round, glass bowl hung from the middle of the chicken wire; when the blues were played it turned slowly and a baby spotlight worked over it. There was a floor show and a master of ceremonies named King Jones. He would stand in front of Oliver and shout, "Oh! One more chorus, King!" Oliver and Louis, would roll on and on, piling up choruses, with the rhythm section building the beat until the whole thing got inside your head and blew your brains out. There was a place near the band reserved for musi-

---

* While I'm alive.

cians who came to listen and to learn; we sat there, stiff with education, joy, and a licorice-tasting gin purchased from the waiters for
two dollars a pint. You could bring your own but it didn't matter
much; in the end the effect was the same—the band playing
"Froggie Moore," "Chimes Blues," "Sweet Baby Doll," "Jazzin'
Babies' Blues," "Mabel's Dream," "Room Rent Blues," "High Society Rag," "Where Did You Stay Last Night," "Working Man
Blues," and everything and everybody moving, sliding, tapping out
the rhythm, inhaling the smoke, swallowing the gin.

After ninety days the union allowed me to take a steady job. I
went to work at the Palace Gardens, a cabaret in the 600 block on
North Clark Street, the heart of the tenderloin. There were five
blocks almost solid with cabarets—The Derby, The Erie, Liberty
Inn, 606, etc., ad infinitum. Most of them were like the Palace
Gardens, which had a small band with hag singers going from
table to table moaning gold-toothed ballads full of moons and Junes.
Harry Greb, the fighter who trained in night clubs and was afraid
of nobody, listened to them and melted. Babe Ruth was another
customer; he would clout a few over the fence in Comiskey Park in
the afternoon and listen to "When You Look in the Heart of a
Rose" at night.

Nobody went to bed; there must have been people who slept at
night and who worked by day but I didn't see them during those
months. Charlie Straight's orchestra played at the Rendezvous up
the street until two o'clock, then an overtime band took up. It was
a pickup outfit and it played jazz. One night it had a cornet player
who sounded somewhat like King Oliver—a miraculous sense of
time, pulling the whole band along with him, and a mellow tone,
with drive. He had a face stuck together with shamrocks; he said
his name was Muggsy Spanier and that he was a local boy, South
Side. "What do you do besides this?" I asked. "I'm at the Colum-
bia Ballroom," he said. "I should have known," I said. The Colum-
bia, also on North Clark Street, had the best dance band in town—
Sig Myer's Druids. They played a Sunday matinee and I was there
to hear Muggsy's cornet. "I was christened Francis," he told me,
"but my mother calls me Muggsy. I don't know whether to be a

baseball player or a doctor." "What's the matter with music?" I asked. "It isn't hard to do," he said.

Spring hit the Palace Gardens and I was back at the union shooting pool. One day I missed the side pocket on an easy shot. "The hotter it gets the more often it will happen," Al Beller, a fiddle player, said. "By August you won't even be able to make your room rent at this racket. Why don't you take a resort job for the summer?" "My white flannels are packed," I said. "When do I leave and for where?" He made the shot I had missed. "There's a job at Lake Delavan with Wop Waller," he said. "He's been there for years. Right now he needs a banjo player." I missed another shot. "You don't have to stay if you don't like it," Al said. Again he made the shot I had missed. The word "lake" had shoved me off balance; I was thinking of canoes and red-headed girls. The next day I left for Delavan, Wisconsin. . . .

As I packed up to leave Lake Delavan a new idea nudged me. The college kids I had met during the summer were like me but they had a different manner. "Who is Proust?" I asked Wop one day. "What does he play?" Wop said. That was it. Education was something you couldn't see but it was there, like being able to throw a curve. I decided to get some for myself. It doesn't come in bottles, I figured, so it can't do me any harm.

Back in Chicago I went to live with brothers John and Jim at the Allerton House, a hotel for men at 700 Michigan Avenue. John was working for our brother-in-law, Jack Dunn, . . . who had a wholesale and retail jewelry business in the Loop. Jim had succeeded in tuning his banjo and was playing club dates. We found two other banjo players and formed a quartet, doing specialty numbers with bands. One of the quartet was Herbie Kaumyer; later he changed his name to Herbie Kay, started an orchestra and married his singer, a girl named Dorothy Lamour.

My summer money went into a winter wardrobe. Now that I was going to get an education I had to be careful about the difference between a gentleman and a dude. A dude, I figured, is a fellow who makes a business of dressing correctly; a gentleman is a guy who can't help putting on the right clothes; he doesn't know any better.

My school was located on Catalpa Avenue on the North Side. It was the home of Mrs. Reid, a retired Northwestern University professor, who occupied herself with tutoring and whose credits were accepted at Northwestern. She had half a dozen boys and girls in addition to myself; I was due at nine in the morning and I had to take a bus to get there. It was grim, but I had something to find out —who was Proust? I began with French, English, mathematics, and some other stuff. I never got time to do homework and I never got time to sleep. I arrived at nine o'clock with my eyelids taped. When the questions were asked and the other students began writing their answers I sneaked into the kitchen, lighted a cigarette on the pilot of the gas stove, and looked out of the window. What the hell am I doing here, I asked myself. I can stay home, get some sleep, and be just as stupid. This way I don't get any sleep and I'm still stupid. But I kept going. Somewhere ahead of me was Proust.

Barbara wrote to me from her school in Massachusetts. When she came to town for the Christmas holidays I swapped overcoats with Benny Goodman to take her on dates; Benny and I were the same size then and he had a new outdoor job. I told Barbara about my schoolwork and she was very happy. About the time I got back my own coat I ran into Milton Mezzrow, who was addicted to the saxophone. Mezz knew the leader of the band at Ike Bloom's Rendezvous on Randolph Street, a fiddler named Irving Rothschild. He got jobs for both of us and we went to work with Rothschild and with Johnny Fortin on piano, Don Carter on drums, and Murphy Steinberg on trumpet. It was steady and pleasant work; by now the customers were providing most of the entertainment in night clubs and speak-easies. Everyone was friendly with the band and the band was friendly with everyone else. We did our best to help the tone of Mezzrow's saxophone. We put cigarette and cigar butts, ashtrays and damp paper napkins, into the bell, but they didn't help. Mezz had a couple of breaks to take on his tenor saxophone during "Eccentric." Somehow he always got nervous and flubbed them. "This is a serious thing, Mezz," we told him. "Unless you break this fixation now it will ruin your career. We'll stick with you, no matter how long it takes." We kept playing "Eccentric" and Mezz kept flubbing his breaks. "Maybe we ought to forget it for a while," Mezz suggested. "No," we said, "you have got to break it now." But he didn't, although we played "Eccentric" all winter long.

Bix came to town that spring. He left the Wolverines when they went on the road; Jimmy MacPartland replaced him. Charlie Straight, at the other Chicago Rendezvous, on North Clark Street, wanted to hire him. The union pointed to its ninety-day clause. Straight made a statement which probably sums up what musicians thought of Bix; he said that Beiderbecke was a unique attraction, that he was not just a cornet player, and that if it were possible to find his equal anywhere in Chicago he, Straight, would hire the equal rather than Beiderbecke. The union agreed with him; Bix was allowed to take the job.

For the opening night I moved the population of the Allerton House to the Rendezvous. There was a floor show with dancing in between—tunes like "Alabamy Bound," "Collegiate," "If You Knew Susie," and "Valencia." All this was drool; we were waiting for Bix to cut loose. One of his Wolverine records for Gennett was "Riverboat Shuffle"; on it Bix took a chorus and hit a high note that became famous. A hasty arrangement of the tune had been made for the Straight band. When Bix stood up to take his chorus we waited for the high note. It never came. That night Bix blew a clinker. But he made up for it later, when the floor shows were over and Straight let the band have its own way.

Bix stayed at the Rienzi Hotel, down the street from the Rendezvous. Often he came to the Allerton House and played the grand piano. Jim and I sat listening to him by the hour, as hopped up as if we had been blown through an opium pipe. My schoolbooks stayed on the table, unopened. One day Bix saw them. "What are these?" he asked. I explained that I was getting an education. He looked perplexed. "What are you going to do with it?" he said. "If you can't read music why do you want to read books?" He sat down at the piano. "By the way," I said, "who is Proust?" He hit a chord, listened to it, and then said, casually, "A French writer who lived in a cork-lined room. His stuff is no good in translation." I leaned over the piano. "How the hell did you find that out?" I demanded. He gave me the seven-veils look. "I get around," he said.

First trumpet in Straight's band was played by Gene Caffarelli, a thorough musician. He interested Bix in the idea of reading music and began to teach him. It was a curious setup; Gene and the rest of the boys were contributing part of their salary to make up the fee Straight was paying Bix, the only member in the band who couldn't read music. Bix didn't know about this financial arrangement. When he found it out he quit and left town.

He was having the usual trouble with his pivot tooth; it was in front, upstairs, and it frequently dropped out, leaving Bix unable to blow a note. Wherever he worked it was customary to see the boys in the band down on the floor, looking for Bix's tooth. Once in Cincinnati at five o'clock in the morning while driving over a snow-covered street in a 1922 Essex with Wild Bill Davison and Carl Clove, Bix shouted, "Stop the car!" There was no speak-easy in sight. "What's the matter?" Davison asked. "I've lost my tooth," Bix said. They got out and carefully examined the fresh snow. After a long search Davison sighted a tiny hole; in it he found the tooth, quietly working its way down to the road. Bix restored it to his mouth and they went on to The Hole in the Wall, where they played every morning for pork-chop sandwiches and gin. It was natural for Bix not to get the tooth permanently fastened; he couldn't be bothered going to the dentist.

He ran into some of Jean Goldkette's boys while he was at the Rendezvous. They were playing a prom date at Indiana University; Bix had a strong following there, led by a piano-playing student named Hoagy Carmichael. He was asked to go down and play the date with the band. He turned up at the Allerton House in the usual dilemma—no tuxedo. Jim and I put him together: Jim's jacket and trousers and shirt, my studs and tie. For good measure and the cool spring nights we gave him a topcoat and a hat. A few days later he returned and brought us the borrowed articles. There was a tuxedo, complete with studs, tie, and shirt. But the tuxedo was not Jim's, the shirt was not his, and the studs and tie were not mine. The topcoat and hat were also different from those we had given him. "Did you have a good time?" we asked politely. "I don't know," Bix said.

That spring Bessie Smith also came to town; we went to hear her at the Paradise, a battered joint with the buttons off at thirty-fifth and Calumet. The first night Bix turned his pockets inside out and put all his dough on the table to keep her singing. We had been raised on her records; we knew she was the greatest of all the blues singers; but she was better than any of us could possibly have anticipated. She had timing, resonance, volume, pitch, control, timbre, power—throw in the book and burn it; Bessie had everything. She was a likable gal and a large piece of woman, with long, beautiful hands, and a thirty-six inch smile. The setting in which she worked didn't quite live up to its name. Rats as big as your arm prowled around casing the customers. Mitch, a hunchback, played cornet; he almost touched Oliver and Armstrong. Tubby Hall was on drums. The place was small, unventilated, gin-soaked, and had been slept in by everyone but George Washington. Bessie rocked it. We heard her sing "Baby Won't You Please Come Home?," "Jailhouse Blues," "I'm Goin' Back to My Used to Be," "Downhearted Blues," "Tain't Nobody's Business if I Do," "Ticket Agent Ease Your Window Down," "Nobody in Town Can Bake a Jelly Roll Like Mine," "Careless Love," "Gulf Coast Blues," "Jazzbo Brown from Memphis Town," "Empty Bed Blues," "A Good Man Is Hard to Find," "I Used to Be Your Sweet Mama," "Nobody Knows You When You're Down and Out." When they finally poured us into the street we could only mumble one thing, "Well, we've heard Bessie." We were back that night and every night thereafter, sitting and listening. Once I turned to Bix and said, "How do you think Bessie would sound in that cork-lined room of Proust's?" Bix didn't hear me. He was leaning on the table, eyes glazed, listening to Bessie.

Between midnight and dawn in those days you met all sorts of people in Chicago. You might be sitting quietly in a speak-easy and be informed that for the rest of the evening drinks were on the house; Capone, the owner, had wandered in, ordered the doors closed, and settled down to enjoy himself. Once Dave Tough played in a cabaret which had a clientele composed almost exclu-

sively of baseball players, gangsters, and detectives. It was managed by an ex-prize fighter named Jake, who weighed three hundred pounds and who had a little brother named Joe who weighed
two hundred and fifty pounds. Capone, of course, was the owner.
Jake was bad-tempered and moody, particularly on rainy
nights, when the weather got into his battered sinuses. Sometimes he
would turn off the lights at midnight, order the customers out, and
take the band into the bar to play for him. He had a passion for
crossword puzzles, the easy ones in the Hearst papers. One night in
the bar Dave helped him with a couple of words. From then on
Jake grabbed him every night and asked him *all* the words. If
Dave got stuck Jake would reach across the table, put his six-pound
hand on Dave's shoulder, and say, "Come on, think!" So Dave
worked the puzzles at home in the afternoon and went to work prepared; anything else for a drummer weighing one hundred and
eight pounds would have been suicide.

One night after finishing the puzzle and grabbing a double rye at
the bar Dave was hurrying to the bandstand. An inconspicuous-
looking man standing in front of him didn't move. Dave put both
hands against the man's shoulders. "Get the hell out of my way!" he
said. One of the boys on the bandstand looked at Dave with admiration as he sat down at the drums. "I guess you don't care
how long you live," he said. "Or aren't you afraid of Bottles Capone?" Bottles was Al's kid brother. Dave played the set involun-
tarily; he shook enough to beat the drums in perfect time. But Jake
saved him; he couldn't afford to have his crossword puzzle expert
damaged.

Once when Jim Lannigan was playing at the Friars' Inn after
the New Orleans Rhythm Kings had left, some of the Capone
mob came in and took the place over for the night. The other customers left and the doors were closed; the band played and the
hoods drank. One of them noticed Jim's bass fiddle. The bulge
on its underside caught the light and made an attractive target. The
hood kept looking at it, measuring the distance and cocking one eye.
Finally he took out a revolver and fired. The bullet hit the fiddle on
the seam and the whole back opened up. The band kept on playing;

the hood asked Jim how much the fiddle cost and stripped off enough from his roll to have it repaired.

In all of the joints the bands kept on playing no matter what happened, though sometimes the drummer would hold his bass drum over his head to keep it from being smashed. Muggsy Spanier saw two people killed in front of him one night; he kept on playing but he was so nervous that afterward he couldn't remember what tune it was. His clothes were so drenched with perspiration he had to change even his shoes. Customers often shoved five- ten- and even twenty-dollar bills into Muggsy's horn. Sometimes he sat and played at their tables. There were no command performances for the gangsters, but sometimes the hoods took Muggsy with them from place to place. "We brought our own entertainment," they would say. They all liked jazz. "It's got guts and it don't make you slobber," one of them said.

All this was educational. . . .

The Goldkette Band broke up in New York. Some of the boys, including Bix, went with Paul Whiteman, who had an outfit as massive as himself. Late in the fall they hit the Balaban-Katz circuit, opening at the Chicago Theater for a week. Bix arrived in the usual predicament—no tuxedo. Jimmy MacPartland contributed the jacket and pants; I dug up the fixtures: studs, shirt, and tie. When Bix stood up to take his chorus on "Sugar," Jimmy's pants hit him halfway to the knees. He was wearing white socks.

The show had everything but a slack wire juggler. The Rhythm Boys sang, one of the trombone players did a number on a bicycle pump, and Henry Busse, who wrote "Hot Lips," soloed on "When Day Is Done." Whiteman, always a gag man, announced that Henry would hit a note never before played on a trumpet. When the moment came Busse held the trumpet to his lips and closed his eyes in rapture. The note soared away and hung in the air. After a while Busse got tired and lowered his horn, but the note kept going. Then a spotlight picked up the clarinet player standing behind him, still blowing. Ferde Grofé did the scoring for the band; there was a hot group in which Bix performed. With him were both Dorseys. Jimmy

got married during that first week in Chicago, to the Miss Detroit of
that year.

After the show I met Bix and took him to a speak-easy around
the corner at 222 North State Street. It was a no-knock place, just
walk in, with a lot of five- and ten-cent bums, Burnett's White
Satin gin, and a cellar with cement walls and an upright piano.
About two o'clock we took our drinks downstairs and Bix played.
Some of the other Whiteman boys followed us. Suddenly everybody
was there and everybody was playing along with Bix. Some singers
arrived but they kept quiet and listened. They were the Rhythm
Boys—Al Rinker, Harry Barris, Bing Crosby—sharp-looking lads,
slightly young.

We played until dawn; I bought a quart of milk off the wagon
on my way home. The next night we were back again; Bud Freeman dropped in, the Dorsey brothers were there, Harry Gale and
Ben Pollack played drums. At half past seven the following morning Bix was playing "In a Mist" and Joe Sullivan was sitting next to
him, hypnotized. The room was getting crowded; customers were
coming down to listen—the Whiteman players and their wives were
enough to put the place on a paying basis. Tesch and MacPartland
showed up; George Wettling and young Gene Krupa helped out on
the drums. There was a lot of music, a lot of gin, and a lot of talk.
It was noon before I got home. Without prearrangement we all
turned up again twelve hours later in the cellar.

One night I called for Bix backstage and he said, "We are going
to a party out in Cicero. Some guy has invited Crosby. He is going to send a car." The three of us stood outside the theater and
waited. Crosby was slim, dapper, casual, and full of laryngitis. "It's
the water in Chicago," Bix explained. "It's full of germs." I asked
Crosby who the friend was who had invited him to Cicero.
Cicero, a suburban district of Chicago, had a not too fragrant reputation at the time. "Some big shot," Crosby said. "He's throwing a party at a place called the Greyhound."

A long, black car drove up to the curb and we were told to get
into the back seat. At the Greyhound we were greeted with open
arms and bulging hips. There was a lot of drinking and talking
and pretty soon Bix was at the piano and Crosby was trying to

sing through his laryngitis. About the time I began to worry about internal drowning, the long black car returned and we were put into the back seat again. The guests waved us off with the same open arms and bulging hips.

As we drove along Bix said drowsily, "Lovely party."

"Lovely people," Crosby croaked.

After a while I said to Bix, "Remember the guy you kept telling to shut up?"

"Sure," Bix said. "Why didn't I knock him down? I'm too good-natured."

"I thought you'd like to know his name," I said.

"The hell with his name," Bix said.

"His name is Capone," I said. "Bottles Capone."

"Lovely people," Crosby croaked.

Poor Bottles! He was always getting pushed around.

After the Whiteman band left town we continued to gather at 222 North State Street. Naturally we called it the Three Deuces, since Capone had a place called the Four Deuces, on Wabash Avenue. The Four Deuces had no music. One night Red McKenzie, the St. Louis ex-jockey, dropped in at the Three Deuces. He was in town scouting talent for the Mound City Blue Blowers. They had toured the country and been to England since making their first hit record in 1924. Red was still singing and blowing through a comb. He listened to our conversation for a while, then turned to me. He looked like a mad bartender.

"Say, boy," he said, "you're running down some pretty good guys —Red Nichols and his Five Pennies. Do you pop off for exercise or does it help you to breathe?"

"We're talking about music," I said, "not about guys. We don't care who the player is, it's what he plays."

"What's the matter with those Nichols records?"

"The music is planned," I said. "Jazz can't be scored."

Red lowered one eye. "You talk big," he said. "What do you do?"

"I play the banjo and mind my own business. Why don't you try it?"

"You can't be doing so good, not with those funny clothes you're wearing. Where did you catch them, on the other side of the wringer?"

"I'm playing with Louis Panico. When I have to ride a horse I'll dress like you."

"So you don't like that music Nichols plays. Do you know anybody who can play half as good?"

"I know a dozen guys who can play twice as good. If you don't agree when you hear them play I'll shut up and buy you a horse so you won't look so silly walking around in that suit."

"Where can I hear them?"

"At my apartment in the Lincoln Park West Hotel tomorrow afternoon."

"The Lincoln Park West Hotel? So you're a Gold Coaster! Does your old man let you clip your own coupons?"

"I'll expect you at five o'clock. Come formal. Wear shoes."

I rounded up Tesch, Bud, Jimmy MacPartland, Lannigan, Sullivan, and Gene Krupa. The next afternoon McKenzie heard us drop a rock on "Nobody's Sweetheart."

"You win," he said. "I'm going to get you a record date with Tommy Rockwell of Okeh. He's in town for two weeks. I'll see him tomorrow. This band is as hot as a cheap sidewalk on August fifteenth."

"You know Rockwell?" I said.

"Who do you suppose pulled Bix and Frankie Trumbauer out of Goldkette's band in New York to make those Okeh records?"

"Red Nichols?"

"McKenzie. I'll call you tomorrow. Try to learn English in case you meet Rockwell."

He left. The guys in the band blinked and looked at me. "Is he on the level?" Bud asked. "I don't know," I said. "He's a gruff mick but he knows music—he liked us. Maybe he'll do something." Tesch got dreamy-eyed. "Gee," he said, "maybe we'll get on records. Then we'll be famous." "Let's practice some numbers," Jimmy MacPartland suggested, "in case we get a date."

What McKenzie told Rockwell I'll never know, but it worked. In New York Bix had made some records for Okeh—"Clarinet Marmalade" and "Singin' the Blues." McKenzie had sold the idea to

Rockwell; the men were hand-picked—Bill Rank on trombone, Don Murray on clarinet, Adrian Rollini on bass saxophone, Frankie Signorelli on piano, Howdy Quicksell on banjo, and Chauncey Moorehouse on drums. The records, to Rockwell's surprise, were successful. "I told him you guys were just like that mob in New York," McKenzie said when he called up. "Here's the date—he had to cancel something else to put it in so be there on time and be good—December ninth at ten in the morning. What's the name of the band?"

"It hasn't any name," I said. "The only time it ever played together was for you."

"Then it's your band. Stick your name on it."

"No, it's your band," I said. "I got it together so you could listen."

There was a moment of silence, indicating thought.

"The McKenzie-Condon Chicagoans," McKenzie said.

"Fine," I said. "Tell that to Rockwell. We'll be there at ten o'clock next Friday."

We decided on our numbers—"China Boy" and "Sugar," the latter in honor of Bix and also for Ethel Waters, who had made a record of it which I played for breakfast. We arrived on time at the Okeh studio, a barnlike place at the corner of Washington and Wells. McKenzie brought Tommy Rockwell to meet us. Rockwell was polite but dubious. Except for Jim Lannigan I was the oldest member of the band, and I had just turned twenty-two. Mezzrow was helping Krupa set up his drums. "What are you going to do with those?" Rockwell asked. "Play them," Krupa said simply. Rockwell shook his head. "You can't do that," he said. "You'll ruin our equipment. All we've ever used on records are snare drums and cymbals." Krupa, who had been practicing every day at home, looked crushed. "How about letting us try them?" I asked. "The drums are the backbone of the band. They hold us up." I could see that Rockwell was leery of the whole business; drums or no drums, I figured, we are probably going to get tossed out. "Let the kids try it," McKenzie said. "If they go wrong I'll take the rap." I didn't know until long afterward that Red had guaranteed our pay for the job. "All right," Rockwell said, "but I'm afraid the

bass drum and those tom-toms will knock the needle off the wax
and out into the street."

The rules and regulations were explained to us; one white light—
get ready, one red light—play. We were to run through the numbers and hear them played back to us so we could iron out the
rough spots; then the master records would be cut. We warmed up
and told the engineer we were ready. Rockwell and McKenzie went
into the control room. I could hear the boys fidgeting behind me.
Someone muttered, "Damn!" Somebody else whispered, "Where did
you put the bottle?" The white light flashed. I swallowed. The red
light came on. I gave the boys the beat and we jumped into "China
Boy." We opened on the nose, all playing, with everyone knitting
from his own ball of yarn. The nights and years of playing in cel-
lars and saloons and ballrooms, of practicing separately and together, of listening to Louis and Joe Oliver and Jimmy Noone and
Leon Rappolo, of losing sleep and breathing bad air and drinking
licorice gin, paid off. We were together and apart at the same time,
tying up a package with six different strings. Krupa's drums went
through us like a triple bourbon. Joe Sullivan took a chorus and
all the good things he had learned from Earl Hines came out in
his left hand. MacPartland followed him for half a chorus. Tesch
finished it; then we went into ensemble, followed by Bud on tenor
saxophone. Lannigan took a release of eight bars and we finished
on an ensemble, with the tom-toms coming through strong.

Quietly we waited for the playback. When it came, pounding out
through the big speaker, we listened stiffly for a moment. We had
never been an audience for ourselves. Then Joe's piano chorus
started and smiles began to sprout. MacPartland, Tesch, Bud, Lannigan—as each heard himself he relaxed. At the finish we were all
laughing and pounding each other on the back. We were the happiest kids since the founding of Fort Dearborn. Rockwell came out
of the control room smiling. "We'll have to get some more of this,"
he said. "Can you boys come again next week?" "We could come tomorrow," I said. "How were the drums?" Rockwell nodded toward
Krupa. "Didn't bother the equipment at all," he said. "I think we've
got something."

We tried "Sugar" then, a lazy rhythm. Tesch had rigged a brief three horn introduction for himself, MacPartland, and Bud. After that we rolled along from horn solos to ensemble; Rockwell was more than satisfied. Finally we began to cut the masters, and right in the middle of "China Boy" Bud laughed and ruined it. He was taking his solo when suddenly joy overcame him. He was so happy he leaned back and guffawed. We tried again and this time I was so excited I played along with Jim Lannigan for a bar before I remembered that he was supposed to be on his own. Rockwell had a luncheon date and came to say good-by to us. "How about the nineteenth, same time?" he said. We agreed without reluctance.

When it was over we stood around trying to realize what we had done. "You're in," McKenzie said. "Now all you've got to do is learn to blow your nose by yourself and you can hit Broadway." Bud began to laugh again. He couldn't stand the excitement. We packed our instruments and headed for the Three Deuces. . . .

The records sold well and the drums were a sensation among musicians. In New York Wingy Mannone got Vic Berton out of bed —Vic had been king of the dance-band drummers for years—and played a side for him. "Man," Wingy said, "that's the way drums ought to sound." Later, when Vic heard Krupa play in New York, he stuck out his hand and said, "Shake, kid; you're the champ." Joe Sullivan's piano solo caused excitement, too, and nobody believed that Tesch had been playing the clarinet for only two years. On the strength of his performance on the tenor saxophone Bud Freeman got a job with Ben Pollack, who already had Jimmy MacPartland. Pollack was playing then at Pershing Palace, a residential hotel on the South Side; he had, in addition to MacPartland and Freeman, Benny Goodman and a trombone player from Denver named Glenn Miller.

FLAPPERS AND JELLYBEANS*

Meyer Levin

THIS excerpt from *The Old Bunch* is taken from Mr.
Levin's best-known novel. Excerpts from novels, as a general rule, make unsatisfactory reading, except when they
are culled from the beginnings of books and are very good
at the same time. This excerpt stands on its own feet easily.
It is lively, colorful, jumpy, true to the West Side material
it deals with.

The words "flapper" and "jellybean" sound anachronistic
today. In fifteen years or less, "squares" and "dig me" will
also have gathered dust. The shifting nomenclature of slang
does not vitiate the quality of good writing, however.

Meyer Levin was born in Chicago. He worked on the
Chicago *Daily News* as a cub reporter. Then he began to
wander. New York, Paris, Germany, Palestine. He has
made semidocumentary movies about Israeli people. His
autobiography, *In Search,* hit the headlines over a full year
after its publication when Willie "The Actor" Sutton, the
big-time bank robber, was apprehended in Brooklyn and
led the police to his room, where *In Search* reposed on the
gangster's shelf.

AFTER graduation, there was no place or no excuse for Harry
Perlin to meet anybody, except taking a walk down Twelfth Street
—pardon me, Roosevelt Road—on the chance of running into
somebody looking over the movie stills in front of the Central Park.

Harry meandered as far as St. Louis Avenue, taking a squint
through the drugstore window to see if Rudy Stone was behind the
counter. Rudy wasn't there. Harry turned on St. Louis, thinking

maybe he'd run into Lou Margolis, who lived in one of the newer three-story red-brick fronts that were stuck in, breaking the gray rows of identical two-flat houses. Fellows like Lou Margolis had something that always kept a crowd turning around them; in fact they had to make excuses to get away from people.

Kids were playing peg. One of them slammed a peg that hit Harry's ankle. "That's all right," Harry forgave, glad to see the scared look fade off the kid's face. The kid doubled down and began to count the sticks. It had been a good long hit.

These summer days, kids stayed out late, playing. The twenty-first was the longest day of the year. It gave Harry a kick to remember facts like that. Motorists turn on lights at 7:40. Automatically, he looked at his wrist watch. It had the latest radium-lite numerals.

Now it was getting towards dark; the air was the same dirty gray as the stone building fronts. Suddenly he heard a bunch of kids yell: "Yay!" then realized the street lights had just gone on. He had used to yell Yay himself, and straighten up with wonder every time the lights went on.

Now he turned up Douglas Boulevard. Naturally this was a sweller street; most of the buildings were six flats, six-room apartments, red-brick sunparlor fronts. Occasionally there remained a large private residence, built when the Irish ran the neighborhood.

Signs hung in the lighted basement windows of many of the apartment buildings: Spartan A.C., or Bluebirds, or Aces. The Lawndale Sportsmen even had a special blue and white electric-box sign, but they could afford to be fancy, they were in good with Rube Moscowitz, who even gave them baseball uniforms. A bunch of fellows would be hanging around in front of each club, making cracks at girls who paraded in pairs along the street. Just taking a walk. On Friday and Saturday nights a lot of the clubs would have victrolas going, and the girls, having accidentally met the fellows, would stop in for a while; there would be dancing.

It was Harry Perlin's idea not to have a club like those other clubs: most of them existed only for a baseball team or to have some fun with the broads. But Pearly thought if fellows like Lou Margolis and Rudy Stone and maybe Mitch Wilner and Joe Freedman could be drawn into the club, serious-minded fellows, they would have a club of a higher type, and they would keep something alive.

Turning again onto Independence Boulevard was like walking up the last side of a rectangle bounding that world. Almost everybody lived inside that rectangle. Well, Sam Eisen lived down on Troy Street, and the Meisels over on Sixteenth; but the half-mile square that he had bounded was somehow warmer, full of life, it was the body containing the guts of the neighborhood though there might be limbs spreading outward.

Across the parkway that ran in the middle of the boulevard, making it such a swell street, Harry could see some of the girls gathered on the stairs of the Moscowitz house. He blushed, even though they were at such a distance.

It was funny how on some streets one side seemed dead, the other alive. Take in business. Rudy Stone had told him that Mrs. Kagen's drugstore was a dying proposition because it was on the wrong side of Roosevelt Road. Rents on the other side were twice as high, but worth it. The Central Park was on the busy side.

But further along the boulevard, when he saw Joe Freedman getting into the Buick, he waved and crossed over. They circled around to Garfield Park and back, Harry listening to the motor. The valve tappets were making a racket again.

"I'll come over Sunday morning and tighten them up," he offered. He got out and lifted the hood of the engine; he could just make out the valves popping. If there had been a little more daylight left he would have started to work right away. Joe was a lousy driver and was killing the car. Between him and his sister Aline what chance did a car have? But you could hardly blame Aline as girls are always hard on a car.

"She had it out yesterday," Joe complained. "Every time she has it out she comes back with something on the blink."

Aline emerged. She was wearing a bright red little skirt, like all the girls were wearing. It had white buttons. Through her georgette waist he could see the straps of her chemise. "Well, what's the matter now? Hello, Harry," she said, and he could feel her standing near him. He wanted to offer to drive her wherever she was going, but after all it wasn't his car.

She was just going over to Rose Heller's but Aline was so lazy she had to take the car even if it was around the corner to the grocery. She admitted it: "What's the use of walking if you have a car?"

As she clashed gears, the fellows looked at each other, wincing.

The Freedman house had one of those high English basements, ideal for a clubroom. Harry figured he could build a crystal set and have it at the club; everybody would take turns listening on his set.

"Say, nobody uses that basement of yours, do they?"

"No," Joe said. "The old man has some ideas of renting it, but you know how he is, he wouldn't spend the dough to fix it up first."

"It's got a nice entrance all right."

"Yah. My mother has got it in her head that I ought to be a doctor, just so I could have an office there," Joe said sarcastically.

"I'll bet it would make a swell clubroom," Harry said.

Joe cast a glance at the dark windows. "They don't want a club in the building. It's supposed to cheapen the building." He grinned.

"Greetings and salutations. What can I do you for?" Rudy was wiping glasses behind Mrs. Kagen's soda fountain. He came out and sat down with Joe and Lou Margolis, ready for a conference.

The first idea was to limit the club to ten.

"If we have it at all," Joe Freedman said, "it ought to mean something to belong. I mean we want something different. We don't want just another club."

Joe's idea was to have each member represent some different field of interest. For instance, Rudolph, going into medicine, could represent that. And Lou naturally would be the law. Joe, himself, would represent, well, the arts. Everyone would bring something to everyone else.

That was a good idea, Rudy agreed, but wouldn't it cut out too many good fellows? For instance, they would want Mitch Wilner.

"Oh, sure."

"Oh, sure."

But that would make two doctors.

"Well, it wouldn't have to be strictly that way, I mean . . ."

The main idea was fellows that would do something. Fellows that weren't just ordinary.

Each leaned back a little. Now they were looking around themselves, seeing what fellows they would go with, whom they would recognize.

"How about Sam Eisen?" Lou offered. This was strange coming from him as everyone had thought Lou and Sam were on the outs. Something funny had happened between them when Lou, as editor of the *Ogdenite,* refused to support Sam for re-election as school mayor, and put in that goy McGowan instead. But that school stuff was all over. Lou, at least, was showing that he harbored no grudges.

"Sam's a fine fellow. He'll get somewhere," Rudolph agreed.

They discussed Mort Abramson.

"All Mort would be in for would be the social end," Joe pointed out.

"Well, I haven't anything against being social," Rudy said, "but—"

"Well, I mean, according to that idea we had—what could Mort contribute? He'll probably end up in his old man's business."

"It might be a good idea to have one businessman!" Lou Margolis cracked.

Just then they realized that Dave Plotkin had come into the store.

"What is this, the Black Hand?" Runt said, sitting down with them. Trust him to horn in on anything.

He put in Sol Meisel, because Sol was a star athlete, and had been on the championship basketball team—Dave Plotkin, manager. Then they had to have Ben Meisel, because he was Sol's brother.

That made nearly ten.

Harry Perlin was almost left out, as there was nothing special about him, but his friend Joe Freedman insisted that the club had been Pearly's idea in the first place.

Lou Margolis pulled in his shadow, Big Ears Lou Green, who wasn't much. Big Ears soon had another name. It was Second-the-Motion.

"The Ten Aces," Chesty Meisel offered for a name.

"How about the Ten Spot?" Runt Plotkin said.

"The Decas," was Mitch Wilner's studious idea.

"The Ten Turks," Lou Green suggested, with his eyes hopefully on Lou Margolis.

Lou went his shadow one better and said: "The Ten Terrible Turks." There was laughter, but Second-the-Motion thought it was a good name, seriously.

"The Ten Spot," Runt Plotkin insisted. Once he got something in his head! "I move we put it to a vote!"

"Any second?" Lou Margolis asked.

"Point of order!" cried Droopy Ben Meisel.

"There's a motion on the floor."

"A point of order is always in order," Ben argued, and they argued about that. Finally Lou conceded: "Well, what's your point of order?"

"I forgot," Droopy said, and he didn't hear the last of that all night. Whenever an argument about anything got hot, Lou Margolis would mimic: "I forgot," and that would send the fellows into convulsions.

Other names suggested were the Ten Stars, the Ten-Alls; then somebody said did the name have to have Ten in it, and they thought of the Rainbow, the All-Stars, the Independents, the Kibitzers Klub, the Eagles, the Hawks, the Lions, the Tigers, the Bears, the Black Cats, the Blue Elephants, ha ha ha, now get serious fellows, the Arrows, the Owls, the White Owls, then Harry Perlin said:

"How about the Big Ten?"

"Naw, that's—well, that's conceited."

"No, I mean like the Big Ten colleges." Some of the fellows had never even heard of the Conference; but Harry suggested that each club member could represent one of the schools.

Runt Plotkin said it was no better than the Ten Spot. Sol Meisel, to kid Runt, suggested the Little Ten, and Ben Meisel made a motion, Lou Green seconded the motion, and Little Ten it was, six to four.

"Point of order," Lou Green said, as the vote was counted. "What's it about?"

"I forgot," Lou burbled, convulsed with his own laughter. But somehow the joke wasn't as funny as when the Sharpshooter did it.

Harry offered to calcimine the place if some of the boys would come over Sunday morning and help him. It was okayed for him to go ahead and buy the stuff and the club would repay him.

He came over and did the job, but there was only one brush so Joe Freedman mostly stood around watching. Runt dropped in just as the job was finished. The calcimine had cost seventy-four cents and Harry gave the bill to Runt, who had somehow become Secretary-Treasurer. It was never paid. He could take it out of his dues, but that would make him feel a piker.

In the Morning, in the Evening

Lil beaded her lashes. With her round little face stuck almost against the mirror, and her big round eyes, everybody said they were big round eyes, held hard open, she fingered the twitching lid and carefully brushed a drop of the black goo onto the edge of her lashes. My, she had long golden lashes, but what good were they if they didn't show? After the stuff had hardened she moved her eyelid slowly downward in an experimental wink at herself. She turned quick to catch herself unexpectedly. She dropped a quick wink. She ran her palm up her arm to feel the delight of herself. All up and down her arms and along her sides she felt little wiggles and jumps of delight. . . . In the morning, in the evening, ain't we got fun! . . . She had many kinds of lipstick. Her father owned the building on the corner of St. Louis and Roosevelt, in which there was Mrs. Kagen's drugstore, and she liked to vamp old Dr. Meyerson who was always hanging around the drugstore. Mrs. Kagen had a special little drawer, where she dropped the samples that salesmen left. Lil would go into the store and rubber through the counter; every time a salesman left a new lipstick, trust her to get hold of it. Kissproof! That was the latest. "What do you want with Kissproof?" Dr. Meyerson growled. "Wouldn't you like to know!" and she stuck out her lips at him. It was all for Rudy Stone's benefit, he was afraid of her. He always hid behind the prescription partition. "Look at the little vampire!" Dr. Meyerson would remark, trying to slap her behind as she skirted past him. "Would you believe it, only last year she would come in here to steal all-day suckers, now lipstick! Kissproof! Flappers!" he would philosophize. He was a nice man with a fat bald head and she had him completely vamped. "I'll tell your father!" he would promise, all the while Mrs. Kagen sighed resignedly.

Now Lil had got the Kissproof on her mouth, she put her lips out toward the mirror. "Oh, you beautiful baby," she said. "Oh, you beautiful baby," keeping her mouth out in the shape of a kiss. They said that in swell finishing schools for society girls the girls had to sit for two hours a day saying prunes and prisms so their lips would come out in a bow. Prunes and prisms, oh, baby, her lips were a perfect cupid's bow! It just comes to me natural!

She jumped up, bent over to straighten her stockings.

"Flappers!" her father would say. "Sixteen years old! flappers!" And while he was lecturing her, she would bend down just like this to fix the roll of her stocking because that was what got him mad and yet he couldn't say anything. Stockings had to be pulled up every so often and she liked to do it right in the street. Right when standing talking to Mort Abramson or Lou Margolis she could just bend down and pull up her stockings and they tried to keep on talking making fresh and clever remarks.

Lil set the stocking an inch above her knee, so that almost any movement swishing around would flash the naked flesh above the stocking. It almost scared her sometimes, being so daring. I've got rings on my fingers and bells on my toes. . . . She stared at her face in the mirror lid of her big box purse, licked her lips, worked her beaded lashes carefully up and down. . . . That would be a cute idea, bells on your toes. Little weentsy sleigh bells. Gee, if she only dared start a fad like that! She touched the tip of her finger to her tongue and slicked the golden spit curl that made an S on her forehead. She had practiced and she could make it into an O for Oscar but she didn't know any Oscar.

It would be terrible if she fell in love with a T or a W! But S was her natural. Who it stood for was a secret. It might be Sol Meisel. Or maybe Sam Eisen. Boo, wouldn't Sam die if he knew! Serious Sam. Two S's. It was nice when her head went back into the cup of a boy's hand. Sol had great big hands, he was an athlete. Lil shivered and danced with herself, she felt so full of life, and she had a big green-stone ring that she put on her engagement finger to kid the kids, rings on my fingers and bells on my toes, and as she walked out onto Roosevelt Road she felt she could almost hear the little bells of herself ringing all around her as she walked. . . . The rich get richer and the poor get . . . (children!) . . . Oh, but honey, ain't we got fun!

Passing Rosen's barber shop, Lil Klein looked inside because at a certain angle you could see your whole figure mirrored, and who should be sitting there but Estelle Green! She was getting a bob! Celia Moscowitz was standing beside her holding her hand and giving directions to Mr. Rosen.

Oh, my god, Lil thought, if I had beautiful red hair like that I would never have it cut! And why didn't Estelle have her own father bob her hair, he was a barber and they didn't have dollars to throw away. Bet she would catch it when she got home!

Mr. Rosen, finishing, held up a mirror for Estelle to see the back. Estelle's shoulders began to shake; Lil couldn't tell whether she was crying or laughing. Then Estelle jumped out of the chair and ran for the door.

"Kid, I've gone and done it!" Estelle burst out, meeting Lil. She stood trembling as if one word would make her cry.

"It's beautiful!" Lil said. "Honest!"

"Oh! Does it look all right? Honest?" Estelle clutched Lil's arm.

"Honest, kid! Oh, it's awful cute! It makes you look so snappy!"

"Honest?" Estelle said, staring first at Lil and then at Celia. And suddenly she wailed: "Oh, my mother'll kill me"

"Oh, don't be a gump," Celia said. "You look cute."

"Oh, you don't know my mother." She began to tremble all over. "I can't go home. She'll kill me!"

Lil and Celia had to pull her into a side street, as everybody was stopping to stare at Estelle.

"My mother didn't like it either at first," Celia said, "but now she says she's going to get her own hair bobbed."

"Anyway, what can she do, it's cut," Lil pointed out.

But that only made Estelle wilder. "Oh, you don't know my mother," she wailed. "She said if I ever cut my hair she'd cut my head off, she's got some crazy idea only bad women do it, oh, she just wants to ruin my life, she just wants me to sit in the house and be crazy like her, oh, you don't know what I have to stand for——'

"I know what, kid," Celia said, putting her thick arm around Estelle and leading her like a child; "listen, you come to my house, and we'll have my mother call her up and break it to her."

The Moscowitz house was fancier than any house in the neighborhood. Mrs. Moscowitz was up to date and you would never see a Yiddish newspaper in her hands. She dressed spiffy with wrap-around sport skirts, and even rolled her stockings, just like the girls. The apartment was swell, too, with a full-width sunparlor and French doors. Near the gas-log fireplace was a grand piano—not a baby grand. A great red and yellow Spanish shawl was slung over its propped-up top. There were at least a dozen lamps, floor lamps and table lamps, and Celia's mother was always buying marvelous new lamp shades at Field's. Yellow silk shades with domes growing out of domes, and pagoda shapes with gorgeous long bead fringes. There was a big oriental vase that was always full of flowers. The only time Estelle ever had flowers was at graduation, and she supposed she would get some when she got married.

Well, the Moscowitzes could afford it. With his political pull, Rube Moscowitz made plenty of money.

Just to sink into the beautiful overstuffed sofa, made Estelle feel better, safer.

Mrs. Moscowitz looked at her sitting there bawling, and burst out laughing.

"Why, a great big girl like you!" she said.

Then Mrs. Moscowitz marched around her inspecting her bob from all angles. She even stepped up and arranged a lock of hair.

"Why, I think it looks *very* cute," she said. "My, if Celia only had red hair like that!"

"I wish I had hair like that!" Lil agreed, waiting for someone to cry: "What! With your golden locks!"

"I think it brings out the color to cut it," Mrs. Moscowitz said. "Anyway, why have long hair? It's such a bother. Believe me!"

Estelle stopped sniffling. She began thinking of a campaign to make her mother buy a new front-room set.

"Now, dearie," said Mrs. Moscowitz, "I'll talk to your mother if you want me to, or why don't you just walk in and surprise her? That's what Celia did to me."

"Oh, you don't know my mother!" Estelle began all over again. "She—well, she doesn't understand things the way other people do."

"That's right!" Lil put in. "Didja read in the paper only the other day some Polack caught his daughter with a bob and he broke her nose? Honest! It was in the paper! He was arrested and fined $5!"

"They should have broken his nose for him," said Celia.

"Can you beat that!" said Mrs. Moscowitz. "But some people are such ignorants! They just can't understand this is a free country and a girl can bob her hair if she wants to. They're greenhorns." There was a strained moment; Estelle blushed as red as her hair.

When the telephone rang, Mrs. Greenstein was sitting on a kitchen chair, waiting for something terrible to happen. Fear of the strange forces of this outside world had been in her ever since, as a girl, she had left her village in Poland in a horse-drawn cart, to go on trains and in the dark thrumming hold of a terrifying boat, for the new country. It had seemed that the trains must collide, that the boat must sink.

Twenty-two years of this life had passed, and yet it was a

strange life to her. First one lit gas jets and then one turned on electric lights, but still the only real life, the only safe life, was under the glow of the oil lamp, those first sixteen years back home.

She sat in her kitchen, just another dumpy West Side mother, in a shapeless housedress. Although she kept her house clean, she let herself go sloppy around the house, tying strips of rags just under her knees to hold up her stockings, no matter how many pairs of garters Estelle bought her. Mrs. Greenstein's mouth was fallen, her eyes always wore an expression of deep inner tragedy.

"What is so terrible in her life?" Estelle would sometimes burst out. She would think of all the mothers who had had sons killed in the war; they really had something to be tragic about!

Now, waiting for trouble, Mrs. Greenstein sat looking out at the crisscross of gray painted stairways and back porches. A gang of kids were walking a fence; each seemed to be her boy Louie, who was walking on a thread agonizingly stretched from one point to another of her own heart, and would surely fall and break his neck.

When the telephone rang she was startled exactly as if she had seen one of the children fall. The telephone must some day bring her news of a terrible disaster; each time it rang might be that time.

But it might be a boy calling up Estelle for a date. Perhaps she could find out who; from her daughter she never learned anything.

"Hahlo," she said carefully. "Who is this?"

"Hello, mother." With the others listening, Estelle said mother instead of ma.

Mrs. Greenstein said: "Yeh?" and waited.

"I've got a surprise for you," said Estelle, and a nervous giggle came out of her.

"What kind of a surprise?" said Mrs. Greenstein. Then she could bear the strangeness of it no longer, this telephone, what was the girl trying to tell her, what terrible thing—had she run away with a goy?

"Where are you?" she cried.

"Oh, I can't tell her!" wailed Estelle, putting her hand over the mouth of the phone. "She'll kill me!"

"Where are you? What is the matter?" cried Mrs. Greenstein.

"Listen, ma, don't get sore—I'll tell you if you won't get sore."

"What has happened!"

"Don't get sore! I had a bob!"

"Hah?" said her mother.

"A bob! I bobbed my hair!" Estelle shrieked, and began to giggle.

"No! I told you not to do it! How many times did I told you not to do it!" Mrs. Greenstein's whole body was trembling. It was just as if her daughter had called her up to say she had done something bad with a man. The wildness of her. She saw the nakedness of her daughter, the young, white, evil flesh, the girl naked with shorn hair under the lustful eyes of men. Her daughter would become a whore in the streets, her daughter with the breasts that she had seen budding, and been ashamed to tell her daughter anything, with the hips that she had felt rounding under her own fingers every time she made her daughter a dress; but how could she talk when even their languages were different, how could she tell a girl such important things when she couldn't think of the English words for them, while in Yiddish you always felt you were talking up, not down to your children? And the girl would laugh at her. The girls knew everything already, with their smart eyes, and their tongues licking their lips. Such young snips, wild, they were wild, something wild in them, like wild animals.

"Well, aren't you going to say something?" Estelle said.

"Where are you?" Mrs. Greenstein sputtered. She wanted to get a stick, a whip in her hands, and hit until red welts were raised. Then she would know! That Esther!

"I'm at Celia's. I—I—" Oh, it would have been better if she had gone straight home.

Now Mrs. Greenstein understood. Now it was all clear. It was the others who were leading her daughter. Mrs. Moscowitz, fancy and stylish, who had a *shikseh* in the house. And her daughter with the great bulging breasts that a girl should be ashamed to show in the street.

"All right! You are by Mrs. Moscowitz! Stay there! Don't come home, do you hear me, you haven't a home any more! I should never live to see you again!"

Estelle began to bawl. "Listen, ma, listen, ma, oh, stop it! stop it!"

"Why, what's the matter, Estelle? Here, let me talk to her." Mrs. Moscowitz took the phone. "I know how you feel, Mrs. Greenstein, but, honest, it isn't so bad. All the girls are doing it and you ought to see, Estelle looks real cute."

"Listen, Mrs. Moscowitz," Estelle's mother shrilled, "you don't have to tell me how to raise my children. Your girl you can raise like you want. But let me tell you there are still some people maybe they are not so swell and stylish but they are still respectable. For your girl she should go around painting her face and staying out all night with the boys, all right! Her family shows her the way! But as long as I am still alive I would not let my girl be such a cheap, fresh, dirty thing! You know what I mean!"

SOUTH SIDE BOY*

Richard Wright

WHEN *Native Son* was published in 1940, it created a literary sensation. It made all other books written by Negroes and whites dealing with Negro material look puny and weak. Richard Wright, before the book's publication, had served his apprenticeship. He had written hundreds of poems, dozens of short stories, and several novels which did not quite get published. One of the unpublished novels, he once told me, was about the Chicago Post Office where he had been employed as a night-shift sorter.

Richard Wright was born in Mississippi, came to Chicago as a boy and lived for years on the South Side, the locale of *Native Son*. He is the author of *Uncle Tom's Children, Black Boy,* and *12,000,000 Black Voices.* After leaving Chicago, he resided for several years in New York. At present he lives in Paris.

The excerpt printed here from *Native Son* is taken from the opening chapter of the book. Its realism did not bother the members of the Book-Of-The-Month Club, to whom the novel was sent as a selection, and I do not think it will bother, today, any readers of this volume.

The novel opens with Bigger Thomas, the book's protagonist, arising in the morning in the tenement flat of his family, faced with the prospect of getting a promised job that day, a job he does not want. After quarreling with his mother and young sister, he leaves the flat in a surly mood and wanders down the chilly street, heading toward his favorite poolroom. The excerpt follows.

HE WALKED toward the poolroom. When he got to the door he saw Gus half a block away, coming toward him. He stopped and

* From *Native Son,* by Richard Wright, published by Harper & Bros. Copyright, 1940, by Richard Wright.

waited. It was Gus who had first thought of robbing Blum's.

"Hi, Bigger!"

"What you saying, Gus?"

"Nothing. Seen G.H. or Jack yet?"

"Naw. You?"

"Naw. Say, got a cigarette?"

"Yeah."

Bigger took out his pack and gave Gus a cigarette; he lit his and held the match for Gus. They leaned their backs against the red-brick wall of a building, smoking, their cigarettes slanting white across their black chins. To the east Bigger saw the sun burning a dazzling yellow. In the sky above him a few big white clouds drifted. He puffed silently, relaxed, his mind pleasantly vacant of purpose. Every slight movement in the street evoked a casual curiosity in him. Automatically, his eyes followed each car as it whirred over the smooth black asphalt. A woman came by and he watched the gentle sway of her body until she disappeared into a doorway. He sighed, scratched his chin and mumbled,

"Kinda warm today."

"Yeah," Gus said.

"You get more heat from this sun than from them old radiators at home."

"Yeah; them old white landlords sure don't give much heat."

"And they always knocking at your door for money."

"I'll be glad when summer comes."

"Me too," Bigger said.

He stretched his arms above his head and yawned; his eyes moistened. The sharp precision of the world of steel and stone dissolved into blurred waves. He blinked and the world grew hard again, mechanical, distinct. A weaving motion in the sky made him turn his eyes upward; he saw a slender streak of billowing white blooming against the deep blue. A plane was writing high up in the air.

"Look!" Bigger said.

"What?"

"That plane writing up there," Bigger said, pointing.

"Oh!"

They squinted at a tiny ribbon of unfolding vapor that spelled out the word: USE. . . . The plane was so far away that at times the strong glare of the sun blanked it from sight.

"You can hardly see it," Gus said.

"Looks like a little bird," Bigger breathed with childlike wonder.

"Them white boys sure can fly," Gus said.

"Yeah," Bigger said, wistfully. "They get a chance to do everything."

Noiselessly, the tiny plane looped and veered, vanishing and appearing, leaving behind it a long trail of white plumage, like coils of fluffy paste being squeezed from a tube; a plume-coil that grew and swelled and slowly began to fade into the air at the edges. The plane wrote another word: SPEED. . . .

"How high you reckon he is?" Bigger asked.

"I don't know. Maybe a hundred miles; maybe a thousand."

"I could fly one of them things if I had a chance," Bigger mumbled reflectively, as though talking to himself.

Gus pulled down the corners of his lips, stepped out from the wall, squared his shoulders, doffed his cap, bowed low and spoke with mock deference:

"Yessuh."

"You go to hell," Bigger said, smiling.

"Yessuh," Gus said again.

"I *could* fly a plane if I had a chance," Bigger said.

"If you wasn't black and if you had some money and if they'd let you go to that aviation school, you *could* fly a plane," Gus said.

For a moment Bigger contemplated all the "ifs" that Gus had mentioned. Then both boys broke into hard laughter, looking at each other through squinted eyes. When their laughter subsided, Bigger said in a voice that was half question and half statement:

"It's funny how the white folks treat us, ain't it?"

"It better be funny," Gus said.

"Maybe they are right in not wanting us to fly," Bigger said.

" 'Cause if I took a plane up I'd take a couple of bombs along and drop 'em as sure as hell. . . ."

They laughed again, still looking upward. The plane sailed and dipped and spread another word against the sky: GASO-LINE. . . .

"Use Speed Gasoline," Bigger mused, rolling the words slowly from his lips. "God, I'd like to fly up there in that sky."

"God'll let you fly when He gives you your wings up in heaven," Gus said.

They laughed again, reclining against the wall, smoking, the lids of their eyes drooped softly against the sun. Cars whizzed past on rubber tires. Bigger's face was metallically black in the strong sunlight. There was in his eyes a pensive, brooding amusement, as of a man who had been long confronted and tantalized by a riddle whose answer seemed always just on the verge of escaping him, but prodding him irresistibly on to seek its solution. The silence irked Bigger; he was anxious to do something to evade looking so squarely at this problem.

"Let's play 'white,' " Bigger said, referring to a game of play-acting in which he and his friends imitated the ways and manners of white folks.

"I don't feel like it," Gus said.

"General!" Bigger pronounced in a sonorous tone, looking at Gus expectantly.

"Aw, hell! I don't want to play," Gus whined.

"You'll be court-martialed," Bigger said, snapping out his words with military precision.

"Nigger, you nuts!" Gus laughed.

"General!" Bigger tried again, determinedly.

Gus looked wearily at Bigger, then straightened, saluted and answered:

"Yessuh."

"Send your men over the river at dawn and attack the enemy's left flank," Bigger ordered.

"Yessuh."

"Send the Fifth, Sixth, and Seventh Regiments," Bigger said, frowning. "And attack with tanks, gas, planes, and infantry."

"Yessuh!" Gus said again, saluting and clicking his heels.

For a moment they were silent, facing each other, their shoulders thrown back, their lips compressed to hold down the mounting impulse to laugh. Then they guffawed, partly at themselves and partly at the vast white world that sprawled and towered in the sun before them.

"Say, what's a 'left flank'?" Gus asked.

"I don't know," Bigger said. "I heard it in the movies."

They laughed again. After a bit they relaxed and leaned against the wall, smoking. Bigger saw Gus cup his left hand to his ear, as though holding a telephone receiver; and cup his right hand to his mouth, as though talking into a transmitter.

"Hello," Gus said.

"Hello," Bigger said. "Who's this?"

"This is Mr. J. P. Morgan speaking," Gus said.

"Yessuh, Mr. Morgan," Bigger said; his eyes filled with mock adulation and respect.

"I want you to sell twenty thousand shares of U. S. Steel in the market this morning," Gus said.

"At what price, suh?" Bigger asked.

"Aw, just dump 'em at any price," Gus said with casual irritation. "We're holding too much."

"Yessuh," Bigger said.

"And call me at my club at two this afternoon and tell me if the President telephoned," Gus said.

"Yessuh, Mr. Morgan," Bigger said.

Both of them made gestures signifying that they were hanging up telephone receivers; then they bent double, laughing.

"I bet that's *just* the way they talk," Gus said.

"I wouldn't be surprised," Bigger said.

They were silent again. Presently, Bigger cupped his hand to his mouth and spoke through an imaginary telephone transmitter.

"Hello."

"Hello," Gus answered. "Who's this?"

"This is the President of the United States speaking," Bigger said.

"Oh, yessuh, Mr. President," Gus said.

"I'm calling a cabinet meeting this afternoon at four o'clock and you, as Secretary of State, *must* be there."

"Well, now, Mr. President," Gus said, "I'm pretty busy. They raising sand over there in Germany and I got to send 'em a note. . . ."

"But this is important," Bigger said.

"What you going to take up at this cabinet meeting?" Gus asked.

"Well, you see, the niggers is raising sand all over the country," Bigger said, struggling to keep back his laughter. "We've got to do something with these black folks. . . ."

"Oh, if it's about the niggers, I'll be right there, Mr. President," Gus said.

They hung up imaginary receivers and leaned against the wall and laughed. A streetcar rattled by. Bigger sighed and swore.

"Goddammit!"

"What's the matter?"

"They don't let us do *nothing.*"

"Who?"

"The *white* folks."

"You talk like you just now finding that out," Gus said.

"Naw. But I just can't get used to it," Bigger said. "I swear to God I can't. I know I oughtn't think about it, but I can't help it. Every time I think about it I feel like somebody's poking a red-hot iron down my throat. Goddammit, look! We live here and they live there. We black and they white. They got things and we ain't. They do things and we can't. It's just like living in jail. Half the time I feel like I'm on the outside of the world peeping in through a knothole in the fence. . . ."

"Aw, ain't no use feeling that way about it. It don't help none," Gus said.

"You know one thing?" Bigger said.

"What?"

"Sometimes I feel like something awful's going to happen to me," Bigger spoke with a tinge of bitter pride in his voice.

"What you mean?" Gus asked, looking at him quickly. There was fear in Gus' eyes.

"I don't know. I just feel that way. Every time I get to thinking about me being black and they being white, me being here and they being there, I feel like something awful's going to happen to me. . . ."

"Aw, for Chrissakes! There ain't nothing you can do about it. How come you want to worry yourself? You black and they make the laws. . . ."

"Why they make us live in one corner of the city? Why don't they let us fly planes and run ships. . . ."

Gus' hunched Bigger with his elbow and mumbled good-naturedly, "Aw, nigger, quit thinking about it. You'll go nuts."

The plane was gone from the sky and the white plumes of floating smoke were thinly spread, vanishing. Because he was rest-less and had time on his hands, Bigger yawned again and hoisted his arms high above his head.

"Nothing ever happens," he complained.

"What you want to happen?"

"Anything," Bigger said with a wide sweep of his dingy palm, a sweep that included all the possible activities of the world.

Then their eyes were riveted; a slate-colored pigeon swooped down to the middle of the steel car tracks and began strutting to and fro with ruffled feathers, its fat neck bobbing with regal pride. A streetcar rumbled forward and the pigeon rose swiftly through the air on wings stretched so taut and sheer that Bigger could see the gold of the sun through their translucent tips. He tilted his head and watched the slate-colored bird flap and wheel out of sight over the edge of a high roof.

"Now, if I could only do that," Bigger said.

Gus laughed.

"Nigger, you nuts."

"I reckon we the only things in this city that can't go where we want to go and do what we want to do."

"Don't think about it," Gus said.

"I can't help it."

"That's why you feeling like something awful's going to hap-pen to you," Gus said. "You think too much."

"What in hell can a man do?" Bigger asked, turning to Gus.

"Get drunk and sleep it off."

"I can't. I'm broke."

Bigger crushed his cigarette and took out another one and offered the package to Gus. They continued smoking. A huge truck swept past, lifting scraps of white paper into the sunshine; the bits settled down slowly.

"Gus?"

"Hunh?"

"You know where the white folks live?"

"Yeah," Gus said, pointing eastward. "Over across the 'line'; over there on Cottage Grove Avenue."

"Naw; they don't," Bigger said.

"What you mean?" Gus asked, puzzled. "Then, where do they live?"

Bigger doubled his fist and struck his solar plexus.

"Right down here in my stomach," he said.

Gus looked at Bigger searchingly, then away, as though ashamed.

"Yeah; I know what you mean," he whispered.

"Every time I think of 'em, I *feel* 'em," Bigger said.

"Yeah; and in your chest and throat, too," Gus said.

"It's like fire."

"And sometimes you can't hardly breathe. . . ."

Bigger's eyes were wide and placid, gazing into space.

"That's when I feel like something awful's going to happen to me. . . ." Bigger paused, narrowed his eyes. "Naw; it ain't like something going to happen to me. It's. . . . It's like I was going to do something I can't help. . . ."

"Yeah!" Gus said with uneasy eagerness. His eyes were full of a look compounded of fear and admiration for Bigger. "Yeah; I know what you mean. It's like you going to fall and don't know where you going to land. . . ."

Gus' voice trailed off. The sun slid behind a big white cloud and the street was plunged in cool shadow; quickly the sun edged forth again and it was bright and warm once more. A long sleek black car, its fenders glinting like glass in the sun, shot past them at high speed and turned a corner a few blocks away. Bigger pursed his lips and sang:

"Zooooooooooom!"

"They got everything," Gus said.

"They own the world," Bigger said.

"Aw, what the hell," Gus said. "Let's go in the poolroom."

"O.K."

They walked toward the door of the poolroom.

"Say, you taking that job you told us about?" Gus asked.

"I don't know."

"You talk like you don't want it."

"Oh, hell, yes! I want the job," Bigger said.

They looked at each other and laughed. They went inside. The poolroom was empty, save for a fat, black man who held a half-smoked, unlit cigar in his mouth and leaned on the front counter. To the rear burned a single green-shaded bulb.

"Hi, Doc," Bigger said.

"You boys kinda early this morning," Doc said.

"Jack or G.H. around yet?" Bigger asked.

"Naw," Doc said.

"Let's shoot a game," Gus said.

"I'm broke," Bigger said.

"I got some money."

"Switch on the light. The balls are racked," Doc said.

Bigger turned on the light. They lagged for first shot. Bigger won. They started playing. Bigger's shots were poor; he was thinking of Blum's, fascinated with the idea of the robbery, and a little afraid of it.

"Remember what we talked about so much?" Bigger asked in a flat, neutral tone.

"Naw."

"Old Blum."

"Oh," Gus said. "We ain't talked about that for a month. How come you think of it all of a sudden?"

"Let's clean the place out."

"I don't know."

"It was your plan from the start," Bigger said.

Gus straightened and stared at Bigger, then at Doc who was looking out of the front window.

"You going to tell Doc? Can't you never learn to talk low?"

"Aw, I was just asking you, do you want to try it?"

"Naw."

"How come? You scared 'cause he's a white man?"

"Naw. But Blum keeps a gun. Suppose he beats us to it?"

"Aw, you scared; that's all. He's a white man and you scared."

"The hell I'm scared," Gus, hurt and stung, defended himself.

Bigger went to Gus and placed an arm about his shoulders.

"Listen, you won't have to go in. You just stand at the door and keep watch, see? Me and Jack and G.H.'ll go in. If anybody comes along, you whistle and we'll go out the back way. That's all."

The front door opened; they stopped talking and turned their heads.

"Here comes Jack and G.H. now," Bigger said.

Jack and G.H. walked to the rear of the poolroom.

"What you guys doing?" Jack asked.

"Shooting a game. Wanna play?" Bigger asked.

"You asking 'em to play and I'm paying for the game," Gus said.

They all laughed and Bigger laughed with them but stopped quickly. He felt that the joke was on him and he took a seat alongside the wall and propped his feet upon the rungs of a chair, as though he had not heard. Gus and G.H. kept on laughing.

"You niggers is crazy," Bigger said. "You laugh like monkeys and you ain't got nerve enough to do nothing but talk."

"What you mean?" G.H. asked.

"I got a haul all figured out," Bigger said.

"What haul?"

"Old Blum's."

There was silence. Jack lit a cigarette. Gus looked away, avoiding the conversation.

"If old Blum was a black man, you-all would be itching to go. 'Cause he's white, everybody's scared."

"I ain't scared," Jack said. "I'm with you."

"You say you got it all figured out?" G.H. asked.

Bigger took a deep breath and looked from face to face. It seemed to him that he should not have to explain.

"Look, it'll be easy. There ain't nothing to be scared of. Between three and four ain't nobody in the store but the old man. The cop is way down at the other end of the block. One of us'll stay outside and watch. Three of us'll go in, see? One of us'll throw a gun on old Blum; one of us'll make for the cashbox under the counter; one of us'll make for the back door and have it open so we can make a quick getaway down the back alley. . . . That's all. It won't take three minutes."

"I thought we said we wasn't never going to use a gun," G.H. said. "And we ain't bothered no white folks before."

"Can't you see? This is something *big*," Bigger said.

He waited for more objections. When none were forthcoming, he talked again.

"We can do it, if you niggers ain't scared."

Save for the sound of Doc's whistling up front, there was silence. Bigger watched Jack closely; he knew that the situation was one in which Jack's word would be decisive. Bigger was afraid of Gus, because he knew that Gus would not hold out if Jack said yes. Gus stood at the table, toying with a cue stick, his eyes straying lazily over the billiard balls scattered about the table in the array of an unfinished game. Bigger rose and sent the balls whirling with a sweep of his hand, then looked straight at Gus as the gleaming balls kissed and rebounded from the rubber cushions, zigzagging across the table's green cloth. Even though Bigger had asked Gus to be with him in the robbery, the fear that Gus would really go made the muscles of Bigger's stomach tighten; he was hot all over. He felt as if he wanted to sneeze and could not; only it was more nervous than wanting to sneeze. He grew hotter, tighter; his nerves were taut and his teeth were on edge. He felt that something would soon snap within him.

"Goddammit! Say something, somebody!"

"I'm in," Jack said again.

"I'll go if the rest goes," G.H. said.

Gus stood without speaking and Bigger felt a curious sensation —half sensual, half thoughtful. He was divided and pulled against himself. He had handled things just right so far; all but Gus had consented. The way things stood now there were three against Gus, and that was just as he had wanted it to be. Bigger was afraid of robbing a white man and he knew that Gus was afraid, too. Blum's store was small and Blum was alone, but Bigger could not think of robbing him without being flanked by his three pals. But even with his pals he was afraid. He had argued all of his pals but one into consenting to the robbery, and toward the lone man who held out he felt a hot hate and fear; he had transferred his fear of the whites to Gus. He hated Gus because he knew that Gus was afraid, as even he was; and he feared Gus because he felt that Gus would consent and then he would be compelled to go through with the robbery. Like a man about to shoot himself and dreading to shoot and yet knowing that he has to shoot and feeling it all at once and powerfully, he watched Gus and waited for him to say yes. But Gus did not speak. Bigger's teeth clamped so tight that his jaws ached. He edged toward Gus, not looking at Gus, but feeling the presence of Gus over all his body, through him, in and out of him, and hating himself and Gus because he felt it. Then he could not stand it any longer. The hysterical tensity of his nerves urged him to speak, to free himself. He faced Gus, his eyes red with anger and fear, his fists clenched and held stiffly to his sides.

"You black sonofabitch," he said in a voice that did not vary in tone. "You scared 'cause he's a white man."

"Don't cuss me, Bigger," Gus said quietly.

"I *am* cussing you!"

"You don't have to cuss me," Gus said.

"Then why don't you use that black tongue of yours?" Bigger asked. "Why don't you say what you going to do?"

"I don't have to use my tongue unless I *want* to!"

"You bastard! You scared bastard!"

"You ain't my boss," Gus said.

"You yellow!" Bigger said. "You scared to rob a white man."

"Aw, Bigger. Don't say that," G.H. said. "Leave 'im alone."

"He's yellow," Bigger said. "He won't go with us."

"I didn't say I wouldn't go," Gus said.

"Then, for Chrissakes, say what you going to do," Bigger said.

Gus leaned on his cue stick and gazed at Bigger and Bigger's stomach tightened as though he were expecting a blow and were getting ready for it. His fists clenched harder. In a split second he felt how his fist and arm and body would feel if he hit Gus squarely in the mouth, drawing blood; Gus would fall and he would walk out and the whole thing would be over and the robbery would not take place. And his thinking and feeling in this way made the choking tightness rising from the pit of his stomach to his throat slacken a little.

"You see, Bigger," began Gus in a tone that was a compromise between kindness and pride. "You see, Bigger, you the cause of all the trouble we ever have. It's your hot temper. Now, how come you want to cuss me? Ain't I got a right to make up my mind? Naw; that ain't your way. You start cussing. You say I'm scared. It's *you* who's scared. You scared I'm going to say yes and you'll have to go through with the job. . . ."

"Say that again! Say that again and I'll take one of these balls and sink it in your Goddamn mouth," Bigger said, his pride wounded to the quick.

"Aw, for Chrissakes," Jack said.

"You *see* how he is," Gus said.

"Why don't you say what you going to do?" Bigger demanded.

"Aw, I'm going with you-all," Gus said in a nervous tone that sought to hide itself; a tone that hurried on to other things. "I'm going, but Bigger don't have to act like that. He don't have to cuss me."

"Why didn't you say that at first?" Bigger asked; his anger amounted almost to frenzy. "You make a man want to sock you!"

". . . I'll help on the haul," Gus continued, as though Bigger had not spoken. "I'll help just like I always help. But I'll be Goddamn if I'm taking orders from *you,* Bigger! You just a scared coward! You calling me scared so nobody'll see how scared *you* is!"

Bigger leaped at him, but Jack ran between them. G.H. caught Gus' arm and led him aside.

"Who's asking you to take orders?" Bigger said. "I never want to give orders to a piss-sop like you!"

"You boys cut out that racket back there!" Doc called.

They stood silently about the pool table. Bigger's eyes followed Gus as Gus put his cue stick in the rack and brushed chalk dust from his trousers and walked a little distance away. Bigger's stomach burned and a hazy black cloud hovered a moment before his eyes, and left. Mixed images of violence ran like sand through his mind, dry and fast, vanishing. He could stab Gus with his knife; he could slap him; he could kick him; he could trip him up and send him sprawling on his face. He could do a lot of things to Gus for making him feel this way.

"Come on, G.H.," Gus said.

"Where we going?"

"Let's walk."

"O.K."

"What we gonna do?" Jack asked. "Meet here at three?"

"Sure," Bigger said. "Didn't we just decide?"

"I'll be here," Gus said, with his back turned.

When Gus and G.H. had gone Bigger sat down and felt cold sweat on his skin. It was planned now and he would have to go through with it. His teeth gritted and the last image he had seen of Gus going through the door lingered in his mind. He could have taken one of the cue sticks and gripped it hard and swung it at the back of Gus' head, feeling the impact of the hard wood cracking against the bottom of the skull. The tight feeling was still in him and he knew that it would remain until they were actually doing the job, until they were in the store taking the money.

"You and Gus sure don't get along none," Jack said, shaking his head.

Bigger turned and looked at Jack; he had forgotten that Jack was still there.

"Aw, that yellow black bastard," Bigger said.

"He's all right," Jack said.

"He's scared," Bigger said. "To make him ready for a job, you

have to make him scared two ways. You have to make him more
scared of what'll happen to him if he don't do the job than of
what'll happen to him if he pulls the job."

"If we going to Blum's today, we oughtn't fuss like this," Jack
said. "We got a job on our hands, a real job."

"Sure. Sure, I know," Bigger said.

Bigger felt an urgent need to hide his growing and deepening
feeling of hysteria; he had to get rid of it or else he would succumb
to it. He longed for a stimulus powerful enough to focus his attention and drain off his energies. He wanted to run. Or listen to
some swing music. Or laugh or joke. Or read a *Real Detective
Story Magazine*. Or go to a movie. Or visit Bessie. All that morning he had lurked behind his curtain of indifference and looked
at things, snapping and glaring at whatever had tried to make him
come out into the open. But now he was out; the thought of the
job at Blum's and the tilt he had had with Gus had snared him
into things and his self-trust was gone. Confidence could only
come again now through action so violent that it would make him
forget. These were the rhythms of his life: indifference and violence; periods of abstract brooding and periods of intense desire;
moments of silence and moments of anger—like water ebbing and
flowing from the tug of a faraway, invisible force. Being this way
was a need of his as deep as eating. He was like a strange plant
blooming in the day and wilting at night; but the sun that made
it bloom and the cold darkness that made it wilt were never
seen. It was his own sun and darkness, a private and personal
sun and darkness. He was bitterly proud of his swiftly changing
moods and boasted when he had to suffer the results of them. It
was the way he was, he would say; he could not help it, he would
say, and his head would wag. And it was his sullen stare and
the violent action that followed that made Gus and Jack and G.H.
hate and fear him as much as he hated and feared himself.

"Where you want to go?" Jack asked. "I'm tired of setting."

"Let's walk," Bigger said.

They went to the front door. Bigger paused and looked round
the poolroom with a wild and exasperated expression, his lips tightening with resolution.

"Goin'?" Doc asked, not moving his head.

"Yeah," Bigger said.

"See you later," Jack said.

They walked along the street in the morning sunshine. They waited leisurely at corners for cars to pass; it was not that they feared cars, but they had plenty of time. They reached South Parkway smoking freshly lit cigarettes.

"I'd like to see a movie," Bigger said.

"*Trader Horn's* running again at the Regal. They're bringing a lot of old pictures back."

"How much is it?"

"Twenty cents."

"O.K. Let's see it."

Bigger strode silently beside Jack for six blocks. It was noon when they reached Forty-seventh Street and South Parkway. The Regal was just opening. Bigger lingered in the lobby and looked at the colored posters while Jack bought the tickets. Two features were advertised: one, *The Gay Woman,* was pictured on the posters in images of white men and white women lolling on beaches, swimming, and dancing in night clubs; the other, *Trader Horn,* was shown on the posters in terms of black men and black women dancing against a wild background of barbaric jungle. Bigger looked up and saw Jack standing at his side.

"Come on. Let's go in," Jack said.

"O.K."

He followed Jack into the darkened movie. The shadows were soothing to his eyes after the glare of the sun. The picture had not started and he slouched far down in a seat and listened to a pipe organ shudder in waves of nostalgic tone, like a voice humming hauntingly within him. He moved restlessly, looking round as though expecting to see someone sneaking upon him. The organ sang forth full, then dropped almost to silence.

"You reckon we'll do all right at Blum's?" he asked in a drawling voice tinged with uneasiness.

"Aw, sure," Jack said; but his voice, too, was uneasy.

"You know, I'd just as soon go to jail as take that damn relief job," Bigger said.

"Don't say that. Everything'll be all right."

"You reckon it will?"

"Sure."

"I don't give a damn."

"Let's think about how we'll do it, not about how we'll get caught."

"Scared?"

"Naw. You?"

"Hell, naw!"

They were silent, listening to the organ. It sounded for a long moment on a trembling note, then died away. Then it stole forth again in whispering tones that could scarcely be heard.

"We better take our guns along this time," Bigger said.

"O.K. But we gotta be careful. We don't wanna kill nobody."

"Yeah. But I'll feel safer with a gun this time."

"Gee, I wished it was three o'clock now. I wished it was over."

"Me too."

The organ sighed into silence and the screen flashed with the rhythm of moving shadows. There was a short newsreel which Bigger watched without much interest. Then came *The Gay Woman* in which, amid scenes of cocktail drinking, dancing, golfing, swimming, and spinning roulette wheels, a rich young white woman kept clandestine appointments with her lover while her millionaire husband was busy in the offices of a vast paper mill. Several times Bigger nudged Jack in the ribs with his elbow as the giddy young woman duped her husband and kept from him the knowledge of what she was doing.

"She sure got her old man fooled," Bigger said.

"Looks like it. He's so busy making money he don't know what's going on," Jack said. "Them rich chicks'll do anything."

"Yeah. And she's a hot-looking number, all right," Bigger said. "Say, maybe I'll be working for folks like that if I take that relief job. Maybe I'll be driving 'em around. . . ."

"Sure," Jack said. "Man, you ought to take that job. You don't know what you might run into. My ma used to work for rich white folks and you ought to hear the tales she used to tell . . ."

"What she say?" Bigger asked eagerly.

"Ah, man, them rich white women'll go to bed with anybody, from a poodle on up. Shucks, they even have their chauffeurs. Say, if you run into anything on that new job that's too much for you to handle, let me know. . . ."

They laughed. The play ran on and Bigger saw a night club floor thronged with whirling couples and heard a swing band playing music. The rich young woman was dancing and laughing with her lover.

"I'd like to be invited to a place like that just to find out what it feels like," Bigger mused.

"Man, if them folks saw you they'd run," Jack said. "They'd think a gorilla broke loose from the zoo and put on a tuxedo."

They bent over low in their seats and giggled without restraint. When Bigger sat up again he saw the picture flashing on. A tall waiter was serving two slender glasses of drinks to the rich young woman and her lover.

"I bet their mattresses is stuffed with paper dollars," Bigger said.

"Man, them folks don't even have to turn over in their sleep," Jack said. "A butler stands by their beds at night, and when he hears 'em sigh, he gently rolls 'em over. . . ."

They laughed again, then fell silent abruptly. The music accompanying the picture dropped to a low, rumbling note and the rich young woman turned and looked toward the front door of the night club from which a chorus of shouts and screams was heard.

"I bet it's her husband," Jack said.

"Yeah," Bigger said.

Bigger saw a sweating, wild-eyed young man fight his way past a group of waiters and whirling dancers.

"He looks like a crazy man," Jack said.

"What you reckon he wants?" Bigger asked, as though he himself was outraged at the sight of the frenzied intruder.

"Damn if I know," Jack muttered preoccupiedly.

Bigger watched the wild young man elude the waiters and run in the direction of the rich woman's table. The music of the swing band stopped and men and women scurried frantically into corners and doorways. There were shouts: *Stop 'im! Grab 'im!* The wild man halted a few feet from the rich woman and reached inside of his coat and drew forth a black object. There were more screams: *He's got a bomb! Stop 'im!* Bigger saw the woman's lover leap to the center of the floor, fling his hands high into the air and catch the bomb just as the wild man threw it. As the rich woman fainted, her lover hurled the bomb out of a window, shattering a pane. Bigger saw a white flash light up the night outside as the bomb exploded deafeningly. Then he was looking at the wild man who was now pinned to the floor by a dozen hands. He heard a woman scream: *He's a Communist!*

"Say, Jack?"

"Hunh?"

"What's a Communist?"

"A Communist is a red, ain't he?"

"Yeah; but what's a red?"

"Damn if I know. It's a race of folks who live in Russia, ain't it?"

"They must be wild."

"Looks like it. That guy was trying to kill somebody."

The scenes showed the wild man weeping on his knees and cursing through his tears. *I wanted to kill 'im,* he sobbed. Bigger now understood that the wild bomb-thrower was a Communist who had mistaken the rich woman's lover for her husband and had tried to kill him.

"Reds must don't like rich folks," Jack said.

"They sure must don't," Bigger said. "Every time you hear about one, he's trying to kill somebody or tear things up."

The picture continued and showed the rich young woman in a fit of remorse, telling her lover that she thanked him for saving her life, but that what had happened had taught her that her husband needed her. *Suppose it had been he?* she whimpered.

"She's going back to her old man," Bigger said.

"Oh, yeah," Jack said. "They got to kiss in the end."

Bigger saw the rich young woman rush home to her millionaire husband. There were long embraces and kisses as the rich woman and the rich man vowed never to leave each other and to forgive each other.

"You reckon folks really act like that?" Bigger asked, full of the sense of a life he had never seen.

"Sure, man. They rich," Jack said.

"I wonder if this guy I'm going to work for is a rich man like that?" Bigger asked.

"Maybe so," Jack said.

"Shucks. I got a great mind to take that job," Bigger said.

"Sure. You don't know what you might see."

They laughed. Bigger turned his eyes to the screen, but he did not look. He was filled with a sense of excitement about his new job. Was what he had heard about rich white people really true? Was he going to work for people like you saw in the movies? If he were, then he'd see a lot of things from the inside; he'd get the dope, the low-down. He looked at *Trader Horn* unfold and saw pictures of naked black men and women whirling in wild dances and heard drums beating and then gradually the African scene changed and was replaced by images in his own mind of white men and women dressed in black and white clothes, laughing, talking, drinking and dancing. Those were smart people; they knew how to get hold of money, millions of it. Maybe if he were working for them something would happen and he would get some of it. He would see just how they did it. Sure, it was all a game and white people knew how to play it. And rich white people were not so hard on Negroes; it was the poor whites who hated Negroes. They hated Negroes because they didn't have their share of the money. His mother had always told him that rich white people liked Negroes better than they did poor whites. He felt that if he were a poor white and did not get his share of the money, then he would deserve to be kicked. Poor white people were stupid. It was the rich white people who were smart and knew how to treat people. He remembered hearing somebody tell a story of a Negro chauffeur who had married a rich white girl and the girl's family had shipped the couple out of the country and had supplied them with money.

Yes, his going to work for the Daltons was something big.

Maybe Mr. Dalton was a millionaire. Maybe he had a daughter who was a hot kind of girl; maybe she spent lots of money; maybe she'd like to come to the South Side and see the sights sometimes. Or maybe she had a secret sweetheart and only he would know about it because he would have to drive her around; maybe she would give him money not to tell.

He was a fool for wanting to rob Blum's just when he was about to get a good job. Why hadn't he thought of that before? Why take a fool's chance when other things, big things, could happen? If something slipped up this afternoon he would be out of a job and in jail, maybe. And he wasn't so hot about robbing Blum's, anyway. He frowned in the darkened movie, hearing the roll of tom-toms and the screams of black men and women dancing free and wild, men and women who were adjusted to their soil and at home in their world, secure from fear and hysteria.

"Come on, Bigger," Jack said. "We gotta go."

"Hunh?"

"It's twenty to three."

He rose and walked down the dark aisle over the soft, invisible carpet. He had seen practically nothing of the picture, but he did not care. As he walked into the lobby his insides tightened again with the thought of Gus and Blum's.

"Swell, wasn't it?"

"Yeah; it was a killer," Bigger said.

He walked alongside Jack briskly until they came to Thirty-ninth Street.

"We better get our guns," Bigger said.

"Yeah."

"We got about fifteen minutes."

"O.K."

"So long."

He walked home with a mounting feeling of fear. When he reached his doorway, he hesitated about going up. He didn't want to rob Blum's; he was scared. But he had to go through with it now. Noiselessly, he went up the steps and inserted his key in the lock; the door swung in silently and he heard his mother singing behind the curtain.

Lord, I want to be a Christian,
In my heart, in my heart,
Lord, I want to be a Christian,
In my heart, in my heart. . . .

He tiptoed into the room and lifted the top mattress of his bed
and pulled forth the gun and slipped it inside of his shirt. Just as
he was about to open the door his mother paused in her singing.

"That you, Bigger?"

He stepped quickly into the outer hallway and slammed the
door and bounded headlong down the stairs. He went to the vestibule and swung through the door into the street, feeling that ball
of hot tightness growing larger and heavier in his stomach and
chest. He opened his mouth to breathe. He headed for Doc's and
came to the door and looked inside. Jack and G.H. were shooting
pool at a rear table. Gus was not there. He felt a slight lessening of
nervous tension and swallowed. He looked up and down the street;
very few people were out and the cop was not in sight. A clock in
a window across the street told him that it was twelve minutes to
three. Well, this was it; he had to go in. He lifted his left hand and
wiped sweat from his forehead in a long slow gesture. He hesitated a moment longer at the door, then went in, walking with firm
steps to the rear table. He did not speak to Jack or G.H., nor they
to him. He lit a cigarette with shaking fingers and watched the
spinning billiard balls roll and gleam and clack over the green
stretch of cloth, dropping into holes after bounding to and fro from
the rubber cushions. He felt impelled to say something to ease
the swelling in his chest. Hurriedly, he flicked his cigarette into a
spittoon and, with twin eddies of blue smoke jutting from his black
nostrils, shouted hoarsely,

"Jack, I betcha two bits you can't make it!"

Jack did not answer; the ball shot straight across the table and
vanished into a side pocket.

"You would've lost," Jack said.

"Too late now," Bigger said. "You wouldn't bet, so *you* lost."

He spoke without looking. His entire body hungered for keen
sensation, something exciting and violent to relieve the tautness.
It was now ten minutes to three and Gus had not come. If Gus

stayed away much longer, it would be too late. And Gus knew
that. If they were going to do anything, it certainly ought to be
done before folks started coming into the streets to buy their food
for supper, and while the cop was down at the other end of the
block.

"That bastard!" Bigger said. "I knew it!"

"Oh, he'll be along," Jack said.

"Sometimes I'd like to cut his yellow heart out," Bigger said, fin-
gering the knife in his pocket.

"Maybe he's hanging around some meat," G.H. said.

"He's just scared," Bigger said. "Scared to rob a white man."

The billiard balls clacked. Jack chalked his cue stick and the
metallic noise made Bigger grit his teeth until they ached. He
didn't like that noise; it made him feel like cutting something with
his knife.

"If he makes us miss this job, I'll fix 'im, so help me," Bigger
said. "He oughtn't be late. Every time somebody's late, things go
wrong. Look at the big guys. You don't ever hear of them being
late, do you? Naw! They work like clocks!"

"Ain't none of us got more guts'n Gus," G.H. said. "He's been
with us every time."

"Aw, shut your trap," Bigger said.

"There you go again, Bigger," G.H. said. "Gus was just talking
about how you act this morning. You get too nervous when something's coming off. . . ."

"Don't tell me I'm nervous," Bigger said.

"If we don't do it today, we can do it tomorrow," Jack said.

"Tomorrow's Sunday, fool!"

"Bigger, for Chrissakes! Don't holler!" Jack said tensely.

Bigger looked at Jack hard and long, then turned away with a
grimace.

"Don't tell the world what we're trying to do," Jack whispered in a mollifying tone.

Bigger walked to the front of the store and stood looking out of
the plate-glass window. Then, suddenly, he felt sick. He saw Gus
coming along the street. And his muscles stiffened. He was going
to do something to Gus; just what, he did not know. As Gus

neared he heard him whistling: "The Merry-Go-Round Broke Down. . . ." The door swung in.

"Hi, Bigger," Gus said.

Bigger did not answer. Gus passed him and started toward the rear tables. Bigger whirled and kicked him hard. Gus flopped on his face with a single movement of his body. With a look that showed that he was looking at Gus on the floor and at Jack and G.H. at the rear table and at Doc—looking at them all at once in a kind of smiling, roving, turning-slowly glance—Bigger laughed, softly at first, then harder, louder, hysterically; feeling something like hot water bubbling inside of him and trying to come out. Gus got up and stood, quiet, his mouth open and his eyes dead-black with hate.

"Take it easy, boys," Doc said, looking up from behind his counter, and then bending over again.

"What you kick me for?" Gus asked.

" 'Cause I wanted to," Bigger said.

Gus looked at Bigger with lowered eyes. G.H. and Jack leaned on their cue sticks and watched silently.

"I'm going to fix you one of these days," Gus threatened.

"Say that again," Bigger said.

Doc laughed, straightening and looking at Bigger.

"Lay off the boy, Bigger."

Gus turned and walked toward the rear tables. Bigger, with an amazing bound, grabbed him in the back of his collar.

"I asked you to say that again!"

"Quit, Bigger!" Gus spluttered, choking, sinking to his knees.

"Don't tell me to quit!"

The muscles of his body gave a tightening lunge and he saw his fist come down on the side of Gus' head; he had struck him really before he was conscious of doing so.

"Don't hurt 'im," Jack said.

"I'll kill 'im," Bigger said through shut teeth, tightening his hold on Gus' collar, choking him harder.

"T-turn m-m-m-me l-l-loose," Gus gurgled, struggling.

"Make me!" Bigger said, drawing his fingers tighter.

Gus was very still, resting on his knees. Then, like a taut bow finding release, he sprang to his feet, shaking loose from Bigger and turning to get away. Bigger staggered back against the wall, breathless for a moment. Bigger's hand moved so swiftly that nobody saw it; a gleaming blade flashed. He made a long step, as graceful as an animal leaping, threw out his left foot and tripped Gus to the floor. Gus turned over to rise, but Bigger was on top of him, with the knife open and ready.

"Get up! Get up and I'll slice your tonsils!"

Gus lay still.

"That's all right, Bigger," Gus said in surrender. "Lemme up."

"You trying to make a fool out of me, ain't you?"

"Naw," Gus said, his lips scarcely moving.

"You Goddamn right you ain't," Bigger said.

His face softened a bit and the hard glint in his bloodshot eyes died. But he still knelt with the open knife. Then he stood.

"Get up!" he said.

"Please, Bigger!"

"You want me to slice you?"

He stooped again and placed the knife at Gus' throat. Gus did not move and his large black eyes looked pleadingly. Bigger was not satisfied; he felt his muscles tightening again.

"Get up! I ain't going to ask you no more!"

Slowly, Gus stood. Bigger held the open blade an inch from Gus's lips.

"Lick it," Bigger said, his body tingling with elation.

Gus' eyes filled with tears.

"Lick it, I said! You think I'm playing?"

Gus looked round the room without moving his head, just rolling his eyes in a mute appeal for help. But no one moved. Bigger's left fist was slowly lifting to strike. Gus' lips moved toward the knife; he stuck out his tongue and touched the blade. Gus' lips quivered and tears streamed down his cheeks.

"Hahahaha!" Doc laughed.

"Aw, leave 'im alone," Jack called.

Bigger watched Gus with lips twisted in a crooked smile.

"Say, Bigger, ain't you scared 'im enough?" Doc asked.

Bigger did not answer. His eyes gleamed hard again, pregnant with another idea.

"Put your hands up, way up!" he said.

Gus swallowed and stretched his hands high along the wall.

"Leave 'im alone, Bigger," G.H. called weakly.

"I'm doing this," Bigger said.

He put the tip of the blade into Gus' shirt and then made an arc with his arm, as though cutting a circle.

"How would you like me to cut your belly button out?"

Gus did not answer. Sweat trickled down his temples. His lips hung wide, loose.

"Shut them liver lips of yours!"

Gus did not move a muscle. Bigger pushed the knife harder into Gus' stomach.

"Bigger!" Gus said in a tense whisper.

"Shut your mouth!"

Gus shut his mouth. Doc laughed. Jack and G.H. laughed. Then Bigger stepped back and looked at Gus with a smile.

"You clown," he said. "Put your hands down and set on that chair." He watched Gus sit. "That ought to teach you not to be late next time, see?"

"We ain't late, Bigger. We still got time. . . ."

"Shut up! It *is* late!" Bigger insisted commandingly.

Bigger turned aside; then, hearing a sharp scrape on the floor, stiffened. Gus sprang from the chair and grabbed a billiard ball from the table and threw it with a half sob and half curse. Bigger flung his hands upward to shield his face and the impact of the ball struck his wrist. He had shut his eyes when he had glimpsed the ball sailing through the air toward him and when he opened his eyes Gus was flying through the rear door and at the same time he heard the ball hit the floor and roll away. A hard pain throbbed in his hand. He sprang forward, cursing.

"You sonofabitch!"

He slipped on a cue stick lying in the middle of the floor and tumbled forward.

"That's enough now, Bigger," Doc said, laughing.

Jack and G.H. also laughed. Bigger rose and faced them, holding his hurt hand. His eyes were red and he stared with speechless hate.

"Just keep laughing," he said.

"Behave yourself, boy," Doc said.

"Just keep laughing," Bigger said again, taking out his knife.

"Watch what you're doing now," Doc cautioned.

"Aw, Bigger," Jack said, backing away toward the rear door.

"You done spoiled things now," G.H. said. "I reckon that was what you wanted. . . ."

"You go to hell!" Bigger shouted, drowning out G.H.'s voice.

Doc bent down behind the counter and when he stood up he had something in his hand which he did not show. He stood there laughing. White spittle showed at the corners of Bigger's lips. He walked to the billiard table, his eyes on Doc. Then he began to cut the green cloth on the table with long sweeping strokes of his arm. He never took his eyes from Doc's face.

"Why, you sonofabitch!" Doc said. "I ought to shoot you, so help me God! Get out, before I call a cop!"

Bigger walked slowly past Doc, looking at him, not hurrying, and holding the open knife in his hand. He paused in the doorway and looked back. Jack and G.H. were gone.

"Get out of here!" Doc said, showing a gun.

"Don't you like it?" Bigger asked.

"Get out before I shoot you!" Doc said. "And don't you ever set your black feet inside here again!"

Doc was angry and Bigger was afraid. He shut the knife and slipped it in his pocket and swung through the door to the street. He blinked his eyes from the bright sunshine; his nerves were so taut that he had difficulty in breathing. Halfway down the block he passed Blum's store; he looked out of the corners of his eyes through the plate-glass window and saw that Blum was alone and the store was empty of customers. Yes; they would have had time to rob the store; in fact, they still had time. He had lied to Gus and G.H. and Jack. He walked on; there was not a policeman in sight. Yes; they could have robbed the store and could have gotten away. He hoped the fight he had had with Gus covered up what he was trying to hide. At least the fight made him feel the equal of them. And he felt the equal of Doc, too; had he not slashed his table and dared him to use his gun?

He had an overwhelming desire to be alone; he walked to the middle of the next block and turned into an alley. He began to laugh, softly, tensely; he stopped still in his tracks and felt something warm roll down his cheek and he brushed it away. "Jesus," he breathed. "I laughed so hard I cried." Carefully, he dried his face on his coat sleeve, then stood for two whole minutes staring at the shadow of a telephone pole on the alley pavement. Suddenly he straightened and walked on with a single expulsion of breath. "What the hell!" He stumbled violently over a tiny crack in the pavement. "Goddamn!" he said. When he reached the end of the alley, he turned into a street, walking slowly in the sunshine, his hands jammed deep into his pockets, his head down, depressed.

He went home and sat in a chair by the window, looking out dreamily.

"That you, Bigger?" his mother called from behind the curtain.

"Yeah," he said.

"What you run in here and run out for, a little while ago?"

"Nothing."

"Don't you go and get into no trouble, now, boy."

"Aw, Ma! Leave me alone."

He listened awhile to her rubbing clothes on the metal washboard, then he gazed abstractedly into the street, thinking of how he had felt when he fought Gus in Doc's poolroom. He was relieved and glad that in an hour he was going to see about that job at the Dalton place. He was disgusted with the gang; he knew that what had happened today put an end to his being with them in any more jobs. Like a man staring regretfully but hopelessly at the stump of a cutoff arm or leg, he knew that the fear of robbing a white man had had hold of him when he started that fight with Gus; but he knew it in a way that kept it from coming to his mind in the form of a hard and sharp idea. His confused emotions had made him feel instinctively that it would be better to fight Gus and spoil the plan of the robbery than to confront a white man with a gun. But he kept this knowledge of his fear thrust firmly down in him;

his courage to live depended upon how successfully his fear was hidden from his consciousness. He had fought Gus because Gus was late; that was the reason his emotions accepted and he did not try to justify himself in his own eyes, or in the eyes of the gang. He did not think enough of them to feel that he had to; he did not consider himself as being responsible to them for what he did, even though they had been involved as deeply as he in the planned robbery. He felt that same way toward everyone. As long as he could remember, he had never been responsible to anyone. The moment a situation became so that it exacted something of him, he rebelled. That was the way he lived; he passed his days trying to defeat or gratify powerful impulses in a world he feared.

HOW A NIGHTHAWK SAVED ITS EGGS FROM BEING MEASURED*

Leonard Dubkin

EVERY large American city has its nature lovers and bird watchers. Most of them are loosely organized into clubs and go on field trips. Once in a while, however, you see lone figures in the parks, or suburbs, standing silently like hunter dogs, their heads lifted, observing something in the trees.

In Chicago one occasionally notices a man or woman looking at the wheeling gulls from one of the city's many bridges. It has always seemed to me to be a wonderful thing to do, just standing there above the hurrying water, studying the intricate design of the flights.

In the following story you will read about a Chicago boy whose love for birds took him to a West Side roof top, and what he found when he got up there.

OF ALL the birds that inhabit our city the species that receives the least notice, and is probably the least understood, is the night-hawk. I do not know why this should be so, for these birds are certainly not rare in the city; I have heard and seen them in every neighborhood except the Loop, where there are not enough insects to suit them. Nighthawks feed exclusively on insects caught high in the air, in the early evening and at night, and so they do not come under the benevolence of "bird-lovers," who dispense their largess only to those species which come to bird trays and feeding troughs to eat. Most citizens do not even know there

* From *Murmur of Wings,* by Leonard Dubkin, published by Whittlesey House, 1944. Reprinted by permission of the publishers.

are nighthawks in our city, and yet wherever you may happen to
be at twilight you hear their peculiar rasping "chweenk," and if
you look up at the sky you will see one or perhaps two of them
fluttering about, barely distinguishable against the darkening sky,
but flying with an erratic, jerky flight that easily identifies them.

Nighthawks are migratory birds, and when I think of them at all
in winter I imagine them fluttering crazily from side to side over
the low thatched roofs of some South American village. Does it
ever occur to them to compare the way of life of the South Americans with that of the human inhabitants of the cities in the North,
and do they wonder at the absence of double-decker buses, elevated railroads, and steam locomotives in their winter habitat? Or
is our modern civilization no more to them than carbon monoxide
fumes in the air and strange-colored lights shining in the darkness?

I seldom think of them in winter, however, and I am not aware
of their departure in the fall. All summer long, every night just before twilight sets in, I hear through the open window of our
fifth-floor apartment their "chweenk, chweenk, chweenk," like
the raping of a huge file on the side of a bell. All evening this
rasping continues, and into the night. From our window we can
watch the sky darkening, and as the deep black silence settles
over the city the rasping of the nighthawk becomes a part of the
mystery of twilight, a pathetic little voice crying in the hush of approaching night. Later, when the blackness fills our windows, the
rasping seems to take on a new note; it becomes more confident,
more self-assured, as though now at last this swift-winged bird was
in its proper element.

Every night in the summer this happens, and then, when it
ceases, I am not aware of it, as one does not notice that a clock in
the room has stopped ticking. The winter nights come and go
with never a rasping "chweenk," and no awareness of its absence,
no consciousness of a void somewhere in the twilight. Only when
spring has almost passed, on the evening of the nighthawk's return
to our neighborhood, do I realize that I have missed its cry. Then,
as I sit at home working, the continuous "chweenk, chweenk,
chweenk" beats against my mind for a long time before I remember

that I have not heard this sound for more than six months, and I strain toward the open window to drink it in.

When I was a boy, before James Warren Bailey induced me to give up my ambition to be a naturalist, I often climbed to the roof of our home on the West Side to watch a pair of nighthawks through my field glasses. Hour after hour until it was too dark to see I would watch them chasing each other around a church steeple or fluttering lazily high in the air, rasping out their call every few seconds. I never saw them except in the air, but it seemed to me I had seen them disappear a number of times in the vicinity of a roof a few buildings down the street, and I decided that was where they had a nest. Being, in those days, nothing if not methodical, I took my ruler and my field glasses and went to investigate.

I discovered that the only way to reach the roof was through a trap door leading from the back porch on the third floor, and I would have to get permission from the owner of the building, who lived in the basement and did his own janitor work. This man, a foreigner, glared at me through half-closed eyes when I asked permission to go on his roof, as though he suspected there was some treasure there.

"What you want to go on roof for?" he asked.

"Some birds have got a nest up there," I said. (There was no use trying to explain to him what a nighthawk was.) "I just want to go up for a few minutes to see it. I'm studying natural history." Here I held up my field glasses to confirm my statement.

He looked at my field glasses and then at me. "No," he said, "no birds on my roof. You go home."

I went home, but I was more determined than ever to get up on that roof. The next evening I walked into the back yard, tiptoed up the three flights of stairs, climbed a ladder that led to the trap door, and pulled myself through. I put the trap door back in place and looked about me. The roof was perfectly flat, open on three sides, with some decorative stonework in front. I would have to be careful in looking for the eggs, I decided, or I might fall off the roof at one of the sides.

I walked slowly back and forth on the roof, looking carefully among the pebbles for the eggs. I knew there would not be a nest of any sort, for I had read in my bird guide that the female night-hawk lays two mottled gray and white eggs on the bare ground or on a gravel roof. As I approached one edge of the roof there was a sudden rush of wings, and a bird whirred by my head. I searched that corner, and finally I saw them, just as the bird guide had pre-dicted, two mottled gray and white eggs on the bare gravel roof. I took out my ruler and was about to stoop to measure the eggs when I became aware of an object high in the air, swooping down on me in what I would now describe as a power dive, though of course I had never heard of such a thing then. It was only a bird, a harm-less nighthawk, and yet I was a little frightened to see it coming straight at me as though it intended to knock me off the roof.

I did not have time to raise my arm in front of my face, but I closed my eyes instinctively, and just as I did so pandemonium broke loose. A deafening, horrible booming broke out all about me, swept me off my feet, and rolled me over on the roof. I re-member thinking I had made a mistake in identifying the object that had swooped down toward me, that it was not a bird but an airplane, and that now it was shooting at me. We were at war with Germany then, and though I had never seen an airplane I had read stories of them, and of the machine guns that shot between the propeller blades. But this was only a passing thought; it was too fantastic to be true. I was sure I had seen a bird in the air before I closed my eyes.

When I came to my senses again I was hanging from the edge of the roof with both hands, a three-story drop below me, and I could hear the voice of the landlord shouting at me from the ground. Quickly I pulled myself up, and without another look at the eggs I ran to the trap door. As I rushed down the stairs I bumped into the landlord. "Now I show you," he shouted, grabbing me by the collar. He rushed me down the stairs, whacking at me all the way, and then booted me into the street. "Now you stay away from my roof," he bellowed as I picked myself up and started for home, the tears streaming from my eyes.

It was not until years later that the mystery of the incident on the roof was cleared up, when I read in a scientific book an account of the "booming" of nighthawks. "Sometimes in May or June," the account read, "a nighthawk will dive with wings set from a great height, with what appears to be suicidal intent. When within a few yards of the earth it will turn suddenly upward, and at this moment there is heard a strange, loud, booming sound, doubtless made by the air passing through the bird's stiffened wing quills."

POEMS

Carl Sandburg

THE work of Carl Sandburg needs no lengthy introduction. No one can mention the Windy City without naming the "good gray poet of Chicago," who helped so much to pin her literary flag upon the map. He belongs to the pioneer period which produced Dreiser, Sherwood Anderson, Masters, and Hecht.

His first volume of poems (*Chicago Poems,* 1916) constitutes a literary landmark. Almost at once it established his reputation and put him in the front rank of the nation's poets.

FISH CRIER*

I know a Jew fish crier down on Maxwell Street, with a voice like a north wind blowing over corn stubble in January.
He dangles herring before prospective customers evincing a joy identical with that of Pavlova dancing.
His face is that of a man terribly glad to be selling fish, terribly glad that God made fish, and customers to whom he may call his wares from a pushcart.

* From *Chicago Poems,* by Carl Sandburg. Copyright, 1916, by Henry Holt & Co., Inc.; 1944, by Carl Sandburg. Reprinted by permission of the publishers.

PICNIC BOAT*

Sunday night and the park policemen tell each other it is dark as
a stack of black cats on Lake Michigan.
A big picnic boat comes home to Chicago from the peach farms
of Saugatuck.
Hundreds of electric bulbs break the night's darkness, a flock of
red and yellow birds with wings at a standstill.
Running along the deck railings are festoons and leaping in curves
are loops of light from prow and stern to the tall smokestacks.
Over the hoarse crunch of waves at my pier comes a hoarse answer
in the rhythmic oompa of the brasses playing a Polish folk-
song for the homecomers.

LOST*

Desolate and alone
All night long on the lake
Where fog trails and mist creeps,
The whistle of a boat
Calls and cries unendingly,
Like some lost child
In tears and trouble
Hunting the harbor's breast
And the harbor's eyes.

BLACKLISTED*

Why shall I keep the old name?
What is a name anywhere anyway?
A name is a cheap thing all fathers and mothers leave each child:
A job is a job and I want to live, so
Why does God Almighty or anybody else care whether I take a new
name to go by?

* From *Chicago Poems*

FOG*

The fog comes
on little cat feet.
It sits looking
over harbor and city
on silent haunches
and then moves on.

JUNGHEIMER'S*

In western fields of corn and northern timber lands,
    They talk about me, a saloon with a soul,
    The soft red lights, the long curving bar,
    The leather seats and dim corners,
    Tall brass spittoons, a nigger cutting ham,
And the painting of a woman half dressed thrown reckless across
    a bed after a night of booze and riots.

* From *Chicago Poems*

BRONZEVILLE*

Horace R. Cayton and
St. Clair Drake

IN 1945 there appeared a thick book concerning itself
with Chicago's South Side Negro population. For scholarship, penetration, analysis, and readability, it is unequaled
in American sociological writing. The authors doubtless
learned a lot from reading *Middletown,* written by the
Lynds. But they carried their book forward to a farther
outpost, and so its impact is stronger.

Today, the question of color is of mounting world-wide
importance. It is an immense subject, and it is with us for
keeps. Any nation or government which does not recognize
the paramount importance of color relationships here and
throughout the entire world is a nation or government with
blinkers on its eyes—a nation, a government, inviting the
holocaust.

Black Metropolis describes and analyzes the lives of
people who live in the Negro Belt of Chicago's South Side.
The authors tell us, in this excerpt, about several South
Side lives, Negroes and whites alike—a little about all of
us, today.

Ezekiel saw a wheel—
Wheel in the middle of a wheel—
The big wheel run by faith,
An' the little wheel run by the grace of God—
Ezekiel saw a wheel.
                              —NEGRO SPIRITUAL

STAND in the center of the black belt—at Chicago's Forty-seventh Street and South Parkway. Around you swirls a continuous eddy of faces—black, brown, olive, yellow, and white. Soon you will realize that this is not "just another neighborhood" of Midwest Metropolis. Glance at the newsstand on the corner. You will see the Chicago dailies—the *Tribune,* the *Times,* the *Herald-American,* the *News,* the *Sun.* But you will also find a number of weeklies headlining the activities of Negroes—Chicago's *Defender, Bee, News-Ledger,* and *Metropolitan News,* the Pittsburgh *Courier,* and a number of others. In the nearby drugstore colored clerks are bustling about. (They are seldom seen in other neighborhoods.) In most of the other stores, too, there are colored salespeople, although a white proprietor or manager usually looms in the offing. In the offices around you, colored doctors, dentists, and lawyers go about their duties. And a brown-skinned policeman saunters along swinging his club and glaring sternly at the urchins who dodge in and out among the shoppers.

Two large theaters will catch your eye with their billboards featuring Negro orchestras and vaudeville troupes, and the Negro great and near-great of Hollywood—Lena Horne, Rochester, Hattie McDaniels.

On a spring or summer day this spot, "Forty-seventh and South Park," is the urban equivalent of a village square. In fact, Black Metropolis has a saying, "If you're trying to find a certain Negro in Chicago, stand on the corner of Forty-seventh and South Park long enough and you're bound to see him." There is continuous and colorful movement here—shoppers streaming in and out of stores; insurance agents turning in their collections at a funeral parlor; club reporters rushing into a newspaper office with their social notes; irate tenants filing complaints with the Office of Price Administration; job-seekers moving in and out of the United States Employment Office. Today a picket line may be calling attention to the "unfair labor practices" of a merchant. Tomorrow a girl may be selling tags on the corner for a hospital or community house. The next day you will find a group of boys soliciting signatures to place a Negro on the All-Star football team. And always a beggar or two will be in the background—a blind man, cup in hand, tapping his way along, or a legless veteran propped up against the side of a building. This is Bronzeville's central shopping district, where rents are highest and Negro merchants compete fiercely with whites for the choicest commercial spots. A few steps away from the intersection is the "largest Negro-owned department store in America," attempting to challenge the older and more experienced white retail establishments across the street. At an exclusive "Eat Shoppe" just off the boulevard, you may find a Negro Congressman or ex-Congressman dining at your elbow, or former heavyweight champion Jack Johnson, beret pushed back on his head, chuckling at the next table; in the private dining room there may be a party of civic leaders, black and white, planning reforms. A few doors away, behind the Venetian blinds of a well-appointed tavern, the "big shots" of the sporting world crowd the bar on one side of the house, while the respectable "élite" takes its beers and "sizzling steaks" in the booths on the other side.

Within a half-mile radius of "Forty-seventh and South Park" are clustered the major community institutions: the Negro-staffed Provident Hospital; the George Cleveland Hall Library (named for a colored physician); the YWCA; the "largest colored Catholic church in the country"; the "largest Protestant congregation in America"; the Black Belt's Hotel Grand; Parkway Community House; and the imposing Michigan Boulevard Garden Apartments for middle-income families.

As important as any of these is the large four-square-mile green, Washington Park—playground of the South Side. Here in the summer thousands of Negroes of all ages congregate to play softball and tennis, to swim, or just lounge around. Here during the Depression, stormy crowds met to listen to leaders of the unemployed.

Within Black Metropolis, there are neighborhood centers of activity having their own drugstores, grocery stores, theaters, poolrooms, taverns, and churches, but "Forty-seventh and South Park" overshadows all other business areas in size and importance.

If you wander about a bit in Black Metropolis you will note that one of the most striking features of the area is the prevalence of churches, numbering some five hundred. Many of these edifices still bear the marks of previous ownership—six-pointed Stars of David, Hebrew and Swedish inscriptions, or names chiseled on old cornerstones which do not tally with those on new bulletin boards. On many of the business streets in the more rundown areas there are scores of "storefront" churches. To the uninitiated, this plethora of churches is no less baffling than the bewildering variety and the colorful extravagance of the names. Nowhere else in Midwest Metropolis could one find, within a stone's throw of one another, a Hebrew Baptist Church, a Baptized Believers' Holiness Church, a Universal Union Independent, a Church of Love and Faith, Spiritual, a Holy Mt. Zion Methodist Episcopal Independent, and a United Pentecostal Holiness Church. Or a cluster such as St. John's Christian Spiritual, Park Mission African Methodist Episcopal, Philadelphia Baptist, Little Rock Baptist, and the Aryan Full Gospel Mission, Spiritualist.

Churches are conspicuous, but to those who have eyes to see they are rivaled in number by another community institution, the policy station, which is to the Negro community what the racehorse bookie is to white neighborhoods. In these mysterious little shops, tucked away in basements or behind stores, one may place a dime bet and hope to win $20 if the numbers "fall right." Definitely illegal, but tolerated by the law, the policy station is a ubiquitous institution, absent only from the more exclusive residential neighborhoods.

In addition to these more or less legitimate institutions, "tea pads" and "reefer dens," "buffet flats" and "call houses" also flourish, known only to the habitués of the underworld and to those respectable patrons, white and colored, without whose faithful support they could not exist. (Since 1912, when Chicago's Red-light District was abolished, prostitution has become a clandestine affair, though open "streetwalking" does occur in isolated areas.) An occasional feature story or news article in the daily press or in a Negro weekly throws a sudden light on one of these spots—a police raid or some unexpected tragedy; and then, as in all communities, it is forgotten.

In its thinking, Black Metropolis draws a clear line between the "shady" and the "respectable," the "sporting world" and the world of churches, clubs, and polite society. In practice, however, as we shall see, the line is a continuously shifting one and is hard to maintain, in the Black Metropolis as in other parts of Midwest Metropolis.

This is a community of stark contrasts, the facets of its life as varied as the colors of its people's skins. The tiny churches in deserted and dilapidated stores, with illiterately scrawled announcements on their painted windows, are marked off sharply from the fine edifices on the boulevards with stained-glass windows and electric bulletin boards. The rickety frame dwellings, sprawled along the railroad tracks, bespeak a way of life at an opposite pole from that of the quiet and well-groomed orderliness of middle-class neighborhoods. And many of the still stately-appearing old mansions, long since abandoned by Chicago's wealthy whites, conceal interiors that are foul and decayed. . . .

"Policy": Poor Man's Roulette

Almost as numerous as the churches (and more evenly distributed) are Bronzeville's five hundred-odd "policy stations," in any one of which a person may place a bet that certain numbers will be announced as lucky by one of fifteen or sixteen "policy companies." Policy is a lottery game.* It is also a "protected busi-

---

* The origin of the term "policy" is obscure, but at least as early as the nineties it was applied to lottery games in which the gambler "purchased" a number and received a duplicate receipt, the original being forwarded to the headquarters of the "pool." Gosnell, in his *Negro Politicians,* states that this type of lottery was so prevalent in New York City around the turn of the century that an antipolicy law was passed by the state in 1901. Illinois passed a similar law in 1905 in an effort to break up the game in Chicago.

In the early policy games the winning numbers were selected by drawing numbered slips from a bowl. In the late twenties, some enterprising New Yorkers hit upon the idea of taking bets on the probable last three numbers of the daily Federal Reserve Clearing House report. This variant form of "policy"—known as the "numbers game"—was very popular on the Eastern seaboard because it placed the game "on the level." No racketeer could tamper with the Clearing House figures, and anyone could read them in the newspaper. During an attempt to smash the racket, newspapers were asked to print these reports in round numbers. The resourceful racketeers then shifted to other published numbers. Throughout this period, "policy" numbers in Chicago were selected by the traditional lottery drawings. Clearing House numbers were never popular in Midwest Metropolis.

ness," operating in defiance of Illinois State Statute No. 413, but under the benevolent patronage of the city political machine. In order to keep up a semblance of respect for the law, about half the stations are "fronted" by legitimate businesses. Most of the others can be easily recognized by the initiated, sometimes by a light over a basement entrance, again by a sign on a window or door: "OPEN"—"4-11-44"—"DOING BUSINESS"—"ALL BOOKS."

A knowing observer can also spot a policy station by the constantly moving stream of customers going in and coming out carrying "drawings"—the slips on which the winning numbers are printed. These slips are distributed three times a day, and at busy stations long queues form as people come to place new bets, collect their winnings, or inquire about results. The unwary person who stands too close to the door of a policy station at certain hours is likely to be hit by the small roll of policy slips—the drawings—which are flung from a speeding car by the "pickup men" as they hasten from shop to shop carrying the latest numbers.

Bronzeville places its bets in one or more of thirty "pools" known colloquially as "books." These pools have distinctive names, such as Monte Carlo, Bronx, Royal Palm, Harlem, Interstate, North and South, East and West. (If you're unlucky in one book today, you may shift to another tomorrow.) The Royal Palm, with twenty-four numbers, is known as a "two-legged book." The Iowa, with twelve numbers, is a "one-legged book."

If a policy addict had gone to a station between noon and midnight on the day of these particular drawings and said, "I want to put a dime on number 56 in the Iowa book," his lucky guess that this number might appear at midnight would have made him the winner of fifty cents. Playing a single number in this fashion is known as playing a "day number."

The most popular "play" in Bronzeville is the "gig." In this case, the player would have guessed at three numbers that might "fall" —for instance, 72-59-4. For his dime he then would have received $20. (The odds against guessing three numbers out of twelve are 76,076 to 1!) Policy players often "saddle their gigs" by investing an additional dime in a bet that at least *two* of the numbers will appear. Then, if the whole gig is lost, the player may still salvage something. The reward for a saddle is a dollar to the dime. To guess on the appearance of four numbers is to play a "Horse." The winner receives $40, but the odds against such a winning are 1,426,425. A five-number bet—a "Jack"—pays $200 for a dime.

Winning numbers are listed three times daily, after selection at a public "drawing." The places where the drawings are made are known as the "wheels." These "wheels" are scattered about the community at strategic spots. The drawings are made from a small drum-shaped container in which seventy-eight capsules or balls, numbered consecutively, are placed. After each turn of the drum, a ball is pulled and its number read aloud. As they are called, a printer sets the numbers and locks them into a special printing press. As soon as the last number is drawn, the press rolls out the policy slips, which are then distributed all over Bronzeville.

In "normal" times, when the "heat is off," a wheel is a beehive of activity, day and night. It is run by a corps of well-trained white-collar experts. Usually, several hundred persons are present to watch, and sometimes the crowd includes a cooperative policeman or two. Many of the onlookers are "walking writers," some two thousand of whom were canvassing Bronzeville in 1938, writing up plays for a twenty per cent commission on the amount played.

Just before the wheel begins to turn, the walking writers arrive, straighten up their books, turn in duplicate slips, and fraternize with one another. Some wheels provide chairs with writing arms; a few even have a lunch counter. All have a "bouncer" or "overlook man" to keep order, to hurry the writers along so they will have the bets recorded before the drawing is made, and to enforce silence during the process. A drawing has been described by an observer as follows:

Up and down the aisle, a large, dark man (I learned later that he was a prize fighter) walked to and fro. He shouted continuously, "All right, get them in, folks. Get those books in." A large sign in front of the room read: ALL BOOKS MUST BE IN FIFTEEN MINUTES BEFORE PULLING TIME. PULLING TIME, 1:30.

•

The overlook man looked in our direction and said, "Baby, is that your chair? If not, you'll have to go downstairs. We don't want any confusion about the chairs. You know how crowded it is here."

By this time it was nearly 1:15 A.M. and the barker continued to prod the writers. "Let's get them in, folks." Everyone seemed in a jocular mood. Then suddenly there was a deep silence. At 1:40 a syndicate official stepped to the office window. A small wooden barrel fixed horizontally on an axle was placed in front of him. He set it spinning, and when it stopped a young lady put in her hand and pulled out a small pellet of paper, which she handed to the man. He opened it and, walking close to the microphone of the public-address system, called out a number. A young man and the young lady pulled numbers alternately, twenty-four times for the North and South book and the same number of times for the East and West book.

The people were rapt. The silence was broken by happy ejaculations or almost inaudible sighs as people saw that they had hit or just missed by a small margin. When the last number had been called, a sudden rushing noise arose, as people began to form in line at the printing press in the back of the room. In less than five minutes, the slips had been printed and were being distributed in the streets. Pickup men were speeding through the Black Belt carrying the news of the latest winning numbers.

At the policy stations throughout the community, the players reach avidly for the slips to see if they have "caught." There are intense little groups discussing the close margins by which they have missed. Occasionally one can hear the rejoicing cry of a winner. A conversation is in progress on a street corner.

"Yes, maybe the jinx is on us, huh?"

"This 9-9-29 [Death Row] is playing right well. It saddled last night and again this morning. The same with the Nigger Baby Row, too—13-32-50."

"Oh, I missed on that Death Row. I don't play it because it made me miss my mother's name once. Man, I would have had good money. You see, my mother is dead and I dreamed about her. Instead of playing her name, I played the Death Row, and missed out because her name fell out in the first sixes. Wheeee, I would have been a rich man."

Suddenly, a shout: "I caught on my son's name, 'Henry'! It's out in the last sixes in the North and South, 27-31-33. Wonder why I didn't put some *real* money on it? Well, anyway, I caught

$5.75 and that's better than nothing. Then, with these saddles, I think I'll clear about $6. Not bad for a dollar. It'll help out a lot at home." . . .

The "Upper Shadies"

The "real uppers" may look askance at "the racketeers" and their wives, but in the decade between the beginning of the Depression and the outbreak of the Second World War, the "Gentlemen Racketeers" and their coterie emerged as the most widely publicized group in Bronzeville. Five Negro policy kings form the core of a "fast set" which has money in abundance and spends it lavishly. This group, who might be called the "upper shadies," is composed of the wealthiest policy men and their wives, a few lawyers and retired undertakers, at least one family with an inherited fortune, and a wealthy Negro manufacturer. The people in this group do not ask, "How did you make your money?" but only, "Have you got money?"

These men with money like good-looking women, and those of them who are married have wives of very light-brown or "fair" complexion. The unmarried ones are usually seen with the pick of Bronzeville's chorus girls, policy-station employees, and "good-timers" of attractive appearance and engaging personality. Rumor has it that there are "kept women" within this group, but there are properly married couples too. The wives of the Gentlemen Racketeers and their associates are women of leisure; unlike many wives of "respectable" uppers, none of them have to work for their living. They can spend their time at the dressmaker's and in the swank downtown shops, or in supervising the details of entertaining in their sumptuous town houses or country homes. The women's lives, like the men's, are centered on conspicuous consumption—display of the most lavish kind.

This set is organized around a cult of clothes. Nothing but the right labels and the right prices will do. Both the men and the women know how to buy and wear clothes—and with taste rather than garishness. Clothes are both an end in themselves and an adjunct to the social ritual of this café au lait society. The ritual can be summed up in a word—entertaining. All through the year there is a continuous round of private informal parties and formal dinners. Into the homes of the "upper shadies" stream nationally known colored theatrical figures and sportsmen. On their tables one will find wild duck and pheasant in season, chicken and turkey in season and out, and always plenty of the finest spirits and champagne. The upper respectables call themselves "good-livers"; the shadies are "high-livers."

In addition to entertaining, the "upper shadies" go in for attending the races, for horseback riding and cabaret parties, and for poker games where the stakes hang high. They also like to travel. They are continually shuttling between Midwest Metropolis and New York; they occasionally visit friends on the West Coast; they have their summer homes in the lake regions of Michigan and northern Illinois. Before the Second World War, the wealthiest families in this set had spent some time in France and one policy king was having his children educated there. After the war began they shifted their attention to "good neighborly" relations and began to explore Mexico and Cuba. One policy king, looking forward to really seeing the world, purchased a yacht. All these activities are reported at length in the Negro press, and on several occasions the Midwest Metropolis dailies have devoted columns to the exploits of the Gentlemen Racketeers.

Despite their wealth and their free and easy mode of life, the "upper shadies" are not unconcerned over what the upper respectables think of them. The Gentlemen Racketeers who form the core of the group have drawn into their circle a few professional men who are by no means wealthy, but who are witty and good dressers and like a good time. These men act as a link between the "shadies" and the respectable uppers, but it is significant that, although the "shadies" have been entertained at the homes of these few upper-class men, they have not been accepted socially by the broader circle of uppers. Two of the most prominent Gentlemen Racketeers are proud that they attended college and that their father was a minister. Further evidence of these two men's orientation toward respectability is furnished by the fact that they have sent their children to the best Northern prep schools and some of their sons to technical colleges; the children are ambitious for the normal upper-class evidences of success and have been pledged to sororities and fraternities. At one time, so it is alleged, one clique hired social secretaries to teach them the know-how of upper-class life and were cultivating an interest in the opera, symphony, and world affairs. The respectable uppers continue to draw the social line against the parents, but not against the children.

In their striving for "respectability" the men among the "upper shady" set have also manifested an active interest in civic affairs and have, to a certain extent, become known as Race Leaders. We have already said, in our discussion of policy, that the policy kings all have legitimate businesses as well as their shady enterprises. They give regularly and generously to all fund-raising drives for Bronzeville charities. With the outbreak of the war they began to play a prominent part in bond rallies and in the sponsoring of a servicemen's center. Their motives appear to be highly mixed, but undoubtedly one motive is their hope that such activities will wipe away the stain of policy.

One of the wealthiest policy kings revealed certain of his experiences and his philosophy of life to an interviewer in the following statement:

I was born in Mississippi. My father was a Baptist minister, my mother a housewife. The financial condition of our family was fair. I went to college for three years and then came to Chicago just after the last war. I went into the taxicab business first. Then I began "running on the road" and made about $100 a month. After I quit railroading—I didn't like being a porter—I went into the gambling business —race horses. I made about $100 a week and employed six or seven people. By 1937, I had a car and a home and several gambling places.

The reason a young man goes into policy or becomes a teacher or doctor or anything else is because he notices outstanding individuals in those fields who are successes. They attract him. So I went into policy.

Now a successful policy king, this Gentleman Racketeer insists that his heart's desire is to "advance The Race" through his large, *legitimate* business, acquired only a few years ago.

What good is a lot of money to a man if he doesn't put it to some use? If you pile it up just for the sake of piling up money, you are selfish. Why not spread it out into business and continue to increase the possibility of employing more of your race?

Stepping out into business was just like another gamble to me. I decided to stick my chin out, and if I got socked on it, O.K. What I want to do now is this—get into a position where I can demand that white business concerns from which I buy my supplies will employ Negroes as distributors and salesmen. We can gradually demand that Negroes be put in various jobs that are related to our business, and sooner or later white meat markets and grocery stores will get used to seeing Negroes come into their stores to deliver supplies.

This Gentleman Racketeer does not put too much confidence in mass action of the "Spend Your Money Where You Can Work" type, "because Negroes are too dependent upon white people for jobs and everything else. If we start boycotting they might start laying us off from this job and that about town." He puts his hope for the salvation of the Negro in the multiplication of legitimate businesses like his own. At the time, he was employing forty girls in his department store and it was his proud verdict that they "do their work just as well as whites." Looking toward the future, he dreamed of organizing a Negro Businessmen's League. He also hoped to organize a bank to replace the House of Binga, destroyed by the Depression.

What I want to do is to go into banking and lending. I am not studying banking, though I realize that theory is necessary. You've got to have men around that know their business.

Yet this Gentleman Racketeer wants to be more than a *Negro* businessman:

I also want to open a department store in a community that's 50-50 white and Negro, because I believe that white people will buy from Negroes if they run their businesses right.

Proud of his ability to run an efficient store, he wants to feel that he is just a man competing with his business peers. He therefore states with some satisfaction:

I guess you've noticed that in my advertisements I never stress that people should buy from me because I am a Negro. I am in business competing with other stores. I'm not trying to play upon any psychology by calling this a "Negro business."

While the "upper shadies" have been displaying some interest in social acceptance by the upper respectables—they like to be invited to dances given by the upper male clubs and the fraternities and sororities—this is not their primary interest. What the "shadies" hope ultimately to do, perhaps, is to displace the older upper class, to outshine it, to incorporate sections of it within their own circles, and to emerge as the bona fide upper class. They have the money, but they are keenly aware that there are some things money won't buy. But they know that once they become known as good Race Men, Bronzeville will forget the source of their income and accord them honor and prestige. And in the eyes of many Bronzeville people they are already *the* upper class. . . .

Doc's Christmas Eve

It was Christmas Eve, 1938. Dr. Maguire had just finished a hard day.* Now for a highball, and then to bed. The doctor stepped back and admired the electric star at the top of the Christmas tree and the gifts neatly stacked beneath it. Judy would certainly be a happy girl in the morning when she bounced downstairs to find the dolls and dishes and baby carriage and candy that Santa Claus had brought her. The doctor smiled, drained his glass, and headed for the bathroom. He caught himself musing in the shower. Not so bad, not so bad. Three years out of med school, in the middle of a depression. A pretty wife with smooth olive skin and straight black hair. A sweet little girl, image of her mother. And buying a home. Well, it was just the "breaks"—lucky breaks ever since he quit picking cotton in Georgia and went off to Howard University in Washington. Plenty of other fellows were better students, but a lot of them were still sleeping in their offices. One or two who were supposed to turn out as distinguished surgeons were Red-Capping. He reflected a moment. Yes—the

* This account of a doctor's Christmas experience is based on an actual incident witnessed by one of the authors, when he was a participant-observer in a group of lower-class households for six months, and on interviews with the physician involved and his wife. The principal characters' inner thoughts are obviously fictionalized. But the other quoted material in this chapter, as throughout the book, has been selected from interview-documents gathered by trained interviewers and has not been subjected to imaginative recasting.

breaks. Suppose he hadn't married a woman like Sylvia. He'd be "on the turf," too, perhaps. Dr. Maguire sharply pulled himself to heel. No, he didn't really believe it had been luck. He prided himself on "having some get-up about him," enough ambition to have made his way anyhow. If he could do it, the other fellows could have, too. He looked at his wife, peacefully sleeping, kissed her lightly on the forehead, and crawled into bed.

Man, what a tough day this Christmas Eve had been! Three appendectomies in the morning and a hernioplasty in the early afternoon. Making the rounds in the midafternoon. Then a few minutes out to help distribute baskets for the Christmas Fund; time out to sign some checks for the legal defense committee of the NAACP; and an emergency meeting of the YMCA executive board. That Y meeting had looked as if it were going to last all night. Negroes talk too damn much. He had hoped to be home by ten o'clock, but it was midnight before he parked his Plymouth. Three late emergency calls—TB patients who ought to be in the sanatorium. Not enough beds—Negro quota filled. Damn this country anyhow. Negroes always get the dirty end of the stick. Christmas! Peace on Earth, Goodwill. . . . Bull. . . . Sometimes I think the Communists are right. And those old fogies over at the hospital yell "socialized medicine" every time somebody wants to extend medical care. Aw, hell, what am I bellyaching about? I haven't had it too tough. He shrugged his shoulders and relaxed. He was just drifting off to sleep when the phone rang.

Sylvia bounded from the bed like a tennis ball coming up after a smash from the net. She was that way, always ready to protect him and conserve his strength. What would he do without her?

"Are you one of the doctor's regular patients? . . . Well, why don't you call your regular doctor? . . . I know, but Dr. Maguire is . . ." He snatched the phone from her hand in time to catch the stream of denunciation: "That's the way you dirty niggers are. You so high 'n' mighty nobody kin reach ya. We kin lay here 'n' die. White doctor'd come right away. Yore own people treat ya like dogs."

Dr. Maguire winced. He always shuddered when this happened. And it happened often. He waited until the hysterical tirade stopped, then said calmly but firmly: "Now listen, you want me to do you a favor. I'll come over there, sure. I'm a doctor. That's my business. But I'm not coming unless you have the money. Have you got $5?" He hung up and began to dress wearily.

"Do they have it?" queried his wife.

"I don't know," he snapped, irritated at himself for having to ask such a question, and at his wife for pressing the point. "You know I'm going whether they have it or not. I'm a doctor. I always go. But you might just as well scare them—it'll be hard enough to collect anyhow." He slammed the door and went down the snowdrifted path that led to the garage.

When he arrived at the building, the squad car was at the door. He and the police went in together. Dr. Maguire pushed his way through the ragged group of children and their excited elders who jammed the hall of the dilapidated building.

"Right this way, Doc," someone called.

"What is it?" he asked jauntily. "Shooting or cutting?"

"She stabbed him," volunteered a little girl.

"Boy, she shore put that blade in him too!" A teen-age boy spoke with obvious admiration, while a murmur of corroboration rippled through the crowd fascinated by tragedy.

For a moment, Dr. Maguire felt sick at his stomach. "Are these my people?" he thought. "What in the hell do I have in common with them? This is 'The Race' we're always spouting about being proud of." He had a little trick for getting back on an even keel when such doubts assailed him: he just let his mind run back over the "Uncle Tomming" he had to do when he was a Pullman porter; the turndown he got when he wanted to interne at the University of Chicago hospital; the letter from the American Medical Association rejecting his application for membership; the paper he wrote for a white doctor to read at a Mississippi medical conference which no Negroes could attend. Such thoughts always restored his sense of solidarity with "The Race." "Yeah, I'm just a nigger, too," he mumbled bitterly.

Then he forgot everything—squalor, race prejudice, his own little tricks of psychological adjustment. He was a doctor treating a patient, swiftly, competently, and with composure. Anger and doubt were swallowed up in pride. His glow of satisfaction didn't last long, however, for the woman who had cut the man was now blubbering hysterically. He barked at her, "Shut up. Get a pan of water, quick! He isn't dead, but he will be if you don't help me." He prepared a hypodermic, gave the shot, and dressed the wound.

"How'dja like to have to give him that needle, honey?" A teen-age girl shivered and squeezed her boy friend's hand, as she asked the question.

"Me? I ain't no doc. But, girl, he flipped that ol' needle in his shoulder sweet. Just like Baby Chile did when she put that blade in Mr. Ben. You gotta have education to be a doc. Lots of it, too."

"I'm gonna be a doctor, I am." A small, self-confident urchin spoke up. The crowd tittered and a young woman said, "That's real cute, ain't it? You be a good one too, just like Doc Maguire." Dr. Maguire smiled pleasantly. An elderly crone mumbled, "Doctor? Humph! Wid a hophead daddy and a booze houn' mammy. How he ever gonna be any doctah? He bettah get his min' on a WPA shovel." Everybody laughed.

"The old man will be all right, now." Dr. Maguire was closing his bag. "Just let him lie quiet all day tomorrow and send him down to the Provident Hospital clinic the day after Christmas. The visit is $5."

Baby Chile went for her purse. There was nothing in it. She screamed a frantic accusation at the crowd. "I been robbed. You dirty bastards!" Then a little girl whispered in her ear, while the crowd tittered knowingly. Baby Chile regained her composure and explained: "Sorry, Doc. I had the money. I was gonna pay you. But them goddam policemen was gonna take me off on a 'sault and batt'ry charge. My little girl had to give 'em the $10 I had in this here bag, and the folks out there had to raise another ten to make 'em go away. Them policemen's got it all. I ain't even got a red cent left for Christmas tomorrow. You got anything, Ben?"

The sick man growled: "You know I ain' got nuthin'! You know I can't holp you."

The doctor didn't say a word. He just picked up his bag and left.

But he ostentatiously took out a pencil and wrote down the number of the apartment before he went out. The crowd seemed pleased at his discomfiture. One woman remarked: "He got the number. Them doctors don't never disremember."

"What was it, dear?" Mrs. Maguire asked as her husband once more prepared for bed.

"Same old thing. Niggers cutting each other up over nothing. Rot-gut whiskey and women, I guess. They ought to start cutting on the white folks for a change. I wonder how they got my number?"

"*Did you get the $5?*" his wife asked.

"Nope. Told me some lie about bribing the police. Maybe they did—I don't know. Let's forget it and go to sleep. Judy will have us both up before daybreak. Tomorrow's Christmas."

Mrs. Maguire turned over and sighed. The doctor went to sleep. . . .

The Kool Kustomers

The Kool Kustomers are among the half-dozen men's clubs that set the social pace for the male clubs in middle-class "Society." There are only thirteen members, but their invitation affairs rival the dances of the much larger upper-class sororities and fraternities, both in size and in expenditure. One of the best-informed middle-class clubmen in Chicago (a barber shop porter), after stating that he hadn't missed a Kool Kustomer dance in ten years, said: "Their affairs are so swanky until other club members ask, six months in advance, 'Please send me a ticket to your next formal.' Their guests are just as elated over attendance at a Kool Kustomer affair as a hungry man is over a banquet. . . . Without a doubt they receive more invitations to formals during the year than any other club in Chicago, because every club wants to receive an invitation from them."

The Kool Kustomers are able to set the pattern primarily because they manage to do, with skill and lavishness, what all male clubs of comparable size would like to do—namely, "throw" a colorful annual formal with hundreds of guests, free drinks, and favorable newspaper publicity. Important, too, is the fact that they manage to stay in the news throughout the year. They always cooperate with other clubs in ticket sales; their members dress fashionably; and, when other clubs give special affairs, they are always ready to spring a sensational surprise. For instance, when the Lions gave a European Ball, all the Kool Kustomers were on hand dressed as members of Louis XIV's court. One Kool Kustomer stated with pride: "We represented the whole court from the King on down. We really stole the show. We were the most correctly attired, in strict accordance with the history books." Bronzeville's band leaders testify that Kool Kustomer formals are "swank affairs."

The Kool Kustomers are willing to spend money for prestige. A few years ago one of the members boasted to an interviewer: "Our entire dance is going to cost about $500. The invitations will cost over $100. I've never seen any invitations like ours before, with all the members' pictures in their full-dress suits. We are the only club which serves wines and drinks. When the guests go to the bar, the drinks are on the house."

The Chicago *Defender* reported the event in glowing terms: "Twelfth annual formal. . . . Comments have been pouring in since then from over two thousand of the élite of Chicago and out-of-town visitors. . . . Grand march . . . hostess perfectly gowned . . . members resplendent in their white ties, top hats, and tails. . . . Wines and liquors served without cost." A bystander commented on the neon sign outside the dance hall, the chauffeured limousines, and women with ermine shoulder wraps. Dazzled by the display, he was sure that "this is a club composed of members of the upper crust of Negroes." Yet an upper-middle-class girl who was present and who also attends upper-class affairs was lively in her ridicule of the Kool Kustomers' affair: "Well, to begin with, the place was too crowded. Every dog and his mammy was there. I told George [a member], 'You had from school-teachers to housemen excusing all the in-betweens. . . . There was every style, color and whatnot of a dress imaginable.' " She criticized the behavior of the women ("throwing up their legs— publicly hugging the men") and dubbed the free wine "junk." "I told them about their wine," she said, "and one of the members answered, 'Since we're giving it away it's good enough. Beggars can't be choosers. Come and take a drink from the private reserve.' " She concluded with a final thrust of class-conscious criticism: "I don't think the affair was worth the expense. They could have spent that money, if they wanted to throw it to the winds, by having several small invitational affairs. They would have had a large attendance of fairly decent people, and not a mob of a little bit of everything." They could have—but only at the price of losing prestige in that vast club world that has come to look upon the Kool Kustomers as the men who set the pattern.

The three original Kool Kustomers began to "run together" in high school during the twenties. Two of them were migrants from Alabama, one from New Orleans. They met on Sunday afternoons with a few other boys, and their parents would "serve a repast." They were first formally organized as the Good Fellows Uplift under the sponsorship of a city truant officer. This venture in adolescent reform was short-lived, however, and the group reorganized in 1928 as a social club with a membership limited to twelve. The dues have increased over a ten-year period from $5 a year to $25 a year, with a $10 joining fee!

The eight regular members of the club and the five honorary members are middle-class men in their late twenties and early thirties with a drive for "getting ahead." Thirteen years before, all of them (except one) were children in the deep South—three in Alabama, three in Louisiana, one in Texas. In 1938 they were distributed throughout Chicago's occupational hierarchy—two as hotel porters in Loop hotels, one as an independent clothes salesman, one as an interior decorator, and three as owners of small businesses: real estate, taxi, and liquor. All had finished high school; none had gone to college.

This lack of formal education and professional occupation had definitely kept them out of the upper class, and while it has not hindered their rising to the top of the middle class, it has resulted in a definite social gulf between them and the fraternity and upper-class clubmen of their own age. This social gulf is recognized within the club by the fact that some of their early associates who went on to college have been accorded the status of *honorary* members. When asked whether club members ever received bids to upper-class affairs, one member replied that he had received such an invitation but hadn't gone. He mentioned that upper-class clubs invited individuals and not entire clubs, and brushed the matter off by saying, "One thing—the Snakes and the Forty Club and the Assembly are all much older groups than we are." (The names are those of upper-class clubs.)

The Kool Kustomers do not think of themselves as frivolous. While the club is dubbed "purely social," organized "to have clean fun," the constitution insists that any prospective member must (1) have high morals; (2) be a good citizen; (3) be a high school graduate; (4) be a good sportsman. Each member is enjoined to "pledge himself whatever he can afford to give for that year toward charity." Meetings open with the Lord's Prayer and close with the club creed. They take pride in aiding any member who suffers financial distress. They also contribute to charity. . . .

Bronzeville's "New Negro"

From the standpoint of "racial advancement," the "middle-class way of life" is perhaps the most significant pattern of living in Bronzeville. It represents a relatively stable pattern that has been emerging since the Flight to Freedom, and has already been defined here as a "model" that emphasizes a type of disciplined public behavior which will distinguish a segment of the population from the "crude" and "unpolished" masses.

These are people interested in maintaining a stable home life, who want to marry and raise a family, who take steady employment when they find it. The older Negro middle class was church-centered; not so the "New Negro." During his leisure time he sees nothing wrong in enjoying life, in playing cards, dancing, smoking, and drinking. At the same time he often maintains membership in a church, attends its services regularly, and helps to raise money for it; but he takes its theology with a grain of salt or ignores it completely, and puts pressure on his minister to work for "racial advancement." He believes in "Negro business" and admires a Race Man.

Because of the narrow occupational base in the Negro community, he has adjusted his thinking to the rise of the labor union movement, which embraces many of the occupations in which Negroes of the middle class are employed. It is not unusual, therefore, to find a person who, though he has finished high school, still works as a laborer in the steel mills and belongs to a CIO union as well as a social club and a church; indeed, membership in some left-wing organization is sometimes added to this pattern.

This is Bronzeville's "New Negro"—usually a fairly well-educated working man or woman who knows the ropes of the urban world, wants to get ahead, and is determined to be "decent." He is likely to be somewhat skeptical of the good intentions of most white people, and suspicious of the disinterestedness of Race Leaders. He is keenly aware that Negroes don't have "their rights," but sees no hope in the extremists of either the racialistic Right or the revolutionary Left, although he may opportunistically support both. If married, he is raising his family and educating his children with the hope that they will "get a break" in the future. The number of such "New Negroes" is set, however, by the iron bands of the Black Ghetto and the pressure of the Job Ceiling. Their future and the future of their children is largely beyond their control.

THE HAYMARKET AFFAIR*

Capt. Michael J. Schaack

IN THE late 1870's and early and middle 1880's, the United States was swept by violent labor unrest. There was agitation for a shorter work week which, later on, snowballed into a country-wide movement for the eight-hour day. The Midwest seemed to be the focal point of the struggle; it was the railroad center, the growing manufacturing belt and the point where European workmen, who had emigrated from Europe because of repressive governments there, gave the American labor movement a sense of direction it had hitherto lacked.

Riots spreading from Pittsburgh and other Eastern cities finally reached Chicago, to crest in the biggest wave of labor upheavals in American history. In the backwash came the Pullman riots, the strikes at the McCormick plants and restlessness at the stockyards.

One day while browsing through the stock of a second-hand Loop bookstore I came across an astonishing volume, *Anarchy and Anarchists,* written in 1889 by a chief of police who had been on duty at the scene of the historic Haymarket riot, where the first bomb in American industrial warfare was thrown. Captain Schaack employed startlingly modern methods of surveillance; he went in for spies, codes, and nighttime cloak-and-dagger work. Parts of his book form a hodgepodge of muddled police thinking, but other parts, the sections that describe the riot (from a police standpoint, of course), the incarceration of the anarchists, and their doom make graphic reading. Captain Schaack hated them, but at their death he could not help but be impressed by them, as were many other Chicagoans. Their execution moved millions of Americans profoundly, many of whom slowly became filled with doubts, remorse, and a disquieting sense of guilt.

* From *Anarchy and Anarchists,* by Captain Michael J. Schaack, F. J. Schulte & Co., Chicago, 1889.

WITH such active work among the conspirators, it was only a question of time when some terrible catastrophe would ensue through the instrumentality of the powerful bombs they had manufactured. The public mind was in a state of fear and suspense, not knowing the direction whence threatened devastation and destruction might appear. The incendiary speeches were enough to excite trepidation, and the appearance of the "Revenge circular" fanned the excitement into general alarm and indignation. The McCormick attack proved conclusively that the Anarchists meant to practice what they preached. After their rout and defeat, they were heard to express regret that they had not taken forcible possession of the works before the arrival of the police and then received the officers with a volley of firearms, as had once been contemplated in a star-chamber session of one of their "revolutionary groups." The air was full of rumors, and the general public was convinced that some great disaster would occur unless the police promptly forbade the holding of further revolutionary meetings. The Mayor's attention had been called to the possible results if such meetings were permitted to continue, and he, in turn, directed the Police Department to keep close watch of the gathering called for the Haymarket Square and disperse it in case the speakers used inflammatory language. During the day many of the Spies circulars had been distributed in the vicinity of the McCormick establishment, and it was expected that many of the enraged strikers from that locality would attend the meeting. It was clear that, in view of the temper of the Socialists, only slight encouragement would be required to produce a disturbance, and it was of the utmost importance that prompt action should be taken at the first sign of trouble. It subsequently transpired that the leaders had intended to make the speeches threatening in order to invite a charge upon the crowd by the police, and then, during the confusion, to carry out the Monday night program.

The city authorities fully comprehended the situation, but concluded not to interfere with the meeting unless the discussion should be attended with violent threats. In order to be prepared for any emergency, however, it was deemed best to concentrate a large force in the vicinity of the meeting—at the Desplaines

Street Station. One hundred men from Capt. Ward's district, the Third Precinct, under command of Lieuts. Bowler, Stanton, Penzen and Beard, twenty-six men from the Central Detail under command of Lieut. Hubbard and Sergt. Fitzpatrick, and fifty men from the Fourth Precinct, under Lieuts. Steele and Quinn, were accordingly assigned for special service that evening. Inspector John Bonfield was ordered to assume command of the whole force, and his instructions were to direct the detectives to mingle with the crowd, and, if anything of an incendiary nature was advised by the speakers, to direct the officers to disperse the gathering.

The meeting had been called for 7:30 o'clock, and at that hour quite a number had assembled in the vicinity of Haymarket Square. This square is simply a widening of Randolph Street between Desplaines and Halsted Streets, and in years past was used by farmers for the sale of hay and produce. It was for this place that the call had been issued, but for certain reasons the meeting was held ninety feet north of Randolph, on Desplaines Street, near the intersection of an alley which has since passed into public fame as "Crane's alley." In sight almost of this alley was Zepf's Hall, on the northeast corner of Lake and Desplaines Streets, and about two blocks further east on Lake Street were Florus' Hall and Greif's Hall—all notorious resorts and headquarters for Anarchists. On the evening in question these places and surrounding streets leading to the meeting place were crowded with strikers and Socialist sympathizers, some within the saloons regaling themselves with beer and some jostling each other on the thoroughfares, either going for liquids or returning to the meeting after having for the moment satisfied the "inner man." Here was a condition of things that would permit an easy mingling in, and ready escape through, the crowd, in the event of inauguration of the revolutionary plan adopted the evening previous. The throngs would serve as a cover for apparently safe operations. Another advantage gained by holding the meeting at the point indicated was that the street was dimly lighted, and, as the building in front of which the speaking took place was a manufacturing establishment—that of Crane Bros.—not used or lighted at night, and as the alley contiguous to the speaker's stand formed an L with another alley leading to Randolph Street, there were points of seeming safety for a conflict with the police. Besides, the point was about 350 feet north of the Desplaines Street Police Station, and it was evidently calculated that when the police should attack the crowd, that part of the Monday night program about blowing up the stations could easily be carried into effect.

These were the undoubted reasons for effecting the change. . . . One of the objections urged by Fischer against holding the meeting on Market Square was that it was a "mousetrap," and one of his potential arguments for the Haymarket was that it was a safer place for the execution of their plot. There was thus a "method in their madness." All the contingencies had evidently been very carefully considered.

But, as I have already stated, the hour had arrived for calling the meeting to order, and as there appeared no one to assume prompt charge, the crowd exhibited some manifestations of impatience. About eight o'clock there were perhaps three thousand people in the vicinity of the chosen place, and some fifteen or twenty minutes later Spies put in an appearance. He mounted the truck wagon improvised as a speaker's stand and inquired for Parsons. Receiving no response, he got down, and, meeting Schwab, the two entered the alley, where there was quite a crowd, and where they were overheard using the words "pistols" and "police," and Schwab was heard to ask, "Is one enough or had we better go and get more?" Both then disappeared up the street, and it is a fair presumption—borne out by the fact that they had entered a group of Anarchists on the corner of Halsted and Randolph Streets, as noted in the preceding chapter, and other circumstances—that they went to secure bombs. Spies shortly returned, and, meeting Schnaubelt, held a short conversation with him, at the same time handing him something, which Schnaubelt put carefully in a side pocket. Spies again mounted the wagon (the hour being about 8:40—Schnaubelt standing near him), and began a speech in English. It is needless, at this point, to reproduce the speech, as its substance appears later on, both as given by the reporters and as written out subsequently by Spies. But both reports fail to give a proper conception of its insidious effect on the audience. It bore mainly on the grievances of labor, the treatment of the strikers by McCormick, and an explanation of his (Spies') connection with the disturbances of the day previous. The lesson he drew from the occurrence at McCormick's was that "workingmen must arm themselves for defense, so that they may be able to cope with the Government hirelings of their masters."

Parsons had meanwhile been sent for, and on the conclusion of Spies' harangue was introduced. He reviewed the labor discontent in the country, the troubles growing out of it, touched on monopoly, criticized the so-called "capitalistic press," scored the banks, explained Socialism, excoriated the system of elections, and terminated his remarks by appealing to his hearers to defend themselves and asserting that, if the demands of the working classes were refused, it meant war. His speech, like that of Spies, was mild as compared with what would be expected on such an occasion. Perhaps this is accounted for by the fact that during their harangues Mayor Harrison mingled in the throng and paid close attention to the sentiments of the speakers. He afterwards characterized Parsons' effort as "a good political speech," and, being apparently satisfied that there would be no trouble, left for the Desplaines Street Police Station, giving his impressions of the gathering to the Captain in charge and telling Bonfield that there seemed to be no further use for holding the force in reserve.

No sooner had Harrison left for the station and thence for his own house, than the next speaker, Fielden, grew bolder in his remarks and sent the words rolling hot and fast over an oily, voluble and vindictive tongue. He opened with a reference to the insecurity of the working classes under the present social system, drifted to the McCormick strike, in which men, he said, were "Shot down by the law in cold blood, in the city of Chicago, in the protection of property," and held that the strikers had "nothing more to do with the law except to lay hands on it, and throttle it until it makes its last kick. Throttle it! Kill it! Stab it! Can we do anything," he asked, "except by the strong arm of resistance? The skirmish lines have met. The people have been shot. Men, women and children have not been spared by the capitalists and the

minions of private capital. It had no mercy—neither ought you.
You are called upon to defend yourselves, your lives, your future.
I have some resistance in me. I know that you have, too."

At this juncture the police made their appearance. During the
remarks of Spies and Parsons, detectives had frequently reported
to the station that only moderate, temperate sentiments were being uttered, but after Fielden had got fairly worked up to his subject, this was changed. The crowd was being wrought up to a
high point of excitement, and there were frequent interjections
of approval and shouts of indignation. Fielden's was just such a
speech as they had expected to hear. Very little was required to
incite them to the perpetration of desperate deeds. Like a sculptor
with his plastic model, Fielden had molded his audience to suit
the purpose of the occasion. With his rough and ready eloquence
he stirred up their innermost passions. His biting allusions to capitalists caught the hearts of the uncouth mob as with grappling
hooks, and his appeals for the destruction of existing laws shook
them as a whirlwind.

It would be as well, he said, for workmen to die fighting as to
starve to death. "Exterminate the capitalists, and do it tonight!"
The officers detailed to watch the proceedings saw that the speech
portended no good, and they communicated the facts to Inspector
Bonfield. Even then the Inspector hesitated. To use his own language, in the report he sent to Superintendent Ebersold: "Wanting
to be clearly within the law, and wishing to leave no room for
doubt as to the propriety of our actions, I did not act on the first
reports, but sent the officers back to make further observations.
A few minutes after ten o'clock, the officers returned and reported
that the crowd was getting excited and the speaker growing more
incendiary in his language. I then felt that to hesitate any longer
would be criminal, and gave the order to fall in and move our force
forward on Waldo Place"—a short street south of the Desplaines
Street Station.

The force formed into four divisions. The companies of Lieuts.
Steele and Quinn formed the first; those of Lieuts. Stanton and
Bowler, the second; those of Lieut. Hubbard and Sergt. Fitzpat-
rick, the third; and two companies commanded by Lieuts. Beard

and Penzen constituted the fourth, forming the rear guard, which
had orders to form right and left on Randolph Street, to guard
the rear from any attack from the Haymarket. These various
divisions thus covered the street from curb to curb. Inspector
Bonfield and Capt. Ward led the forces, in front of the first division. On seeing them advancing in the distance, Fielden
exclaimed:

"Here come the bloodhounds. You do your duty, and I'll do
mine!"

Arriving on the ground, they found the agitator right in the
midst of his incendiary exhortations, that point where he was telling his Anarchist zealots that he had some resistance in him, and
assuring them that he knew they had too. At that moment the police were ordered to halt within a few feet of the truck wagon,
and Capt. Ward, advancing to within three feet of the speaker,
said:

"I command you, in the name of the people of the State, to
immediately and peaceably disperse."

Turning to the crowd, he continued: "I command you and you
to assist."

Fielden had meanwhile jumped off the wagon, and, as he
reached the sidewalk, declared in a clear, loud tone of voice:

"We are peaceable."

This must have been the secret signal—it has about it suggestions of the word *Ruhe*—and no sooner had it been uttered than
a spark flashed through the air. It looked like the lighted remnant
of a cigar, but hissed like a miniature skyrocket. It fell in the
ranks of the second division and near the dividing line between the
companies of Lieuts. Stanton and Bowler, just south of where
the speaking had taken place.

A terrific explosion followed—the detonation was heard for
blocks around. The direction in which the bomb—for such it was
—had been thrown was by way of the east sidewalk from the
alley. It had been hurled by a person in the shadow of that narrow
yet crowded passageway on the same side of, and only a few
feet from, the speaker's stand.

The explosion created frightful havoc and terrible dismay. It was instantly followed by a volley of small firearms from the mob on the sidewalk and in the street in front of the police force, all directed against the officers. They were for the moment stunned and terror-stricken. In the immediate vicinity of the explosion, the entire column under Stanton and Bowler and many of the first and third divisions were hurled to the ground, some killed, and many in the agonies of death.

As soon as the first flash of the tragic shock had passed, and even on the instant the mob began firing, Inspector Bonfield rallied the policemen who remained unscathed, and ordered a running fire of revolvers on the desperate Anarchists. Lieuts. Steele and Quinn charged the crowd on the street from curb to curb, and Lieuts. Hubbard and Fitzpatrick, with such men as were left them of the Special Detail, swept both sidewalks with a brisk and rattling fire.

The rush of the officers was like that of a mighty torrent in a narrow channel—they carried everything before them and swept down all hapless enough to fall under their fire or batons. The masterly courage and brilliant dash of the men soon sent the Anarchists flying in every direction, and a more desperate scramble for life and safety was never witnessed. Even the most defiant conspirators lost their wits and hunted nooks and recesses of buildings to seclude themselves till they could effect an escape without imminent danger of bullets or of being crushed by the precipitate mob.

Fielden, so brave and fearless on the appearance of the police, pulled a revolver while crouching beneath the protection of the truck wheels, fired at the officers, and then took to his heels and disappeared. Spies had friendly assistance in getting off the truck, and hastened pell-mell through the crowd in a frantic endeavor to get under cover. He finally reached safety, while his brother, who was with him on the wagon, got away with a slight wound. Parsons seems to have taken time by the forelock and nervously awaited developments in the barroom of Zepf's Hall. Fischer had been among the crowd while Spies and Parsons spoke, but he was in the company of Parsons at Zepf's when the explosion occurred. Schnaubelt, who had sat on the wagon with his hands in his pockets until Fielden began his speech, hurried through the mob, after sending the missile on its deadly mission, and got away without a scratch. Other lesser yet influential lights in the Anarchist combination found friendly refuge, and, as subsequently developed, lost no time in reaching home as soon as possible. How any of these leaders who were in the midst of the awful carnage managed to escape, while other of their comrades suffered, is not clear, unless they dodged from one secluded spot to another, while the storm raged at its height—and there are many circumstances showing that this was the case. At any rate the point is immaterial: the fact remains that they were all found lacking in courage at the critical moment, and each seemed more concerned about his own safety than that of his fellow revolutionists.

Owing to the masterly charge of the police, the conflict was of short duration, but, while it lasted, it produced a scene of confusion, death and bloodshed not equaled in the annals of American riots in its extent and far-reaching results. The hissing of bullets, the groans of the dying, the cries of the wounded and the imprecations of the fleeing made a combination of horrors which those present will never forget.

No sooner had the field been cleared of the mob than Inspector Bonfield set to work caring for the dead and wounded. They were found scattered in every direction. Many of the officers lay prostrate where they had fallen, and to the north, where the mob had disputed the ground with the police, lay many an Anarchist. On doorsteps and in the recesses of buildings were found wounded and maimed. The police looked after all and rendered assistance alike to friend and foe. The dead, dying and wounded were conveyed to the Desplaines Street Station, where numerous physicians were called into service.

In subsequently speaking of the bravery of his men on this occasion, in his report to the Chief of Police, Inspector Bonfield very truly said:

It has been asserted that regular troops have become panic-stricken from less cause. I see no way to account for it except this. The soldier acts as part of a machine. Rarely, if ever, when on duty, is he allowed to act as an individual or to use his personal judgment. A police officer's training teaches him to be self-reliant. Day after day and night after night he goes on duty alone, and, when in conflict with the thief and burglar, he has to depend upon his own individual exertions. The soldier being a part of a machine, it follows that, when a part of it gives out, the rest is useless until the injury is repaired. The policeman, being a machine in himself, rarely, if ever, gives up until he is laid on the ground and unable to rise again. In conclusion, I beg leave to report that the conduct of the men and officers, with few exceptions, was admirable—as a military man said to me the next day, "worthy the heroes of a hundred battles."

II

I have often been asked how it was that I came to have charge of the detective work which was done in bringing the Anarchists to justice, and I think that the time has now come for the whole story to be told. I think it would be a false delicacy for me, in this book, which I mean to make, as nearly as I can, a fair and truthful record of the Anarchist case, to pass over the notorious incompetency which prevailed at Police Headquarters at that time. It cannot be denied that, had the case been left in the hands of the men of the Central Office, the prosecution would have come to naught, and these red-handed murderers would have gone unwhipped of justice. This was something which every good citizen would have been bound to prevent, and more than others a police officer, for into our hands is intrusted the care of the lives and property of the community and the preservation of law and order. I knew as well as my questioners that the case belonged to the Central Office. There was the Chief; there were the two heads of the detective department; there was the detective corps, supposed to contain the keenest and the best officers on the force.

From the first I was satisfied that the men at headquarters neither appreciated the gravity of the occasion, nor were they able to cope with the conspirators—a set of wily, secret and able men, who had made a special study of the art and mystery of baffling the law and avoiding the police. There was neither order, discipline nor brains at headquarters. Every officer did as he liked, and the department was rent and paralyzed with the feuds and jealousies between the chiefs and the subordinates. This, too, was at a time when the people of Chicago were in a condition of mind almost bordering upon panic. They were looking to us for protection. The red flag was flaunted in the streets, demagogues were shouting dynamite in a dozen parts of the city, riotous mobs had already met the police—and the police were in charge of a man who—it is a charity to say no more—had neither a proper conception of his duties nor the ability to perform them.

For instance, on the evening of May 3 all the captains of the city were ordered to meet at the Chief's office, and, together with Inspector Bonfield, they responded promptly. While the situation was being discussed, there was a rap at the door. I was nearest the entrance, and I opened it. Mr. Hanssen, one of the editors of the *Freie Presse,* was there. He handed in a paper, saying that it was of most serious import—so serious that, as soon as he had seen it, he had felt it his duty to bring it to police headquarters. It was the "Revenge" circular, of which so much is said elsewhere in this book, and which afterwards became so notorious. I handed it to Chief Ebersold, who glanced at it and said it was all nonsense. "Why," said he, "we are prepared for them." Bonfield looked it over, and thought it serious. I was sure that it meant mischief and murder, but the rest treated it as a farce. Now, what was to be expected from men who had no clearer idea of the gravity of the crisis that was upon us than the story of this incident conveys.

On the next evening the crash of dynamite was for the first time heard on the streets of an American city. The Red Terror was upon us.

What was done?

Every citizen of Chicago demanded justice for the brave men who had fallen—justice on the miscreants who had done them to death. Knowing what I did of the manner in which the detective work was apt to be done, it will not be wondered that I at once made up my mind to do what lay in my power to hunt these murderers down. Even had I not so concluded, the events of that day, the fifth of May, would have fastened the determination in my mind. At ten o'clock in the morning I was ordered by tele-

phone to report at the Central Station at once with two companies
—trouble was momentarily expected on the Black Road. When
I had disposed my men at the City Hall, and arranged for the
patrol wagons we were to occupy if a call should come, there was
nothing to do but wait in the Chief's office till we were summoned.
No one ever had a better opportunity of seeing how the police
business of the city was transacted.

It was a time of acute excitement, the day after the Haymarket.
The Chief was in a state of alarm that would have been ridiculous if it had not been pitiable. Whenever the telephone rang,
he would start nervously and demand, "Is that on the prairie, or
the Black Road?" and when assured that there was no trouble,
his relief was absurdly manifest. Among the detectives the topic
was whether they would be called on to work in the Anarchist
case and how many they would be expected to arrest.

Another question that bothered them was: What would the old
man (Mayor Harrison) say if they went to work arresting Anarchists, and how would he like it?

The officers who did their duty after such a stupendous crime
as the slaughter of the police officers would never have lost anything in the end, even if they should have lost their positions. The
question, "How would Harrison like it?" as asked by one of the
detectives, should, therefore, have cut no figure, and possibly it
did not. Probably the officer fell back upon it as an excuse for his
own laziness and incompetence. But one thing is certain, and that
is that the department did nothing to speak of in the case.

I saw some of those red-handed murderers come out of that
office smiling and laughing instead of being made to feel that they
were about to have a rope around their necks.

In fact, the Central Office was run so that no one could tell who
was officer, waiter or janitor. Everybody had a full sweep in
and out of the office, and if a prisoner happened to be brought
in by some well-meaning officer, everybody was allowed to hear
the investigation. It was a sort of town meeting, and it was free to all.

At that time Inspector Bonfield had been receiving a great
deal of favorable mention in the newspapers, in connection with
the labor troubles, and this aroused the jealousy of Chief Eber-

sold. The Chief accordingly concluded to attend to all the business himself, assisted by his pet gang of ignorant detectives, and they made a fine mess of it. But forces were at work, in spite of the internal difficulties, which rescued the case from utter failure.

On the morning of May 5, at an early hour, Inspector Bonfield had a short interview with State's Attorney Grinnell; but exactly what transpired no one but themselves knew. Before noon of that day, however, the result could be plainly seen. Officers James Bonfield, Palmer, Slayton and a few others had by that time succeeded in arresting August Spies, Chris Spies, Schwab, Fischer and Fielden. Of course, this step only served to create more jealousy in the Central Station.

After the prisoners had been brought in, some of the newspaper reporters endeavored to obtain interviews with them, but they were not permitted to get anywhere near the Anarchists.

In the meantime, and while the working officers were out hunting for more of the chief conspirators, the lieutenants in command of the detective department concluded that they would enjoy a little breathing spell. Accordingly they took a stroll among the fashionable saloons on Clark Street. There they met their friends, and while sampling the various decoctions compounded by the cocktail dispensers, they fell in with a party of professional prize fighters, heavyweight and lightweight, and matchmakers for man and beast. They found there was more sport in that party than in taking risks by going out into the suburbs through tough streets and dirty alleyways looking for Anarchists.

At any rate, after a lot of wine had been consumed and good cigars tested, round after round, one of the pug-faced sluggers made the remark to one of the lieutenants that he would like to see the Anarchists who had been arrested, and the officer addressed responded: "Of course you can see them—all you gentlemen can see them. Come right along with us."

They all fell into line, went over to the Central Station, were taken downstairs to the lockup, and there told to go around and look for themselves. This was some time after nine o'clock in the evening, and after the party had satisfied their curiosity, they returned to the saloon which they had left. The vigilant reporters had noticed this proceeding, and, holding a short conference, they resolved to insist on seeing the prisoners also. They told the officials that the public had as much right to know about the parties arrested as a gang of prize fighters, whether Sullivans or lesser lights in the prize-ring firmament, and the lieutenants at once recognized the force of the argument. Between eleven and twelve that night one reporter from each paper in the city was allowed to see the Anarchists, and interviews were secured for publication the next morning.

When I understood how the whole affair was being managed during that day, I came to the conclusion that the case would never be worked up by that department, and I was more resolved than ever that if the opportunity came I would not rest until the criminals were brought to justice.

Inspector Bonfield had likewise become disgusted with the nervous actions of the Chief and the heads of the detective department, and he decided to confine his operations to the West Side. He went over there that day—May 5—and as a result he cleaned out all Lake Street from the river to Halsted Street. He broke up all the Anarchist rendezvous, captured their guns, confiscated their flags, and created general dismay among the reds. Some sought safety by fleeing to the roofs, others escaped through back alleys, and still others got into the dark recesses of basements. When they learned that "Black" Bonfield, as they called him, was on their track, consternation took possession of them all. The Inspector had no easy task. He looked up all their halls and meeting places, hunted for "Revenge" circulars at every place he visited, and in every instance he found plenty of them as evidence of the extensive circulation given that document among Anarchists. He gathered them all together, and in the trial they proved of great service to the State as showing that all had notice to come to the Haymarket meeting with arms and be prepared for a deadly conflict. . . .

III

After motion in arrest of judgment had been overruled by Judge Gary, Spies was asked if he had anything to say why sentence of death should not be passed upon him. The prisoner rose, with pallid cheeks and distended eyes, and advanced toward the bench with a hesitating tread. The moment he faced the court he recovered his equanimity and proceeded with much deliberation to give his reasons why he should not be sent to death on the gallows. He spoke in a firm, almost a menacing tone of voice, and seemed bent on posing as a martyr to the cause of the laboring classes. In his very opening sentence he desired to have that understood. "In addressing this court," he said, "I speak as the representative of one class to the representative of another. I will begin with the words uttered five hundred years ago, on a similar occasion, by the Venetian Doge Falieri, who, addressing the court, said, 'My defense is your accusation. The cause of my alleged crime is your history.' " He then referred to his conviction, holding that there was no evidence to show that he had any knowledge of the man who threw the bomb, or that he had had anything to do with its throwing. There being no evidence to establish his legal responsibility, he maintained, his "conviction and the execution of the sentence would be nothing less than willful, malicious and deliberate murder, as foul a murder as may be found in the annals of religious, political or any sort of persecution." He charged that the representative of the State had "fabricated most of the testimony which was used as a pretense to convict," and that the defendants had been convicted "by a jury picked out to convict." . . .

If you think that by hanging us you can stamp out the labor movement—the movement from which the downtrodden millions, the millions who toil and live in want and misery—the wage slaves—expect salvation—if this is your opinion, then hang us! Here you will tread upon a spark, but there, and there, and behind you and in front of you, and everywhere, flames will blaze up. It is a subterranean fire. You cannot put it out. The ground is on fire upon which you stand. You can't understand it. You don't believe in magical arts, as your grandfathers did, who burned witches at the stake, but you do believe in conspiracies; you believe that all these occurrences of late are the work of conspirators! You resemble the child that is looking for his picture behind the mirror. What you see and what you try to grasp is nothing but the deceptive reflex of the stings of your bad conscience. You want to "stamp out the conspirators"—the agitators? Ah! stamp out every

factory lord who has grown wealthy upon the unpaid labor of his em-
ployés. Stamp out every landlord who has amassed fortunes from the
rent of overburdened workingmen and farmers. Stamp out every
machine that is revolutionizing industry and agriculture, that intensifies
the production, ruins the producer, that increases the national wealth,
while the creator of all these things stands amidst them, tantalized with
hunger! Stamp out the railroads, the telegraph, the telephone, steam
and yourselves—for everything breathes the revolutionary spirit. You,
gentlemen, are the revolutionists. You rebel against the effects of social
conditions which have tossed you, by the fair hand of fortune, into a
magnificent paradise. Without inquiring, you imagine that no one else
has a right in that place. You insist that you are the chosen ones, the
sole proprietors. The forces that tossed you into the paradise, the industrial forces, are still at work. They are growing more active and
intense from day to day. Their tendency is to elevate all mankind to
the same level, to have all humanity share in the paradise you now
monopolize. You, in your blindness, think you can stop the tidal wave
of civilization and human emancipation by placing a few policemen,
a few Gatling guns and some regiments of militia on the shore—you
think you can frighten the rising waves back into the unfathomable
depths whence they have arisen, by erecting a few gallows in the perspective. You, who oppose the natural course of things, *you* are the
real revolutionists. *You* and *you* alone are the conspirators and destruc-
tionists! . . .

Michael Schwab said:

If Anarchy were the thing the State's Attorney makes it out to be,
how could it be that such eminent scholars as Prince Kropotkin and the
greatest living geographer, Elisée Reclus, were avowed Anarchists, even
editors of Anarchistic newspapers? Anarchy is a dream, but only in the
present. It will be realized. Reason will grow in spite of all obstacles.
Who is the man that has the cheek to tell us that human development
has already reached its culminating point? I know that our ideal will
not be accomplished this or next year, but I know that it will be accomplished as near as possible, some day, in the future. It is entirely wrong
to use the word Anarchy as synonymous with violence. Violence is one
thing and Anarchy another. In the present state of society violence is
used on all sides, and therefore we advocated the use of violence against
violence, but against violence only, as a necessary means of defense.
I never read Mr. Most's book, simply because I did not find time to
read it. And if I had read it, what of it? I am an agnostic, but I like
to read the Bible nevertheless. I have not the slightest idea who threw
the bomb on the Haymarket, and had no knowledge of any conspiracy
to use violence on that or any other night. . . .

Oscar Neebe said:

They found a revolver in my house, and a red flag there. I organized
trades unions. I was for reduction of the hours of labor, and the education of laboring men, and the re-establishment of the *Arbeiter-Zeitung*
—the workingmen's newspaper. There is no evidence to show that I
was connected with the bomb-throwing, or that I was near it, or anything of that kind. So I am only sorry, Your Honor—that is, if you can
stop it or help it, I will ask you to do it—that is to hang me, too; for
I think it is more honorable to die suddenly than to be killed by inches.
I have a family and children; and if they know their father is dead, they
will bury him. They can go to the grave, and kneel down by the side
of it; but they can't go to the penitentiary and see their father, who was
convicted for a crime that he hasn't had anything to do with. That
is all I have got to say. Your Honor, I am sorry I am not to be hung
with the rest of the men.

Adolph Fischer rose with some signs of nervousness and proceeded slowly and deliberately with his protest. "I was tried here
in this room," he said, "for murder, and I was convicted of Anarchy." He objected most vigorously to the charge that he was a
murderer, and insisted that he had had nothing to do with the
throwing of the bomb. He confessed to having made arrangements
for the Haymarket meeting, to having been present, but urged
that it had not been called for the purpose of committing violence
or crime. . . .

Louis Lingg was in no gentle frame of mind when he advanced
to enter his objection at the bar of the court. After a thrust at the
court, he said that he had been accused of murder and been convicted; and "what proof," he defiantly asked, "have you brought
that I am guilty?" He acknowledged that he had helped Seliger
to make bombs; "but," he stoutly maintained, "what you have not
proven—even with the assistance of your bought 'squealer,' Seliger, who would appear to have acted such a prominent part in
the affair—is that any of those bombs were taken to the Haymarket." He referred to the testimony of the experts as simply
showing that the Haymarket bomb bore "a certain resemblance
to those bombs of his," and that was the kind of evidence, he held,
upon which he had been convicted. He had been convicted of
murder, but it was Anarchy on which the verdict was based.

"You have charged me with despising 'law and order,'" he said. "What does your 'law and order' amount to? Its representatives are the police, and they have thieves in their ranks." He then opened fire on me because the detectives I had sent out had broken into his room, as he claimed, to effect his arrest, and insisted that he had not been at the Monday night meeting, but at Zepf's Hall, at that time, which I had stated to be false.

Lingg next turned his attention to Mr. Grinnell, and accused him of having "leagued himself with a parcel of base, hireling knaves, to bring me to the gallows." Then the Judge came in for a scoring. "The Judge himself," he held, "was forced to admit that the State's Attorney had not been able to connect me with the bomb-throwing. The latter knows how to get around it, however. He charges me with being a 'conspirator.' How does he prove it? Simply by declaring the International Workingmen's Association to be a 'conspiracy.' I was a member of that body, so he has the charge securely fastened on me. Excellent!" He concluded as follows:

I tell you frankly and openly, I am for force. I have already told Captain Schaack, "If they use cannon against us, we shall use dynamite against them." I repeat that I am the enemy of the "order" of today, and I repeat that, with all my powers, so long as breath remains in me, I shall combat it. I declare again, frankly and openly, that I am in favor of using force. I have told Captain Schaack, and I stand by it, "If you cannonade us, we shall dynamite you." You laugh! Perhaps you think, "You'll throw no more bombs," but let me assure you that I die happy on the gallows, so confident am I that the hundreds of thousands to whom I have spoken will remember my words; and when you shall have hanged us, then, mark my words, they will do the bomb-throwing! In this hope do I say to you: "I despise you. I despise your order, your laws, your force-propped authority." Hang me for it!

George Engel appeared the least concerned of all when it came his turn to respond to the court's question as to any reasons he might have against the infliction of the death penalty. He opened by setting forth his arrival in America in 1872 and gave some reasons which had prompted him to espouse Anarchy. . . .

It is true, I am acquainted with several of my fellow defendants; with most of them, however, but slightly, through seeing them at meet-

ings, and hearing them speak. Nor do I deny that I, too, have spoken
at meetings, saying that, if every workingman had a bomb in his pocket,
capitalistic rule would soon come to an end.

That is my opinion, and my wish; it became my conviction when I
mentioned the wickedness of the capitalistic conditions of the day. . . .

Samuel Fielden entered into a long disquisition on the troubles
of the working classes all over the world, and covered much of
the ground traversed by him when on the witness stand. . . .

Your Honor, I have worked at hard labor since I was eight years of
age. I went into a cotton factory when I was eight years old, and I have
worked continually since, and there has never been a time in my history
that I could have been bought or paid into a single thing by any man
or for any purpose which I did not believe to be true. To contradict the
lie that was published in connection with the bill by the grand jury
charging us with murder, I wish to say that I have never received one
cent for agitating. When I have gone out of the city I have had my
expenses paid. But often when I have gone into communities, when
I would have to depend upon those communities for paying my way, I
have often come back to this city with money out of pocket, which
I had earned by hard labor, and I had to pay for the privilege of my
agitation out of the little money I might have in my possession. Today
as the beautiful autumn sun kisses with balmy breeze the cheek of
every free man, I stand here never to bathe my head in its rays again.
I have loved my fellowmen as I have loved myself. I have hated trick-
ery, dishonesty and injustice. The nineteenth century commits the crime
of killing its best friend. It will live to repent of it. But, as I have said
before, if it will do any good, I freely give myself up. I trust the time
will come when there will be a better understanding, more intelligence,
and above the mountains of iniquity, wrong and corruption, I hope the
sun of righteousness and truth and justice will come to bathe in its
balmy light an emancipated world.

Albert R. Parsons consumed a great deal of time in the delivery of his speech. He began by declaring that the trial had been
conducted with "passion, heat and anger," and pronounced the
verdict as one of "passion, born in passion, nurtured in passion,
and the sum totality of the organized passion of the city of Chicago." For that reason he asked for a suspension of sentence
and a new trial. He said:

Now, I stand here as one of the people, a common man, a workingman, one of the masses, and I ask you to give ear to what I have to say.

You stand as a bulwark; you are as a brake between them and us. You are here as the representative of justice, holding the poised scales in your hands. You are expected to look neither to the right nor to the left, but to that by which justice, and justice alone, shall be subserved. The conviction of a man, Your Honor, does not necessarily prove that he is guilty. Your law books are filled with instances where men have been carried to the scaffold and after their death it has been proven that their execution was a judicial murder. Now, what end can be subserved in hurrying this matter through in the manner in which it has been done? Where are the ends of justice subserved, and where is truth found in hurrying seven human beings at the rate of express speed upon a fast train to the scaffold and an ignominious death? Why, if Your Honor please, the very method of our extermination, the deep damnation of its taking-off, appeals to Your Honor's sense of justice, of rectitude, and of honor. A judge may also be an unjust man. Such things have been known.

Parsons acknowledged being an Anarchist and proceeded to show the ends Anarchy sought. Then he asked:

Now, what is this labor question which these gentlemen treat with such profound contempt, which these distinguished "honorable" gentlemen would throttle and put to ignominious death, and hurry us like rats to our holes? What is it? You will pardon me if I exhibit some feeling? I have sat here for two months, and these men have poured their vituperations out upon my head, and I have not been permitted to utter a single word in my own defense. For two months they have poured their poison upon me and my colleagues. For two months they have sat here and spat like adders the vile poison of their tongues, and if men could have been placed in a mental inquisition and tortured to death, these men would have succeeded here now—vilified, misrepresented, held in loathsome contempt, without a chance to speak or contradict a word. Therefore, if I show emotion, it is because of this, and if my comrades and colleagues with me here have spoken in such strains as these, it is because of this. Pardon us. Look at it from the right standpoint. What is this labor question? It is not a question of emotion; the labor question is not a question of sentiment; it is not a religious matter; it is not a political problem; no, sir, it is a stern economic fact, a stubborn and immovable fact. . . .

He continued:

Who are the mob? Why, dissatisfied people, dissatisfied workingmen and women; people who are working for starvation wages, people who are on a strike for better pay—these are the mob. They are always the mob. That is what the riot drill is for. Suppose a case that occurs. The First Regiment is out with a thousand men armed with the latest improved Winchester rifles. Here are the mobs; here are the Knights of Labor and the trades unions, and all of the organizations without arms. They have no treasury, and a Winchester rifle costs $18. They cannot purchase those things. We cannot organize an army. It takes capital to organize an army. It takes as much money to organize an army as to organize industry, or as to build railroads; therefore, it is impossible for the working classes to organize and buy Winchester rifles. What can they do? What must they do? Your Honor, the dynamite bomb, I am told, costs six cents. It can be made by anybody. The Winchester rifle costs $18. That is the difference. Am I to be blamed for that? Am I to be hanged for saying this? Am I to be destroyed for this? What have I done? Go dig up the ashes of the man who invented this thing. Find his ashes and scatter them to the winds, because he gave this power to the world. It was not I. . . .

The speeches of the defendants occupied three days—the seventh to the ninth of October, inclusive—and when Parsons had finished the court proceeded to pronounce sentence. Judge Gary said:

I am quite well aware that what you have said, although addressed to me, has been said to the world; yet nothing has been said which weakens the force of the proof, or the conclusions therefrom upon which the verdict is based. You are all men of intelligence, and know that, if the verdict stands, it must be executed. The reasons why it shall stand I have already sufficiently stated in deciding the motions for a new trial.

I am sorry beyond any power of expression for your unhappy condition, and for the terrible events that have brought it about. I shall address to you neither reproaches nor exhortation. What I shall say shall be said in the faint hope that a few words from a place where the people of the State of Illinois have delegated the authority to declare the penalty of a violation of their laws, and spoken upon an occasion so solemn and awful as this, may come to the knowledge of and be heeded by the ignorant, deluded and misguided men who have listened to your counsels and followed your advice. I say in the faint hope; for if men are persuaded that because of business differences, whether about labor or anything else, they may destroy property and assault and beat other men and kill the police if they, in the discharge of their duty, interfere to preserve the peace, there is little ground to hope that they will listen to any warning. . . .

The people of this country love their institutions. They love their homes. They love their property. They will never consent that by violence and murder their institutions shall be broken down, their homes despoiled and their property destroyed. And the people are strong enough to protect and sustain their institutions and to punish all offenders against their laws. And those who threaten danger to civil society if the law is enforced are leading to destruction whoever may attempt to execute such threats.

The existing order of society can be changed only by the will of the majority. Each man has the full right to entertain and advance, by speech and print, such opinions as suit himself; and the great body of the people will usually care little what he says. But if he proposes murder as a means of enforcing them he puts his own life at stake. And no clamor about free speech or the evils to be cured or the wrongs to be redressed will shield him from the consequences of his crime. His liberty is not a license to destroy. The toleration that he enjoys he must extend to others, and he must not arrogantly assume that the great majority are wrong and that they may rightfully be coerced by terror or removed by dynamite.

It only remains that for the crime you have committed—and of which you have been convicted after a trial unexampled in the patience with which an outraged people have extended you every protection and privilege of the law which you derided and defied—the sentence of that law be now given.

In form and detail that sentence will appear upon the records of the court. In substance and effect it is that the defendant Neebe be imprisoned in the State Penitentiary at Joliet at hard labor for the term of fifteen years.

And that each of the other defendants, between the hours of ten o'clock in the forenoon and two o'clock in the afternoon of the third day of December next, in the manner provided by the statute of this State, be hung by the neck until he is dead. Remove the prisoners.

IV

The Anarchists of Chicago now became desperate. Many of them had calculated on the worst for some time, and they had formed into small groups to be better able to plot for their imprisoned friends with the least possible danger of police detection. While assembling in large bodies, they had discovered that many of their secrets were in my possession, and after the decision of the Illinois Supreme Court they realized that it was essential to the success of any movement they might decide upon to keep all knowledge of it within the circle of true and trusted men. The leading lights in the order accordingly resorted to private residences. . . .

Sometimes they were joined in meetings of a general nature by some who had previously been anti-Anarchists, but who since the decision of the Illinois court had secretly expressed sympathy with the condemned men. Becoming emboldened by what they thought to be a growing sentiment in favor of the prisoners, these secret abettors finally threw off their masks, and, openly expressing their views, many of them speedily lost the esteem and friendship of neighbors by whom they had previously been highly regarded. With a view to aiding to effect a general change in public sentiment, some of these sympathizers even threw open their doors to Anarchists, as I have indicated in a prior chapter. But whenever some risky project was contemplated the small bands of conspirators saw to it that none but avowed and tried adherents of the red flag were present.

It was at this time that the police discovered the plot to release the doomed men, and one day Detective Schuettler learned of a place where numerous secret conferences were being held from time to time. He was under orders of Mr. Ebersold, who had taken him away from the Chicago Avenue Station with a view to crippling my force, but nevertheless the detective found a way, even while engaged in other directions, to keep a keen eye on secret revolutionary movements. He had been too long in the service to lose his interest in things Anarchistic, and he resolved to get at the bottom of the rumored clandestine gatherings.

Learning that star-chamber sessions were being held in the room of an old-time Communist named Theodore Appell, at No. 234 West Division Street, Schuettler at once rented an adjoining room. In this apartment there was a closet, and after reconnoitering about the premises at a favorable opportunity, he discovered that by cutting a hole in the closet wall he could obtain a good view of those who might be present at future meetings. A hole was accordingly cut. This gave him a fine chance both to see and hear. Everything worked nicely for a time, but finally the conspirators became suspicious, as they found their secrets getting beyond their own circle, and, satisfied that the leakage was not due to members in their own set, they instituted a search. The result was that the officer's peephole was discovered. That closed their deliberations in that place, but they resolved to take revenge on the man who had thus obtruded his attentions upon them. For this purpose they decided to hold a mock meeting in the old quarters, and then and there, when they were satisfied that the concealed individual had his eye at the hole, to discharge a syringe filled with vitriol. This would destroy the eyesight as well as disfigure for life the face of the man who had dared to intrude on their secrecy. I learned of this plan, however, and warned the officer. Schuettler never again went near that closet. But he had already gathered all the information that was needed.

The conspirators left the place like young birds leave the old nest, with a flop and a flourish, never to return; but we had learned that they had in view the liberation of their friends in jail.

This information put the authorities on their guard, and it is possible that this timely discovery averted a jail delivery.

But the Anarchists did not lose hope. When they learned that the United States Supreme Court had refused to interfere with the execution they became more desperate than ever. Where before they had been revengeful, they now were frantic, and their schemes now embraced more drastic and destructive measures. They considered propositions looking to a blowing-up of the jail building with dynamite, and in the turmoil and confusion incident to the wreckage of a part of the building and the destruction of life within they contemplated a rush to the untouched portion containing their comrades, whom they would thus rescue from the hands of the law. This diabolical plot was earnestly debated, and about the time the reds became satisfied that the Governor would not step in between their convicted leaders and the gallows they even went so far as to advocate an explosion that would not only rob the gallows of its victims, but kill those whom curiosity might assemble about the jail a short time before the expected event. If their comrades must die, they should not die alone. The disgrace of an execution must be averted, and a terrible lesson imparted to the enemies of Anarchy.

But the jail officials joined me in most rigid measures to prevent the execution of each and all of the plots, and officers and detectives were stationed in goodly numbers about the building, night and day, to watch the movements of suspicious characters. When the decision of the Governor was finally announced this vigilance was redoubled, and we made sure that no secret mines had been constructed under any of the sidewalks surrounding the building or across under the alley on the west side of the jail structure.

It was not only the liberation of the imprisoned Anarchists that was aimed at in the numerous conspiracies which came to our knowledge about this time. One plot which was reported to me embraced a wanton scheme of incendiarism and pillage, and in order to facilitate this, it was proposed to cut off the water supply of the city by demolishing the stand-pipe in the Waterworks tower. In some manner the conspirators had learned the exact spot in the tower where a charge of dynamite would accomplish the most effective execution, and the reports brought to me showed that this project was debated most minutely. For the space of two months we were required therefore to keep extra guard over the source of Chicago's water supply, and the contemplated attack of the reds was not attempted.

While the plots on the outside of the jail were thus met with vigilance, the doomed conspirators within appeared quiet and resigned. They received the Governor's decision with extraordinary composure, and, having felt throughout that day that they must face the inevitable on the morrow, they busied themselves in arranging their earthly affairs, writing letters to friends and relatives and giving directions as to the disposition of personal matters and the publication of their autobiographies and other manuscripts. Early in the evening they received their immediate friends and relatives to bid them farewell, and through all that trying ordeal they remained unmoved. Tears coursed down the blanched faces of wives, sisters and daughters as the last loving words were spoken, but no emotion of despair or grief seemed to agitate the men. They were solemn and stoical in their demeanor, and their efforts were mainly directed to administering words of cheer and consolation. When the final parting had taken place, they returned to their cells, and their last night on earth was varied with letter-writing and chats with the deathwatch. None of them retired early. Parsons did not seek his couch till after midnight, and then it was some time before the rapid thoughts coursing through his brain would permit him to sleep. Before morning he broke the stillness of his surroundings by singing a favorite song of his earlier days—"Annie Laurie." The clear tones echoing down the corridor startled all then awake, and prisoners and deathwatch eagerly inclined their heads to catch every word and note. When Parsons drew near the closing stanza, his voice tripped and hesitated, unmistakably showing that his feelings were giving way to the recollections of former times.

Spies lay down to rest at a late hour, but his thoughts, as he chatted with his deathwatch, seemed busy with the events that had brought him to a murderer's doom. He denounced the verdict as iniquitous, and declared that the people would shortly see the error of hanging men for seeking the welfare of the laboring classes.

Fischer was the quietest and most self-composed of all, and he had very little to say even to his deathwatch. He soon apparently fell into a slumber and seemed to rest easily.

Engel was also remarkably self-possessed, and he was the last to retire to his couch—not because of thoughts of the morrow occupying his mind, but for another reason, as will appear further along.

During the latter part of the night, if any one of them had happened to be awake, the horrible preparations for the execution could have been distinctly heard. Around the corner, in the corridor north of the one in which their cells were located, the gallows were being placed in position, and, even though the sounds of the hammer were subdued, the echo plainly told the character of the work the carpenters were engaged upon. It was the same scaffold on which the three Italians had two years before atoned for the death of a murdered countryman, and on which the murderer Mulkowsky had also paid the penalty for his foul crime. It was a large structure—large enough to have dropped seven men had the original sentence of the trial court been carried into full execution. At the end of each rope one-hundred-and-eighty-pound weights were attached, so as to give a heavier fall, and, thus arranged, by daylight the trap of death was ready for its victims.

When morning dawned, the four Anarchists arose early, but each seemed to have had a restful night. Their demeanor had not changed perceptibly from that of other mornings. After their ablutions they perused the morning papers and subsequently partook of breakfast, brought in from a neighboring restaurant. They ate quite heartily, and then each turned his attention again to letter-writing. Their communications were mainly directed to their families and to friends in the city, and some to Anarchists in other parts of the country, and very nearly the last they penned were directed to the Sheriff and to the Coroner and had reference to the disposition of their bodies and personal effects after death.

During the fleeting morning hours, the Anarchists were visited by the Rev. Mr. Bolton, of the First Methodist Episcopal Church of Chicago, who came to assist in their spiritual preparation for death, but while each received him courteously, they all declined his kindly proffered ministrations. They had no faith in the gospel and frankly told the clergyman that they did not desire his services. They wanted to die as they had lived, with no faith in God or man as exalted above general humanity. Some of them even went into discussion with the clergyman, stoutly combatting every point he made to reach their hearts; but the talk always ended as it had begun—in a positive refusal to accept any spiritual guidance or advice. The Rev. Mr. Bolton was forced to retire without having made any impression, and the men treated the whole matter afterwards in a most indifferent and flippant manner.

While the unfortunates on the inside were apparently unmoved by their impending fate, commotion and excitement prevailed on the outside of the jail. At a very early hour in the morning a contingent of the police force, numbering three hundred men, was detailed to preserve order and keep away from the immediate vicinity of the building all persons not having proper credentials or not properly vouched for. Across Michigan and Illinois Streets, on the east side of Clark Street, and on Dearborn Avenue at its intersections with the two first-named streets, stout ropes were stretched, and within the inclosure thus formed and at the barriers squads of policemen were marching up and down with glistening bayonets and Winchester rifles. There were also policemen in and about the Criminal Court and jail building and on the roof, commanding the streets below in all directions. There was thus a most complete arrangement to meet any unexpected attack or any violent hostile demonstration.

As the hour approached for the execution the streets beyond the ropes became crowded with people of all grades and descriptions, impelled by curiosity; but they were all kept moving by policemen scattered along the thoroughfares amongst them, so that no groups might gather and under the excitement of the moment precipitate a row or a riot. Along toward ten o'clock Mrs. Parsons, dressed in mourning and accompanied by her two children, presented herself at the ropes and demanded admittance to see her husband "murdered by law." She was, of course, delicately refused, and then she endeavored to create a scene, but the police promptly called a patrol wagon and sent her to the Chicago Avenue Station, where she was detained until after the execution. During the forenoon thousands of people passed in the vicinity of the building, but the only satisfaction they received for their pains was a sight of the somber walls of the jail at a distance. Taking the crowd as a whole, it was remarkably orderly, although there was more or less subdued muttering among the Anarchists who had sought the vicinity only to find themselves ordered to "move on." These generally sought solace for their wounded feelings in neighboring saloons, where they cast dire imprecations upon the police, promising to be avenged in time.

Within the jail everything was quiet, and, except for the presence of those who had come to witness the execution, there seemed to be no special indication of the tragedy to be enacted. The officials moved about quietly while making the preliminary arrangements, and the unfortunate Anarchists smoked, wrote hasty notes and chatted at intervals with their attendants.

At 11:30 o'clock Sheriff Matson, accompanied by Deputies Hartke, Cleveland, Spears and Peters, County Physician Moyer and Jailor Folz, started from the jail office, and repaired to the cell occupied by Spies. The iron-barred door was opened, and

Spies advanced to meet the Sheriff. Mr. Matson at once proceeded to read the death warrant. Spies listened with folded arms, and there was no indication of nervousness nor trace of emotion. His feelings could not be divined from his demeanor. The facial muscles remained unmoved, and no color rose to flush the usual paleness of the cheeks, nor was the pallor of his face heightened when the last fearful words of the warrant had been read. The Sheriff was visibly agitated, and his voice was at times tremulous. On the conclusion of the reading Spies merely bowed his head slightly, and then stepped out into the corridor in obedience to the deputies' request. Around his chest was placed a leather belt about an inch and a half wide, with which to pinion his arms just above the elbows, and his hands were handcuffed behind his back. Then a white muslin shroud was thrown over him and fastened slightly at the neck and waist.

While these details were being carried out, the Sheriff was at Fischer's cell, and the same program of preparation was gone through with. The Anarchist was manacled, pinioned and shrouded, and he gazed upon each operation with curious interest, but with no sign of perturbation or weakness. Now and then he faintly smiled, and he seemed more concerned about the trepidation of the deputies than about his own situation.

Meantime the death warrant had been read to Engel, who was soon arrayed in the habiliments of death. He stood it all unflinchingly, and seemed even less concerned than his comrades. There was also an entire absence of affected indifference.

Parsons was the last to step out of his cell, and, as he stood receiving the ghastly paraphernalia, he endeavored to display no sign of fear. He bore up well, although he evidently wrestled with his inner feelings.

The solemn march to the scaffold began with the Sheriff in the lead. In the east corner of the north corridor stood the scaffold. Below and before it were benches for the two hundred spectators. The death procession moved slowly and with measured tread. As it neared the corner the footfalls became distinctly audible to those assembled. When the shuffling of feet on the iron stairway leading to the first gallery, which was on a level with the gallows, was heard, the buzz of conversation ceased, and every eye was centered on the spot whence the Anarchists would be first seen. It was only a moment, and then Spies, Fischer, Engel and Parsons, one after the other, came into view, each with a deputy by his side. Having reached their respective places on the trap, they faced the spectators. Spies, the moment he caught sight of the audience, gave it a contemptuous look, and thereafter his eyes seemed centered on some invisible object down the corridor above the heads of the spectators. Fischer merely looked down for a moment on the uncovered heads below, and then his eyes wandered in various directions. Engel seemed the most unconcerned of all, and swept the audience with a cool glance as though it might have been composed of friends. Parsons was superbly stiff, and his gaze, after a snap at those below, firmly set itself in the direction of the cell tiers.

As soon as those on the platform had taken the positions assigned, the lower limbs of the four Anarchists were pinioned. This was done very quickly. The nooses dangling overhead were then lifted from their hooks, and Spies was the first to have the rope placed around his neck. The noose had been slipped a little too tight, and, noticing the uneasiness it gave him, the deputy instantly loosened it a trifle. Spies gave a faint smile in acknowledgment of the kindness and again seemed at ease. Not a tremor was visible during the adjustment of the rope. Another deputy next placed the rope around the neck of Fischer, who, to facilitate its proper adjustment, bent his tall form slightly and received it with head inclined until the knot rested in its proper place under the left ear. Engel received the noose as if it had been a decoration about to be placed upon his shoulders by friendly hands, and several times he turned his head around to exchange a word or two with the deputy, accompanying his whispered utterances with a smile. Parsons stood unmoved when his turn came, and appeared entirely indifferent to the operation. Loose-fitting white caps were now produced, and, as these came in sight, Fischer and Engel turned their heads slightly to the left and spoke a second to their respective deputies. Spies first, Fischer next, then Engel, and Parsons last, was the order in which the caps were adjusted, and the heads had no sooner been enveloped, shutting out forever the light of day, than all knew that the fatal moment had arrived. During all the preliminary preparations not a relaxation of nerve or an expression of anguish or despair had been observed. Now the tension of silence was painful. But suddenly there broke from the lips of Spies an exclamation that startled the auditors as if by a shock.

"You may strangle this voice," said he, in clear but sub-dued tones, "but my silence will be more terrible than speech."

Spies had scarcely uttered his last words, when Fischer shouted:

"This is the happiest moment of my life. *Hoch die Anarchie!*"

Engel immediately caught up the sentiment, and in a strong voice, and with a pronounced German accent, cried:

"Hurrah for Anarchy!"

Parsons then lifted his voice, and in firm, deliberate tones, exclaimed:

"O men of America!"

Then, lowering his voice to an appealing accent:

"Mr. Sheriff, may I be permitted to say a few words?"

Raising his voice again, without waiting for an answer, and con-tinuing in the same breath, he said:

"O men of America, let the voice of the people be heard."

The last word had barely escaped his lips, when the signal was given to the unknown and hidden man in the sentry box back of the platform, the rope controlling the trap was cut, and four bodies shot downward into space. The intervals between the adjustment of the caps, the utterances and the drop were only a few moments, but they were moments that seemed like hours. The first instant after the drop, the bodies all seemed motionless, but immediately one after the other began violent contortions, the limbs contracted, the breasts swelled with spasms, and the arms shook convulsively. It was fully eight minutes before the last was limp and lifeless. The bodies, however, were left hanging for twenty-six minutes, and then they were deposited in plain coffins, ready to be turned over to their relatives. The jury selected by the Sheriff to pass upon the death, as required by law, next viewed the remains and then signed the usual legal certificates. Those composing the jury were Dr. Ferdinand Henrotin, Dr. Denslow Lewis, Dr. G. A. Hall, Dr. Harry Brown, Dr. J. B. Andrews, Dr. M. W. Thompson, John N. Hills, William B. Keep, ex-Sheriff John Hoffman, Edwin Wynn, George Lanz, George M. Moulton, John L. Woodward and H. L. Anderson.

It was subsequently ascertained that the necks of none of the Anarchists had been broken, and that death had come in each case through strangulation.

Within an hour and a half the coffins were removed, the bodies of Spies, Parsons and Fischer being receipted for by a committee of the Central Labor Union, and those of Engel and Lingg by a friend of Mrs. Engel. The body of Lingg had reposed in the women's department of the jail. Shortly before his death, the bomb-maker had expressed the wish that his body be allowed to repose by the side of Engel's, and that it be given in charge of Engel's family, as he himself had no relatives in America.

The remains of Spies, Fischer and Parsons were taken to an undertaking establishment at 596 Milwaukee Avenue, and those of Engel and Lingg to a similar place at 186 Milwaukee Avenue, and there costly and ornamental coffins were provided after the bodies had been first embalmed. Subsequently they were removed to the houses of their respective relatives, and arrangements were at once set on foot for a tremendous demonstration at the funeral, the following Sunday.

No sooner had each coffin been taken to the relatives than hundreds of Anarchists flocked in to view the remains. Others, too —men, women and children, moved by morbid curiosity— crowded in to view the dead. The families were in almost constant tears, and deep were the lamentations over the fate of their loved ones. Mrs. Parsons was in paroxysms of grief and had to be almost forcibly removed from beside the bier of her husband. Her curses were loud against the police, and she strenuously refused all comfort. At the Spies residence there were copious tears, and no one was more deeply moved than Miss Van Zandt. The sorrow of Mrs. Engel and her daughter was more subdued, but nevertheless keen and poignant. It was the same at Fischer's home.

Meantime the preparations for the funeral went on, and the

committee having it in charge determined that it should be conducted with the utmost pomp, ceremony and display. They desired that on this occasion the red flag should again be unfurled and wave over the bodies of those whom they regarded as martyrs. The police learned of it, and when a committee waited upon Mayor Roche to secure the necessary permission for the procession, he set his face firmly against the red flag.

"The American flag," said he, "is good enough for us, and it is good enough for you. If that flag don't suit you, I am sorry. No red flag shall ever take its place while I am Mayor of Chicago."

Sunday, November 13, came, and every Anarchistic organization in the city turned out to attend the funeral. The procession, which started at an early hour, first called at the Spies residence, 154 Bryson Street, for the coffin of the editor, and then moved on to Mrs. Parsons' residence at 785 Milwaukee Avenue. After the coffin of Parsons had been placed in the hearse, Fischer's house was reached, and next that of Engel, and when all the hearses were in line, the entire funeral procession proceeded down Milwaukee Avenue, thence to Lake Street, and thence along Fifth Avenue to the depot of the Wisconsin Central Railway. At each of the houses of the executed Anarchists the cortege had been joined by friends and by various societies of which the dead had been members, and with these accessions the procession, as it finally moved on to its destination, numbered not less than six thousand. The hearses were loaded down with flowers, wreaths and other floral tributes, and each was followed by carriages containing the mourners. Close behind the Spies hearse was a carriage containing Mrs. and Miss Van Zandt, mother and daughter, and Mrs. Spies, the mother, and Miss Gretchen, the sister of the deceased. All along the line of march, the sidewalks were thronged, and there must have been over fifty thousand persons who viewed the procession as it passed. Hundreds had gathered at the residences before the procession started, and when they joined the throngs already on Milwaukee Avenue the streets became almost impassable. Policemen were stationed at the various street corners, and these gave the processionists ample room to move unimpeded.

The procession did not lack music, several bands having been engaged, and the "Marseillaise" and "Annie Laurie" were the airs most frequently heard.

The absence of the red banner on the street was commented on, but with a seeming defiance of the Mayor's orders two red flags decked the coffins of Engel and Lingg. What was still more significant was the fact that not a single flag of the Union was borne by the procession. It was only when the Anarchists reached Lake Street that the red, white and blue was unfurled to the breeze, and then it was done, not by an Anarchist, but by Howell Trogden, a veteran of the Civil War. It was a small emblem in size, and of cheap material, but he held it high above his head and proudly carried it before the cortege, clear down to the depot, greatly to the discomfiture and chagrin of the reds. When remonstrated with by some one who was in the crowd that had gathered about him and cheered him on the way, he defiantly exclaimed in plain, though perhaps not elegant, language:

"What, furl the ensign of the nation I fought for? Not much! You bet your life, I'll carry this flag and I'll kill the first man who tries to wrest it from me. I'll shed my blood to keep it there."

And the flag was kept there.

Arriving at the depot, the various organizations boarded the trains in waiting, and shortly after one o'clock all were under way to Waldheim Cemetery, situated some nine miles west of Chicago. It was a gloomy, cold day, but nevertheless an immense concourse of people followed the remains to the vault in which they were temporarily deposited. Those who had immediate charge of the funeral arrangements were Frank A. Stauber, H. Linnemeyer, George Schilling, R. M. Burke, Julius Leon, Edwin Goettge, Charles F. Seib, Ernst Litzman, H. Ulharn, F. G. Bielefeld, William Urban, Dr. Ernst Schmidt and T. J. Morgan, all members of the Defense Committee and the Amnesty Association.

After the coffins had been placed in the vault, Capt. W. P. Black took a position near the entrance and delivered the funeral oration. In concluding his address, he said, speaking of a day "when righteousness should reign":

We look forward to that day. We hope for it. We wait for it, and
with such a hope in our hearts can we not bring the judgment of charity
to bear upon any mistakes of policy or action that may have been made
by any of those who, acknowledging the sublime and glorious hope in
their hearts, rushed forward to meet it? We are not here this afternoon
to weep. We are not here to mourn over our dead. We are here to pay
by our presence and our words the tribute of our appreciation and the
witness of our love. I loved these men. I knew them not until I came
to know them in the time of their sore travail and anguish. As months
went by and I found in the lives of those with whom I talked the witness of their love for the people, of their patience, gentleness and
courage, my heart was taken captive in their cause. For this I have no
apology. If any of you feel that the tears are coming listen to the last
words spoken by one of these, our dead.

"Go not to my grave with your mourning, with your lamentations
and tears, with your forebodings and fears. When my lips are dumb,
do not thus come. Bring no long train of carriages; no hearse with waving plumes, with the gaunt glory of death illumed; but with hands on
my heart let me rest. Ye who are left on this desolate shore, there still
to suffer alone, deeply do I pity you. For me no more are the hardships,
the bitterness, heartache and strife, the sadness and sorrow of life, but
the glory of the divine, that is mine. Poor creatures, afraid of the darkness, who groan at the sight of the anguish in our silent night, go to
my tomb. Peal no solemn bell—I am well."

It has been said that these men knew no religion. I repel the charge.
I know but one religion—the religion which seeks to manifest itself by
its service of God—or of the supreme good—by its service of humanity
in its anguish and its hours of despair. And one of these, our dead,
while within the very gloom of approaching death, gave in these words:
"My religion is this: To live right. To do right is to live right, and the
service of humanity is my worship of God."

I remember that back in the centuries it was written in words that
shall never perish: "He that doeth righteousness is righteous, even as
He is righteous." There is no conception possible to humanity of that
which we call God other than the conception which sets our life aflame
in the service of our fellowmen. But I must not keep you. There is no
necessity for multiplying words in such a presence as this. There are
times when silence is more terrible than speech; when men moving to
the supreme issue of life can say, standing with their feet on earth and
their hands reaching out into the unknown, in a sublime burst of
enthusiasm: "This is the happiest moment of my life" (the last words
of Fischer), and then in that hour can cheer for the cause to which
they have given their lives (as Engel did), and men in that hour, forgetting themselves, can speak of the voice of the people (Parsons' last

words) until utterance is silenced forever, what need is there to stand by such men and multiply words?

I say that a mistake may well be forgotten in the glory of the purpose which we condemn—it may be through undue haste. I say that whatever of fault may have been in them, these, the people whom they loved and in whose cause they died, may well close the volume and seal up the record and give our lips to the praise of their heroic deeds and their sublime self-sacrifice.

Some weeks afterwards arrangements were made for the final interment of the bodies. A suitable lot had been purchased with money collected by the "Defense Committee," and accordingly on Sunday, the eighteenth of December, 1887, the Anarchists were invited out to Waldheim to witness the last rites over the dead conspirators. It was a cold, chilling day, and only about a thousand people were in attendance. The remains of the five Anarchists were removed from the vault, the coffins opened and the bodies viewed by all who desired. They were then placed in one grave, and a heavy flagstone was lowered and firmly cemented to protect them.

STUDS*

James T. Farrell

ON the South Side of Chicago, in back of the "yards" and stretching beyond, lies the city's principal Irish settlement. Because of the shifting migrations of its population, it's not as big as it used to be. But it still remains a sizable community, dotted by churches, parochial schools, Irish undertaking parlors, real estate offices, and taverns bearing the seals of O'Malley's, Kelly's Place, Delaney's Dug-Out, The Shamrock Grill, etc. This sector has been plowed for writing by one of its sons who is known primarily for his long sociological novels.

James T. Farrell not only has written full-length books but also has produced several volumes of short stories which deal for the most part with the same South Side Irish he has put into his novels.

The record shows "Studs" to be a youthful effort, one of Mr. Farrell's earliest stories written for a college English class. In my opinion it's the best short story he has done. It contains the essence of all his worth-while longer work. In its few pages are crammed the promise of a talent and the future author's entire philosophy. Farrell once composed a footnote to "Studs," asserting it was the acorn out of which the *Studs Lonigan* trilogy grew.

IT WAS raining outside; rain pouring like bullets from countless machine guns; rain spattering on the wet earth and paving in endless silver crystals. Studs' grave out at Mount Olivet will be soaked and soppy, and fresh with the wet, clean odors of watered earth and flowers. And the members of Studs' family will be looking out

* Reprinted by permission from *The Short Stories of James T. Farrell*. Copyright, 1934, 1935, 1937, by Vanguard Press, Inc.

of the windows of their apartment on the South Side, thinking of the cold, damp grave and the gloomy, muddy cemetery, and of their Studs lying at rest in peaceful acceptance of that wormy conclusion which is the common fate.

At Studs' wake last Monday evening everybody was mournful, sad that such a fine young fellow of twenty-six should go off so suddenly with double pneumonia; blown out of this world like a ripped leaf in a hurricane. They sighed and the women and girls cried, and everybody said that it was too bad. But they were consoled because he'd had the priest and had received Extreme Unction before he died, instead of going off like Sport Murphy who was killed in a saloon brawl. Poor Sport! He was a good fellow, and tough as hell. Poor Studs!

The undertaker (it was probably old man O'Reedy who used to be usher in the old parish church) laid Studs out handsomely. He was outfitted in a somber black suit and a white silk tie. His hands were folded over his stomach, clasping a pair of black rosary beads. At his head, pressed against the satin bedding, was a spiritual bouquet, set in line with Studs' large nose. He looked handsome, and there were no lines of suffering on his planed face. But the spiritual bouquet (further assurance that his soul would arrive safely in Heaven) was a dirty trick. So was the administration of the last sacraments. For Studs will be miserable in Heaven, more miserable than he was on those Sunday nights when he would hang around the old poolroom at Fifty-eighth and the elevated station, waiting for something to happen. He will find the land of perpetual happiness and goodness dull and boresome, and he'll be resentful. There will be nothing to do in Heaven but to wait in timeless eternity. There will be no can houses, speak-easies, whores (unless they are reformed), and gambling joints; and neither will there be a shortage of plasterers. He will loaf up and down gold-paved streets where there is not even the suggestion of a poolroom, thinking of Paulie Haggerty, Sport Murphy, Arnold Sheehan and Hink Weber, who are possibly in Hell together because there was no priest around to play a dirty trick on them.

I thought of these things when I stood by the coffin, waiting for Tommy Doyle, Red Kelly, Les, and Joe to finish offering a few perfunctory prayers in memory of Studs. When they had showered some Hail Marys and Our Fathers on his already prayer-drenched soul, we went out into the dining room.

Years ago when I was a kid in the fifth grade in the old parish school, Studs was in the graduating class. He was one of the school leaders, a light-faced, blond kid who was able to fight like sixty and who never took any sass from Tommy Doyle, Red Kelly, or any of those fellows from the Fifty-eighth Street gang. He was quarterback on the school's football team, and liked by the girls.

My first concrete memory of him is of a rainy fall afternoon. Dick Buckford and I were fooling around in front of Helen Shires' house bumping against each other with our arms folded. We never thought of fighting but kept pushing and shoving and bumping each other. Studs, Red O'Connell, the Donoghues, and Jim Clayburn came along. Studs urged us into fighting, and I gave Dick a bloody nose. Studs congratulated me, and said that I could come along with them and play tag in Red O'Connell's basement, where there were several trick passageways.

After that day, I used to go around with Studs and his bunch. They regarded me as a sort of mascot, and they kept training me to fight other kids. But any older fellows who tried to pick on me would have a fight on their hands. Every now and then he would start boxing with me.

"Gee, you never get hurt, do you?" he would say.

I would grin in answer, bearing the punishment because of the pride and the glory.

"You must be goofy. You can't be hurt."

"Well, I don't get hurt like other kids."

"You're too good for Morris and those kids. You could trim them with your eyes closed. You're good," he would say, and then he would go on training me.

I arranged for a party on one of my birthdays, and invited Studs and the fellows from his bunch. Red O'Connell, a tall, lanky, cowardly kid, went with my brother, and the two of them convinced my folks that Studs was not a fit person for me to invite. I told Studs what had happened, and he took such an insult decently.

But none of the fellows he went with would accept my invitation, and most of the girls also refused. On the day of the party, with my family's permission, I again invited Studs but he never came.

I have no other concrete recollections of Studs while he was in grammar school. He went to Loyola for one year, loafed about for a similar period; and then he became a plasterer for his father. He commenced going round to the poolroom. The usual commonplace story resulted. What there was of the boy disappeared in slobbish dissipation. His pleasures became compressed within a hexagonal of whores, movies, pool, alky, poker, and craps. By the time I commenced going into the poolroom (my third year in high school) this process had been completed.

Studs' attitude toward me had also changed to one of contempt. I was a goofy young punk. Often he made cracks about me. Once, when I retaliated by sarcasm, he threatened to bust me, and awed by his former reputation I shut up. We said little to each other, although Studs occasionally condescended to borrow fifty or seventy-five cents from me, or to discuss Curley, the corner imbecile.

Studs' companions were more or less small-time amateur hoodlums. He had drifted away from the Donoghues and George Gogarty, who remained bourgeois young men with such interests as formal dances and shows. Perhaps Slug Mason was his closest friend; a tall, heavy-handed, good-natured, child-minded slugger, who knew the address and telephone number of almost every prostitute on the South Side. Hink Weber, who should have been in the ring and who later committed suicide in an insane asylum, Red Kelly, who was a typical wisecracking corner habitué, Tommy Doyle, a fattening, bulldozing, half-good-natured moron, Stan Simonsky and Joe Thomas were his other companions.

I feel sure that Studs' family, particularly his sisters, were appalled by his actions. The two sisters, one of whom I loved in an adolescently romantic and completely unsuccessful manner, were the type of middle-class girls who go in for sororities and sensibilities. One Saturday evening, when Studs got drunk earlier than usual, his older sister (who the boys always said was keen) saw him staggering around under the Fifty-eighth Street elevated station. She was with a young man in an automobile, and they stopped. Studs talked loudly to her, and finally they left. Studs reeled after the car, cursing and shaking his fists. Fellows like Johnny O'Brien (who went to the U. of C. to become a fraternity man) talked sadly of how Studs could have been more discriminating in his choice of buddies and liquor; and this, too, must have reached the ears of his two sisters.

Physical decay slowly developed. Studs, always a square-planed, broad person, began getting soft and slightly fat. He played one or two years with the corner football team. He was still an efficient quarterback, but slow. When the team finally disbanded, he gave up athletics. He fought and brawled about until one New Year's Eve he talked out of turn to Jim McGeoghan, who was a boxing champ down at Notre Dame. Jim flattened Studs' nose, and gave him a wicked black eye, Studs gave up fighting.

My associations with the corner gradually dwindled. I went to college, and became an atheist. This further convinced Studs that I wasn't right, and he occasionally remarked about my insanity. I grew up contemptuous of him and the others; and some of this feeling crept into my overt actions. I drifted into other groups and forgot the corner. Then I went to New York, and stories of legendary activities became fact on the corner. I had started a new religion, written poetry, and done countless similar monstrous things. When I returned, I did not see Studs for over a year. One evening, just before the Smith-Hoover election day, I met him as he came out of the I. C. station at Randolph Street with Pat Carrigan and Ike Dugan. I talked to Pat and Ike, but not to Studs.

"Aren't you gonna say hello to me?" he asked in friendly fashion, and he offered me his hand.

I was curious but friendly for several minutes. We talked of Al Smith's chances in an uninformed, unintelligent fashion and I injected one joke about free love. Studs laughed at it; and then they went on.

The next I heard of him, he was dead.

When I went out into the dining room, I found all the old gang there, jabbering in the smoke-thick, crowded room. But I did not have any desire or intention of giving the world for having seen them. They were almost all fat and respectable. Cloddishly, they talked of the tragedy of his death, and then went about remembering the good old days. I sat in the corner and listened.

The scene seemed tragicomical to me. All these fellows had been the bad boys of my boyhood, and many of them I had admired as proper models. Now they were all of the same kidney. Jackie Cooney (who once stole fifteen bottles of grape juice in one haul from under the eyes of a Greek proprietor over at Sixty-fifth and Stony Island), Monk McCarthy (who lived in a basement on his pool winnings and peanuts for over a year), Al Mumford (the good-natured, dumbly well-intentioned corner scapegoat), Pat Carrigan, the roly-poly fat boy from Saint Stanislaus High School—all as alike as so many cans of tomato soup.

Jim Nolan, now bald-headed, a public accountant, engaged to be married, and student in philosophy at Saint Vincent's evening school, was in one corner with Monk.

"Gee, Monk, remember the time we went to Plantation and I got drunk and went down the alley overturning garbage cans?" he recalled.

"Yeah, that was some party," Monk said.

"Those were the days," Jim said.

Tubby Connell, whom I recalled as a moody, introspective kid, singled out the social Johnny O'Brien and listened to the latter talk with George Gogarty about Illinois U.

Al Mumford walked about making cracks, finally observing to me, "Jim, get a fiddle and you'll look like Paderwooski."

Red Kelly sat enthroned with Les, Doyle, Simonsky, Bryan, Young Floss Campbell (waiting to be like these older fellows), talking oracularly.

"Yes, sir, it's too bad. A young fellow in the prime of life going like that. It's too bad," he said.

"Poor Studs!" Les said.

"I was out with him a week ago," Bryan said.

"He was all right then," Kelly said.

"Life is a funny thing," Doyle said.

"It's a good thing he had the priest," Kelly said.

"Yeh," Les said.

"Sa-ay, last Saturday I pushed the swellest little baby at Rosy's," Doyle said.

"Was she a blonde?" Kelly said.

"Yeh," Doyle said.

"She's cute. I jazzed her, too," Kelly said.

"Yeh, that night at Plantation was a wow," Jim Nolan said.

"We ought to pull off a drunk some night," Monk said.

"Let's," Nolan said.

"Say, Curley, are you in love?" Mumford asked Curley across the room.

"Now, Duffy," Curley said with imbecilic superiority.

"Remember the time Curley went to Burnham?" Carrigan asked.

Curley blushed.

"What happened, Curley?" Duffy asked.

"Nothing, Al," Curley said, confused.

"Go on, tell him, Curley! Tell him! Don't be bashful now! Don't be bashful! Tell him about the little broad!" Carrigan said.

"Now, Pat, you know me better than that," Curley said.

"Come on, Curley, tell me," Al said.

"Some little girl sat on Curley's knee, and he shoved her off and called her a lousy whore and left the place," Carrigan said.

"Why, Curley, I'm ashamed of you," Al said.

Curley blushed.

"I got to get up at six every morning. But I don't mind it. This not workin' is the bunk. You ain't got any clothes or anything when you ain't got the sheets. I know. No, sir, this loafin' is all crap. You wait around all day for something to happen," Jackie Cooney said to Tommy Rourke.

"Gee, it was tough on Studs," Johnny O'Brien said to George Gogarty.

Gogarty said it was tough, too. Then they talked of some student from Illinois U. Phil Rolfe came in. Phil was professional major-domo of the wake; he was going with Studs' kid sister. Phil used to be a smart Jewboy, misplaced when he did not get into the furrier business. Now he was sorry with everybody, and thanking them for being sorry. He and Kelly talked importantly of pallbearers. Then he went out. Some fellow I didn't know started telling one of Red Kelly's brothers what time he got up to go to work. Mickey Flannagan, the corner drunk, came in and he, too, said he was working.

They kept on talking, and I thought more and more that they were a bunch of slobs. All the adventurous boy that was in them years ago had been killed. Slobs, getting fat and middle-aged, bragging of their stupid brawls, reciting the commonplaces of their days.

As I left, I saw Studs' kid sister. She was crying so pitifully that she was unable to recognize me. I didn't see how she could ever have been affectionate toward Studs. He was so outside of her understanding. I knew she never mentioned him to me the few times I took her out. But she cried pitifully.

As I left, I thought that Studs had looked handsome. He would have gotten a good break, too, if only they hadn't given him Extreme Unction. For life would have grown into fatter and fatter decay for him, just as it was starting to do with Kelly, Doyle, Cooney and McCarthy. He, too, was a slob; but he died without having to live countless slobbish years. If only they had not sent him to Heaven where there are no whores and poolrooms.

I walked home with Joe, who isn't like the others. We couldn't feel sorry over Studs. It didn't make any difference.

"Joe, he was a slob," I said.

Joe did not care to use the same language, but he did not disagree.

And now the rain keeps falling on Studs' new grave, and his family mournfully watches the leaden sky, and his old buddies are at work wishing that it was Saturday night, and that they were just getting into bed with a naked voluptuous blonde.

TRAVAIL*

Louis Zara

CHICAGO'S West Side is so huge that besides containing the city's large Polish, Scandinavian, German, Greek, Syrian, Italian, and Czech colonies, it also holds the not inconsiderable Jewish subcity of the metropolis. The main street along which this settlement has developed is Roosevelt Road, once known as Twelfth Street. The sector is called the Lawndale district. Though many of its inhabitants are moving farther west, to Austin, or north, to Albany Park and West Rogers Park, the West Side Jewish settlement still sprawls over a large area which is rapidly acquiring a run-down appearance and losing its old color and ebullience.

This neighborhood not only forms the backdrop of Meyer Levin's book, *The Old Bunch,* but is also the locale for "Travail."

While going through an old pile of (Mencken) *American Mercury* copies, I came across a 1932 issue containing Louis Zara's fine, powerful story. I had read it twenty years ago, and on second reading it seemed better than before. The death of the hundred-year-old grandmother, surrounded by the babble of her relatives and scented by the smells of her own decaying body, contains the essence of life's termination for the extremely aged. The mood and quality of the writing make one suspect the story was written out of direct observation, or out of the immediate milieu of the author's life.

OLD Dvorah Gelberman had been wasting away for ten years, but now Dr. Shulman, counting her pulse, knew that the long race with

* Reprinted from *The American Mercury,* 1932, by special permission of Louis Zara.

Time would soon be over. He marveled that she had lasted so long. Between his pink, scrupulously clean fingers her age-tanned wrist throbbed slowly. Dvorah's strong old heart was giving out. And crowding the small bedroom, its windows sealed airtight despite all the doctor's pleas, were the children and the grandchildren, and the great-grandchildren tugging at their mothers' skirts, and the anxious neighbors who had dropped in to see how Dvorah was getting along, and the sick committee from the Ladies' Auxiliary that had come to console their dying sister.

The doctor completed the evening's inspection and stepped quickly from the room. Feh! he wanted air, fresh air. Chaim Gelberman, the old woman's son, waved to him as he went out, and Dr. Shulman waited obediently in the dining room where the overflow of visitors had assembled. He had tried many times to disperse this idle gathering that haunted the little flat and the sickroom, waiting, waiting, waiting, but Dvorah had insisted on having them around, and her children, especially Chaim, who paid all the bills, were prone to disregard his advice in favor of their mother's caprices. So now the flat was crowded with people who should have been at home preparing to go to bed. Many had come, doubtless, to be remembered with bequests for the causes they represented. They were there to remind Dvorah that they and theirs were worthy. And she, dipping into Chaim's purse, showered the "needy" with her son's cash.

They would not have long to wait now. That old body, wasted by the erosion of the years, could not survive much longer. How old was she, anyway? Mentally the doctor calculated to ninety-eight. Dvorah had admitted to eighty when Chaim had called him in that first time to diagnose a case of indigestion. Ninety-eight? At least that. He was, in fact, fairly certain that she was well over a hundred; but she had feared the envy and jealousy of her friends, and as well the dreaded Evil Eye, and so she had lied, pitifully attempting to conceal what was obvious to all.

This denying one's correct age, it appeared, was something of a family failing. There was Chaim, nearly seventy, yet only the other day the doctor had heard him give his age as sixty-four or -five. And Reuben, who was over sixty and the pauper of the

Gelbermans, also snipped a few annoying years from his age. And of course Leah did the same. Even some of the younger members of the family, whom he could remember as tots, had lied to his office girl in giving their ages. They all did. Perhaps they thought the Angel of Death would alter the records to suit them. An interesting case of mass fear, reflected Dr. Shulman. Thinking of his own sixty-three, he wondered if he would act that way, too, when and if he became much older. Longevity was nothing to be proud of, surely, but why be ashamed of it?

The doctor reached for a cookie from a bowl on the sideboard and poured himself a few fingers of saffron-hued liquor. As he nibbled at the cookie he wondered where Chaim Gelberman had got such brandy. Suddenly he remembered that Chaim was waiting for him. He finished his drink and went back to the sickroom. Impatiently he elbowed his way through the phalanx that walled the doorway, muttering "The doctor! The doctor!" and peered in.

He was shocked. He confessed it to himself. Shocked. The dim electric bulb, through its dirty, white-glass shade, cast a frightening light. It was only because he was familiar with his patient's features, had been so for the past ten years, that he recognized her at all. A gaunt and bony creature lay under the comforter. Its long arms, brown and stiff, were stretched over the sides of the coverlet, the hands lying tensed and open. On the white of the pillow the long, narrow head lay, a cadaverous thing, topped with a coarse wig. The skin of the forehead and chin was cross-hatched with lines.

Looks as though she had been soaking in formaline, thought the doctor, and a sensation of disgust rose in his nostrils as he saw the long, ugly hairs that sprouted from the corners of her lips and the knob of her chin. Her cheeks were furrowed, too, and led innumerable radii toward her eyes. Her eyebrows had grown wildly till they were a dark, bushy bar over the deep black, fireless coals of her eyes, but the lashes had disappeared almost entirely. Longevity also has its disappointments, he mused, as he detected about the bed the revolting odor of the unburied dead.

He was fascinated. He had never had so old a patient, had never seen one struggle so for meaningless life. Suddenly the old lips moved and the sound that issued was hoarse and very mortal.

"Chaim!"

From the semidarkness a figure detached itself and stepped forward. The doctor understood. Chaim had been waiting for her to call him before she sank altogether.

"Mameh, what is it?"

The old woman's eyelids fluttered. She seemed to be looking far out beyond this room, this flat, this world. She whispered again.

"Reuben!"

Another figure stooped over the bed.

"Leah!"

A weeping woman threw herself forward. Leah sobbed as she knelt and laid her head against the coverlet.

"Dovvid . . . Simon . . . Sarah . . ."

Others crowded through the door, standing as silently as shades, but none answered to these last names. Dovvid and Simon and Sarah, indeed, would never answer again: the kind earth had accepted them long ago. Dvorah Gelberman, the old Dvorah, raised herself as she realized that no one had responded to her call.

"Dovvid," the hoarse whisper issued again, and then Dvorah remembered.

"He sleeps," she muttered and beat her bony breast. "Let him sleep."

"Mameh," Chaim began. "What is it, Mameh?"

She shook her head.

"Be good to your father, children. He's not so old, but he can hardly crawl from one chair to another. Don't be angry with him. His mind wanders a little sometimes. His strength grows less day by day."

A murmur ran through the little room, then a long sh! Old Gelberman had been dead now thirty-six years. He had died before Dvorah had consented to come to America to live with her children. And now she spoke of him as one still breathing, as though he were in that very room!

Dvorah looked at her children. Eleven had sought life in her womb, but here stood only three. Of the six that had come to

America only these were yet alive. The others? They were not here. She could not recall them. But these three, these three she would bind upon oath.

"Swear to me, you, Chaim, and you, Reuben," the old woman began. "Give me your hands in oath that you will take care of him. And Leah, in the summer he likes the little red radishes and in the winter dumplings made with unrendered fat, you know the kind. You shouldn't forget!"

"We swear, Mameh," they said. "Be calm! Let your heart be at peace!"

Both men shuddered as her fingers gripped their hands. She grows cold. Soon, soon.

"Now go and let me rest a little," she bade them petulantly. "Don't come again until I call you to say good-by. Let me rest for a while. You are always bothering me. Soon I'll pack and leave. The children have begged so long that I must go and see them in this Golden Land. I have a couple of jars of chicken-fat, a bottle of grape-wine, and some beet-jelly made with sweet walnuts to bring them. But it's such a long way to go. Over the sea . . ."

Chaim played with the heavy gold chain that hung across his vest. Reuben bowed his head and shifted his tobacco quid to a new corner in his jowl. Leah wept in the arms of one of the neighbors.

Dvorah lay quietly for a moment and Mrs. Aaronson, chairman of the sick committee of the Ladies' Auxiliary, crept near. The women had a promise to fulfill before Death claimed their sister.

"Does she draw breath?" someone whispered.

"Dvorah," Mrs. Aaronson began softly.

"Sh! she sleeps!" Chaim said.

The dying woman stirred.

"Who calls? I am Dvorah and the Almighty Himself watches over me!"

"The Almighty Himself should watch over you! It is Rivkah Aaronson, Dvorah. Rivkah. Do you remember what you wanted me for?"

The old hands clutched at the coverlet.

"Rivkah Aaronson? Yeh, yeh."

Suddenly she sat up. The others fell back in fright. Was she coming back to the life that was trying so hard to disown her?

"Yeh, Rivkah," Dvorah continued, "you came to wash me and dress me in my white grave-clothes. Twenty years ago I sewed them up to be ready when the time would come. Yeh, Rivkah, I remember. The old head still works. It goes slow, but it goes. So come, Rivkah! Come, old wives, wash Dvorah, wash her clean! Dvorah goes to America!"

The women gathered around the bed, Dvorah's friends of the Ladies' Auxiliary who had promised to prepare her for her coffin. She would not have the undertaker's men touch her: who can tell what kind of people they are?

The others left, looking back over their shoulders. Slowly they went out, drifting into the dining room, the parlor, the kitchen. Chaim Gelberman had kept his mother in a flat of her own. His wife did not want to have old Dvorah in her home. Too much of a burden. An old person, one foot in the grave—too much responsibility. So Chaim had furnished this place for his mother and had engaged various of her friends to drop in to see her at regular intervals. A fine man, Chaim, well-to-do and respected. His brother Reuben, on the other hand, is something of a good-for-nothing. Always in debt, always failing to make any business pay. He is a paving contractor: so is Chaim. How different two brothers can be!

Chaim beckoned to the doctor. Together they elbowed through the plague of relations, large and small, and sought privacy on the back porch.

"*Nu,* Doctor?" the older man began, hands in pocket, jingling a few coins.

Dr. Shulman rubbed his chin thoughtfully and stared out at the stars that winked roguishly at him and his handicraft.

"It's hard to say," he answered at last. "She has a strong heart for such an old woman——"

"She's not so old!" Chaim retorted almost mechanically, and then he added: "Talk about what you know, Shulman!"

The doctor checked his tongue: no sense in antagonizing Gelberman. He should have remembered how sensitive all the Gelbermans, mother, children, and even grandchildren, were on the point of their ages. And Chaim was the oldest of Dvorah's living children. Plainly, he did not want to be reminded that Death, which was even now preparing to erase his mother, would stand bound to waylay him next, if only out of respect for his seniority.

"She has a strong heart," the doctor went on firmly, "but her breathing is becoming slower. She may not last the night. Yet she may linger for days. One can't tell."

Chaim was silent, and somewhat reproachful. He said nothing for five minutes. Then he rose and without a word to the doctor went back into the house.

"It is a shame to talk about it," Feinman apologized, "while she is yet alive. She might even live till her hundred and twenty years is over. You know, Mr. Gelberman, it's the broken pitcher that goes to the well the most times."

Chaim shuddered.

"Of course, you want a good box for the mameh," the undertaker went on, "and I've got them. Aluminum, steel, copper. The best your money could buy. Guaranteed to give service. It's a pleasure, a box like that——"

"Enough, Feinman! Make me no speeches! The mameh wants a plain wooden box like they had in the old home. So don't argue. And she has her own white grave-clothes. She sewed them up twenty years ago."

The undertaker hesitated.

"A wooden box?"

"Yeh."

"Then I'll make it nice with copper outside. It should look good at the cemetery, no?"

Chaim shrugged his shoulders.

"What's the difference? So long as there's wood in it. The mameh wants wood."

"And the limousines, how many should I have ready?"

"I don't know nothing about that. But let everybody that wants to pay her the last honor have a seat in a car."

Feinman smiled and rubbed his hands.

"Not many mothers have such sons," he sang mournfully.

Gelberman looked at him stonily and he shuffled out.

Rabbi Pearlbloom passed him at the door.

"She'll not die, Mr. Gelberman," the rabbi declared piously. "Such a good heart. The charities she has done will alone earn her a long life. God doesn't forget such things."

"You know that for sure?" Chaim asked with a glare. The rov annoyed him. Plainly, the fellow wanted the job of conducting the ceremonies at the cemetery—it would cost a pretty penny, too—but why did he fawn so?

"For sure? That, of course, I can't say," the rov chanted. "But a woman that has brought such fine children into the world! God can't let her miss her reward on earth. . . . Mr. Gelberman, you will want, of course, a gathering of ten young psalm-singers to repeat the Psalms when—at a hundred and twenty years!—she expires. I'll take care of it myself."

"You'll take care of it? Who said you should?"

Rabbi Pearlbloom halted in dismay. He tugged at the wings of his broad nose perplexedly.

"I've already given an order to have ten of the best pupils of the Hebrew school ready."

Chaim said nothing for a moment. Then he consented with a shrug.

"Now," the rov continued, "I'll go in to see how the mameh is doing."

"Bring me candles!" Dvorah commanded. Her voice rose to a high pitch as she spoke.

"Candles, candles?" Chaim mumbled. "Let some one bring candles. Reuben, run out and buy candles!"

The older brother stuffed a bill into Reuben's hand.

"Run, run!" he bade him.

"Wait, Chaim, Reuben, wait!" Leah begged them. "Maybe the mameh has candles!"

They asked her. Of course, she had them. She had everything prepared. She even had a list of small bequests she desired to make, ready for Chaim. To the great disappointment of the visitors, he tucked the paper in his pocket, promising to have the checks written out as soon as he got home. Dvorah had thought of everything, so of course she had the candles ready. Go in the first wide door of the kitchen cupboard. Reuben slipped the bill into his pocket: Chaim had plenty. Leah hastened and found them, tall, wax candles that one lights near the dead.

"Not these, Mameh!" Leah murmured.

"Yeh, yeh, these!" Dvorah insisted. "Both at my feet where I can see them."

They obeyed. Rabbi Pearlbloom nodded his head solemnly, signifying that it was permissible.

"You shouldn't make a lot of trouble over me!" Dvorah said suddenly. "I don't want anybody to have any trouble over me now."

Chaim wanted to laugh. To laugh here at her deathbed? He controlled himself. For thirty years had she been a problem on his hands. Now she did not want to be any trouble for anyone.

"And if I have made someone angry, let him forgive me!" Dvorah continued. "Forgive me now and I'll put in a good word for you over there!"

"We forgive you, Mameh!" they chorused. "We forgive you, Dvorah!"

And that was all she said that could be clearly understood.

Her eyes now focused on the candle-flames, and she lay quietly, breathing only with effort. Then she began to murmur as in a fever. Once she turned slightly and stared at Chaim.

"Oh, Eliezer," she whispered, "you have grown so tall! I thought I would never live to see you so big."

Chaim squirmed and muttered.

"This is Chaim, Mameh!"

But she did not know him. Again she called him Eliezer. Eliezer had been born and had died a child of six before Chaim had ever seen the light of this world.

Suddenly Dvorah dug her gnarled hands into the coverlet. A fierce tensing of muscles, and then her face relaxed and her jaw dropped, revealing the dark cavern of her mouth. That was all. The travail of death was simpler than the travail of birth. Dr. Shulman felt gently for her pulse; he needed no more. Then he turned away with a manner of reverence. It was over. There was still the formality of the death certificate, but that could be taken care of later. He wanted to say something, words of condolence, but he could think of nothing: Dvorah Gelberman had taken her full measure of life. There should be no mourning here: this physiological machine had functioned till the last ounce of energy had been coerced from it. Truly dust was returning to dust, but what should he say? Rabbi Pearlbloom rose to his aid.

Quickly the rov produced a large, fringed praying-shawl from one of the pockets of his black alpaca coat, unfolded it, and covered the corpse. The *talith* reached only from Dvorah's head down to her knees, but that would do until the undertaker arrived. Feinman would not have to wash the body nor to clothe it. Dvorah's Auxiliary sisters would attend to that. But he would probably want to dress the face, touch it up with color to make a good appearance when the coffin was opened for the last time. And he would place the small fragments of a broken clay dish over the dead eyes to keep the lids closed: symbolic of the character of this life. Feinman would take care of all that.

In a singsong the rov chanted a prayer, the others echoing him with fervent Amens. When he had finished he turned to Chaim and cut his coat lapels in several places with a little scissors that he brought forth from another pocket. There had been silence, the frightened silence that is Death's tribute from the living, but now Leah began to sob violently. Her cries grew shriller; she screamed and collapsed in a faint. Other women screamed and beat their breasts contritely; Dvorah had belonged to many charity societies in her thirty years in America. Tears trickled down Chaim's cheeks as he witnessed the grief of these strangers. Reuben blew his nose, took the little scissors from the rov, and cut his own lapel: mourning. The doctor slipped quietly from the room.

Rabbi Pearlbloom tugged lightly at Chaim's sleeve.

"Mr. Gelberman, when God wills, what can we do? He gives and He takes!" he declaimed eloquently but not without tenderness, and then he changed to a brisker tone. "I'll take care of everything for you. Don't bother yourself for a thing. Right away I'm running out to telephone Feinman to come. He will do his

share. I have been working with him for years already. He will
bring more candles to light around her bed—may she be happy in
Eden!—and everything. And I'm going this minute to order the
youngsters from the Hebrew school to come and chant the Psalms
tomorrow when she is laid out in the coffin—may she rest in her
peace! I'll take care of everything myself, Mr. Gelberman, the
prayers and the sermon at the cemetery, everything. Don't worry,
you can rely on me!"

He was gone with a spryness that belied his bulk. Chaim wiped
his eyes, uttered the kaddish, prayer for the dead, and pushed
through the crowded doorway as Reuben began his kaddish. He
wanted to get away, away from this corpse and these mourners.
There was no one in the dining room, so he poured himself a
short glass of brandy. When he had swallowed it his head felt
clearer. But the wailing and the sobbing came back to him.

Again he thought of his dead lying there in the next room. After
all, she had been his mameh. In his mind he could no longer, try
as he might, see her as a young woman, a young mother, who
had played with him when he had been a child. He could not mus-
ter a single endearing memory of her. For him there existed only
the picture of an old woman struggling stubbornly for years, hanging on to life with her weak, bony fists, refusing to die. She had
become repulsive to her friends, to his wife, to her grandchildren,
even to her own children. But not to him, not to him, he insisted.

To live so long! He denied himself the pleasure of reflecting on
her longevity. Instead, he mused bitterly for a few moments; would
the thread of his own life unravel so far? Then something drew at
his heart. The old mameh was dead. And he began to weep.

MY AUNT DAISY*

Albert Halper

> HERE is a short story of my own. I include it, first, because I am known as a Chicago writer; and, second, because it has met with some favor among readers.

IN THE late spring, just before the hot weather set in, my mother began receiving letters from Boston, and started to wear a frown. She put the letters in the upper right-hand drawer of the old, scratched-up bureau, because the upper right-hand drawer had had no knob for some time now, and if you wanted to open it you had to pry it from side to side with the ice pick, or the little screw driver she kept locked up in the sewing machine.

Finally, after five or six letters had arrived, my mother began to show her agitation, and to drop, here and there, a hint that her youngest sister Daisy wanted to come to Chicago for a few weeks during the summer. We had heard so much about our Aunt Daisy that everybody got excited in the flat and began asking questions—everybody except my father, who sat down to the supper table, chewed his food thoughtfully, and didn't say a word all through the meal. My mother watched him quietly.

"Well," he said at last, "is she as crazy as she used to be?"

He received no answer and went on eating. Later, clearing his throat, reaching over for the sugar bowl with his short fat arm, he asked the question again, this time scowling a bit.

"She's thirty now," my mother said submissively. "She's no girl any longer. She knows how to act."

* Reprinted from *On The Shore,* published by The Viking Press. Copyright, 1934, by Albert Halper.

"She should get married," said my father, finishing his tea, still frowning. "What she needs is a man!" and he put on his hat and went back to the store, leaving a gloomy feeling in the flat.

He knew my mother's youngest sister, and he did not like her. When he spoke of her he called her a *fitchkhe,* which means a skittish little horse. No, he didn't like her. Before he had come to Chicago to settle down he had lived for a time in Boston, and he knew Aunt Daisy very well. It was evident, as he left the flat, that he had no strong desire to see her again.

Later on in the evening, when he came back from the store, he took his shoes off and sat for a while in the old rocker in the front room, his heavy face half cupped in his fist, rocking there for a long time. Finally he yawned, got up tiredly, scratched his head, and went to bed. In the kitchen my mother was putting washing to soak, and her hands fluttered above the tubs.

During the next few weeks the flat was like a powder magazine —everything was tense and silent in the house as soon as my father would come home from the store. If we had been playing in the front room or wrestling on the floor we stopped as soon as we heard that well-known heavy tread on the stairs, so that when our father opened the door he came into a quiet flat. He'd take his hat off, pull up a chair and start eating right away, while my mother began serving him.

She was a large woman, almost a full head taller than my father, but it was he who was boss around the house. When he complained about the bad business in his little grocery, when he wailed that the hot weather was spoiling the few slabs of meat in his dinky icebox and that the chain stores, which had begun to expand rapidly, had already reached Madison Street, half a mile away, my mother had to contract her face with sympathetic suffering, as if she had a toothache. And if she didn't, he'd holler out that of course it made no difference to her where the money came from just as long as she had a place to eat and sleep in. But right after he'd say this, he'd feel sorry, and would sit there frowning, with a low grumble rumbling deep down in his throat. Then he would go back to the store. My mother would take the dishes from the table after he was gone and would stand at the sink for a long while before turning on the hot water.

Sometimes, late at night, from the dark of their bedroom, I could hear my mother and father talking in low tones.

"But we haven't got room for her," my father would argue. "And besides, it costs something to board her."

But my mother who had not seen her youngest sister for many years kept at it. The letters piled up.

Toward the end of June my father, worn away, gave in. My mother wrote to Boston telling her sister to come and when the train arrived my oldest brother met Aunt Daisy at the station. He brought her home. My oldest brother, about twenty at the time, was somewhat of a dandy, wore a wide straw sailor with a colored ribbon, and was thus delegated to be the family's reception committee. I remember we watched him going up the street toward the trolley on his way to the station, and when he reached the corner he waved back at us because he knew that we were looking, though he really could not see us.

He brought Aunt Daisy home. It was late dusk when they came. The street lamps had not yet lit up and from the windows we could see Milt struggling with two heavy bags while a little woman walked jauntily at his side. In the fading light we couldn't see her face and when they got closer to the flat we went away from the front windows because she might look up and see us, so when at last the bell rang we were all excited and her entrance was something of a dramatic event. I could hear the bags bumping as my brother struggled with them up the stairs.

Then we opened the door, Milt set the bags down in the hall and Aunt Daisy, with a little cry, rushed forward into my mother's arms. My mother couldn't talk for a while; she hadn't seen her sister for over fifteen years.

Milt came inside, shut the door and dumped the bags in the parlor. "It's dark here!" he shouted. "What's the matter?" and he struck matches and lit the gas lamps in all the rooms of the flat.

In the sudden light we looked at our mother's sister—we stood there gaping, the whole crew of us, six kids. We saw a small, dark, vivacious woman who looked to be about twenty, flashing us a smile. There was something vibrant about her, about her nostrils, her eyes and hair, and we fell in love with her at once. On her head she wore a small hat with gray and brown feathers, and she had a way of tilting her chin, of flashing her smile, of looking pertly alert that made me think of a bird. Yes, she was a warm little bird.

She took her hat off right away and stared brightly at us in friendship. My mother's eyes were misty as she saw her sister counting us briskly by placing her forefinger saucily against our foreheads, one by one, and trilling "Tra-la-la-la!"

"I'm your Aunt Daisy," she said, then bent down and kissed every one of us while our mother stood by choking and happy. When she came to my oldest brother she stopped, flashing us all another smile. "I kissed Milt at the train, but I guess I can kiss him again," and she gave him a real loud smack on the lips. My kid brother, who was about six at the time, jumped up in the air and clapped his hands, so my aunt had to kiss him again also.

Then she breezed through the flat, through the six large gloomy rooms, her heels rapping against the floor, while my mother, middle-aged, gray, tired out by childbearing and household drudgery, walked behind her.

When we reached the front room we all stood at the windows looking down the darkening street, and at that moment the arc lamps lit up with a sudden burst of light. "See!" she cried as glare and shadow cut the pavement below, and she raised my kid brother in her arms and kissed his cheek again. She was in love with him right away.

On the outskirts my sister, thirteen and lonely in a house of many brothers, edged silently away, and with a sad, lost look stared down at the shining asphalt. She had been dreaming and thinking of our aunt for weeks and wanted so much to have someone to talk to. She stood there with her soft yellow hair in two long plaits hanging down her back, and by the set of her small jaw I knew she was hating her little brother. But Aunt Daisy suddenly turned to her, coddled her hand and brought her over. My sister was awkward at first, but it was evident that she liked Aunt Daisy.

Finally Aunt Daisy said: "Where's Isak?" and the flat went quiet.

"He's at the store," my oldest brother answered after a while. "He'll be home pretty soon."

"Maybe you ought to go down and tell him, Milton," my mother put in, pleading.

"He'll be home," Milt said shortly and stared at his straw hat on a hook.

While we waited for our father our mother showed Aunt Daisy to her room and I started dragging the heavy bags across the floor, kicking at the brothers who sprang for the handles. I was about nine years old at the time, and puffed from the exertion. My mother told Aunt Daisy that she could have the whole room to herself. "Can you manage it?" said our aunt, knowing we were crowded, then changed the subject.

We were to sleep three in a bed and our sister was to sleep on the sofa. "On the sofa?" Aunt Daisy said in alarm. "No, she's to sleep with me!" This made my sister so very happy that she started crying; she looked at Aunt Daisy as though at that moment she would have kissed her feet.

Then we heard that well-known heavy tread on the bottom stairs. All of us stood crowded in Aunt Daisy's bedroom, waiting. The door slammed.

"Is there a show going on?" shouted our father when he saw all the lights in the flat burning. "What's the meaning of this?" and he strode through the house, turning off all the gas except the parlor jet. He was grumbling to himself, a short, stocky, testy man.

At the threshold of the bedroom he stopped. "Oh . . ." he said, taken slightly aback, and stood looking at my mother's sister, at the trembling smile she flashed at him. What fine teeth she had! They greeted each other quietly, and he asked if the train ride had been hot and dusty. Then he went into his bedroom.

After he went to bed all of us sat in the parlor with the gas turned low while Aunt Daisy told our mother about the family in Boston. Milt had a date with the daughter of one of the neighbors down the street, but he ran outside and broke it, and then came back. He didn't want to miss the news. Aunt Daisy, speaking low so as not to disturb our father, gave our hungry mother all of it. At that time my grandmother was still alive and also all five of my mother's sisters, all living in Boston or nearby New England cities. My mother was the oldest and had been the first to leave the little village near the Baltic for America; then all had followed. My father, also from the same town, had sent her passage money.

"And how is Mama? How is she?" asked my mother for the fifth time, and Aunt Daisy said our grandmother was well. Our grandmother ran a little drygoods store in East Boston and was getting along all right, Aunt Daisy said. Then came talk about relatives we had never seen, strange names and little stories connected with everyone of them, with my mother happy and excited and breaking out in her native tongue every so often. We sat up late until all of us began yawning, and then went to bed.

In the days that followed Aunt Daisy and my mother were always talking together in the kitchen, in the bedroom or on the back porch, reminding each other of various happenings of many years ago. They spoke all day long about relatives in Europe, about the little village near Memel on the Baltic, and my mother suddenly remembered old folk tales, and for the first time in my life I saw her face was beautiful as she talked about the things she knew. My father grew a trifle less grouchy, but did not unbend all the way. He still went to bed as soon as he came back from the store at night.

It was now July and the midsummer heat was upon us. It blew in from the plains in huge hot waves which rolled up the streets, stifling the town. In the evenings we sat on the back porch, which overlooked a wide yard below, where all the children of the tenement played ball until full darkness came on, throwing the ball up and back until it looked like a gray streak and you wondered how they caught it. Closer to the wall of the next building the men pitched horseshoes in pairs, the big shoes ringing hard against the iron stakes, and the losing side had to fork up ten cents for a can of beer, which was drunk slowly, going from mouth to mouth, with the kids begging for a chance to blow off the foam.

After the men got tired of playing horseshoes in the dark they sat on the stairs below and sang, slowly at first—sad love songs and ballads of the day. Someone would pull out a mouth organ and the men would sing softly. They were laborers and mechanics mostly, with a sprinkling of single railroad men who boarded with the families in the building. They all liked to sing.

The Midwestern twang of their songs was new to Aunt Daisy and she started calling us Westerners. She herself spoke with a Bostonian accent which sounded brittle and odd at first, until we grew accustomed to it.

For the first week or so the entire life of the flat was keyed up and my mother's thoughtful face lost some of its quiet look. We stayed up later than usual and Milt went down to the drugstore for a quart of ice cream almost every night. Aunt Daisy had come with five or six new summer dresses and wore a different one each night, though she did not go out. I believe that she finally spoke to my mother about it, because at the end of the first week my mother had a talk with Milt and a day later Milt started taking Aunt Daisy out.

She was ten years his senior, but on the street she looked so girlish that people took her for Milt's sweetheart. Milt took her downtown to a couple of shows, introduced her to a few of his friends, and then began to worry because he had heard that his girl in the block had started going with another fellow. He grew nervous, dropped Aunt Daisy right away, and tried to straighten things out with his girl.

But the little sip of Loop night life, the lights and music of the downtown restaurants made Aunt Daisy restless and she began to quarrel with Milt. At first he was polite in his answers, but later on, when she grew quick-tempered and told him he owed her a duty as a nephew to take her around, he flew off the handle and answered sharply. My mother tried to smooth things over, but Milt stalked out of the flat and went striding up the street. Daisy locked herself in her bedroom and cried there a long time.

From then on, her visit was not a happy one. Ben, who was the next to the oldest and eighteen at the time, volunteered to take her out, but he was a quiet fellow and had a youngish face, and lacked the poise and easy manner that Milt possessed.

So the evenings passed, the hot summer nights, and Aunt Daisy remained in the flat. Two weeks went by and she said nothing about leaving. My father spoke to my mother, but my mother said to wait another week. Now that all the news had been exchanged, now that the first flush of meeting had worn off, there was a sharp letdown. We had grown accustomed to Aunt Daisy's Eastern accent and had heard some of her Boston stories for the second and third time. In the daytime we went swimming in the city ponds or in the playgrounds, and only my sister stayed behind. Aunt Daisy, in her loneliness, would read aloud to her from *Ramona* or *Ivanhoe,* and sometimes she liked to braid my sister's heavy yellow hair.

And all the while my father grew grouchier and grouchier. "When is she going?" he would ask my mother. "We're crowded here, the boys have to sleep three in a bed in such hot weather, and you're setting a better table now, a cake or fruit almost every evening. I can't afford it."

My mother would stand there without answering him until my father went back to the store.

At last, during the middle of the third week, my mother must have spoken to her sister about it, for when I came into the flat one hot afternoon I could hear Aunt Daisy crying in her room. My mother stood there, looking helpless. Daisy sobbed out that she had no friends, that she was tired of being unmarried, and she said she had thought she would meet somebody here. "I was looking forward to it so much," she sobbed.

"But the boys are so young," my mother said. "Milton is only twenty. His friends are boys, too."

Aunt Daisy kept on crying. "Besides, I haven't got the railroad fare back," she confessed. "Every penny I could scrape together went into the dresses I brought with me."

My mother stood aghast. Then she saw me.

"God knows, God knows! . . ." she said and Daisy, looking

up, also saw me and began smiling through her tears, to show me she had not been crying. She called me over, laughing softly, and when I came she strained me to her and kissed my face all over. Her arms were trembling. She kept whispering to me and in the end she mussed my hair, laughing nervously. "What did you see? Was I crying?"

I shook my head.

"There!" she cried and flung her arms out happily. "Tra-la-la-la, tra-la-la-la!" and she went singing through the rooms of the flat. In the kitchen my mother, standing over the stove, stirred the heavy soup slowly with a big ladle.

Another week went by and still my mother was afraid to ask my father for Aunt Daisy's return railroad fare. She put the matter off from day to day. But out of her own meager savings she gave her sister a few dollars for stockings, face powder and other things. Aunt Daisy took the money, drew the new hose snug against her shapely little legs, and tousled our heads harder than ever.

"Tra-la-la-la! Tra-la-la-la!"

Milt went out every night now and on Sundays stayed away all day. He bought a pair of flannels and a blue jacket, and went out sporting. The daughter of the neighbor was more gone on him than ever, and just before he used to leave the flat Aunt Daisy would find something to do in her room until he had gone.

Later on, when she was sure that Milt had left the house and when my father had gone to bed, Aunt Daisy would sit on the back porch and wait for a breeze with the rest of us, while a hundred yards to the south the Lake Street elevated roared and crashed along, hurtling its racket through the summer night like long-range artillery. And to the north, a block behind us, were the Northwestern tracks, with freights that passed all night long, their whistles wailing over the town and the black soot of the soft coal they burned floating down upon the people in a thin, sifted ash. The heat brought out the perspiration, and if you rubbed your face with your hand it came away dirty from the train soot.

In the hot night, looking to left and right, you could see all the porches of the building loaded with families, the men sitting in their socks, the women in thin cotton house dresses. Some of the families hauled out mattresses and slept on the porches all night; and in the morning you could see them sprawled out, wearily, and if they were awake they'd pull the sheets over them quickly, wait for you to look away, and then duck inside the house.

No rain fell. In the evenings, when the sun rolled down in the west over the piano factory in Walnut Street, clouds of gray dust rose in the air as the men pitched the horseshoes. Their trousers bottoms would be powdered and they'd have to step back and wait awhile to let the dust settle before looking at the iron shoes. They rushed the can harder than ever and the kids kept fighting to see who would be chosen to blow off the foam.

Then came the tragedy of the summer. One of the young unmarried railroaders had seen Aunt Daisy sitting on the porch and had fallen for her. He was a big, honest, bashful fellow named Harry O'Callahan, and he had the shoulders of a coal heaver. He had a fine voice, too, and could play the harmonica.

He spied Aunt Daisy one evening as he was pitching horseshoes, glancing up at our porch on the second floor. He saw she was small and dark and was dressed in a yellow summer frock. He fell in love right away. Small as I was, I noticed it at once. He played horseshoes very badly all evening and the men bawled him out and none would pair off with him, so he had to play against two of them, walking up and back across the dusty ground, and losing every game.

"What's come over you?" the men asked. "You used to beat us all."

Harry shook his head, forked up another dime and dropped out of the game. And later on, in the hot dark when the men had grouped themselves on the stairs, someone struck up an old railroad song, a ballad about the sweat of the road and the Iron Horse and the whistles of the roundhouse early in the morning. I had never heard that song before. Harry O'Callahan was singing it. The men grew quiet while his fine baritone floated toward us. When he finished, handclapping and footstamping thundered at him from all the porches. They called out to him to sing on.

He sang a few more songs and in the choruses the men hummed

bass for him. Then he took out his harmonica and played, "Down By The Old Mill Stream," and "By The Light Of The Silvery Moon," fluttering his cupped hands over the mouth organ so that quivering notes issued forth.

"Who is that fellow?" Aunt Daisy whispered, asking me in the dark.

I told her.

"Oh, he works on the railroad?" she said and seemed to lose interest, though the music continued to move her. "Is he the big fellow who threw the horseshoes so badly?"

I nodded.

She said nothing more.

The next evening, when the men pitched the shoes again, Harry seemed to have found his former stride and tossed with his old form; he threw like a champion, twirling the heavy iron shoes unerringly so that they rang angrily around the metal stakes with a burst of sparks. He stared hard ahead through the dust to see the ringers he had made, smiled, then looked up toward our porch. My mother sat quietly, but her hands were clenched in her lap.

Later on, when the men played singles, I went down in the yard and watched. Harry was playing against another railroader, a big fellow, too, his best friend; the fellow's name was Frank.

Harry and Frank played three games while the families leaned from the porches, watching. Harry won them all. Someone was sent for the beer and when it came the kids stood around in a pushing circle. As he was the winner, Harry got the first drink. He pointed at me with a grin, held the full can aloft, so I worked myself proudly through the group, gripped the can in my fists and, filling my lungs to the bottom, blew all the foam cleanly from the top. It was a neat job, Harry said, and he slipped me a nickel when the other kids weren't looking.

After that, when full darkness came on, the singing started up again and Harry gave an entire concert with his harmonica. The neighbors seemed to sense that something was up, for they kept looking toward our porch where Aunt Daisy sat in the gloom, only her summer dress showing, a pink one this time. My father had long since gone to bed and Milt was out sparking, but the rest of the family sat on the porch. In one of the pauses my mother called out softly to me, saying it was getting late, but I pretended I didn't hear.

An hour later, after the can had made many trips to the saloon in Lake Street, the men grew boastful and started bragging about their strength. There would be singing, then shouting, then bragging, then singing again. Things grew noisy.

"I can swing the sixteen-pound hammer harder than any man here," a road man shouted. "I drive stakes in with two blows!"

"Well, where's the hammer, where's the hammer to prove it?" the men shouted back.

"That's your affair!" came the answer and the porches howled with laughter.

But pretty soon, because there was so much bragging and counterbragging, it was decided that weight-lifting was the best all-around test of strength, and someone went down into the basement for two big buckets, crossed the alley where the foundation work of a factory was under way, and came back with the pails loaded to the top with heavy mixing sand. The janitor of the building, sitting in his socks and smoking on his porch, came forward hollering that the pails belonged to the owner of the building, but the men pacified him with a long drink of beer. He wiped his mustache and went back to his porch again. Someone got hold of an old broom, broke off the stout handle and tied the two pails to the ends of it with stout cord. Now they had a weight, all right.

The first fellow to step up couldn't lift the two pails higher than his chest. He grunted and strained, but he had to give up. All the smaller men came forward, also the men over forty, but none of them could lift the heavy buckets over their heads. The pails were very big.

Then the day laborers tried. Three of them were able to lift the twin buckets high over their heads, but couldn't hold the pails up there very long. From the porches the families started calling for Harry O'Callahan to try. He sat back in the darkness and did not answer.

Finally his best friend Frank got up and, gripping the wooden handle, raised the weight slowly and gracefully up to his chest, his chin, the top of his head, then high above it, straightening out his arms. Cheering broke out from the porches.

"Anybody can lift the weight up quickly, but the real test is lifting it slowly," Frank said blowing, looking at the day laborers. He sat down, heaving.

"Well, we know who's the strongest now," came from the porches.

Harry stepped from the shadow. Once, twice, three times he lifted the buckets up to his chin and over his head, as slowly as Frank had done and just as gracefully. Then he sat down. Now the cheering was greater than ever and the kids pressed forward to feel Harry's biceps. On the porches the women were impressed and leaned over more from the railings. In the dark I saw a pink blur on our porch move forward, too, and, turning, I noticed that Harry had also seen.

"That was nothing," he said quietly, but he couldn't keep the triumphant ring from his voice.

Frank got up and began thinking of new ways of lifting the weight, of gripping your hands the other way, knuckles up. He and Harry tried it. It was harder, but both managed it.

"Do it with one hand!" someone shouted from the porches, a short fat man sitting in his underwear who was married to a pretty young woman rumored to be carrying on an affair with the neighborhood iceman.

Everybody laughed. Mr. Moser, besides being short and flabby, was bald and couldn't lift an egg from the floor—because he couldn't stoop to pick it up.

At first Frank tried it with one hand. He gripped the wooden bar with his right hand, strained, grunted and wrenched, but but couldn't lift it higher than his waist. He tried his left hand.

The kids started yelling, "Harry, Harry!"

Harry came up. He tried first with his left hand, testing to see how much energy he'd have to use with his right, not straining himself. You could see he had been thinking it out. With his left hand he brought the buckets up to his thigh, a little higher, then lowered them.

"You can't do it!" fat little Mr. Moser shouted, fanning his face excitedly. The families laughed.

Then the yard grew quiet. Bending over, gripping the wooden handle firmly with his right hand, winding his fingers hard around the smooth wood until his fist went white, Harry started lifting. He had a wrist as thick as my leg around the calf. The buckets, ascending slowly, swayed from side to side, went up, up, up, as high as his waist, his chest, his chin, then came down with a plop against the ground. Toward the end of the hoist Harry's whole frame had started to quiver from the strain.

"Take some of the sand from the pails," Moser taunted from his porch, but his wife, leaning away over, had her eyes glued on Harry O'Callahan. Harry smiled at the sally. He looked up, heaving like a spent swimmer, and as he turned toward our porch I saw the sweat break out on his forehead. He wiped it away, then bent once more to the buckets. His friend Frank advised him not to try again. "Don't try it," said Frank. "You're tired out, it isn't worth it."

But already Harry had his fingers wound around the smooth wooden broom handle and now his jaw was like a block of concrete, and his whole fine, young, Irish face was grimly set as if he were about to rush into a burning building to save his heroine.

Slowly, using his strength carefully, he raised the buckets from the ground to his shins, his knees, his thigh, bracing himself, curving his spinal column as the pails rose to his chest. Up, up, up they went, his whole frame quivering like a leaf in the wind, until he had the pails of sand level with his chin, his nose, his eyes. Then with a hoarse, shouting grunt, with a tremendous distortion of facial muscles and baring of teeth, he heaved the weight aloft, grinning like a maniac, his frame quivering so violently you could count the great pitiful shivers of the fellow's big body. A hush fell upon the whole yard. From the rear windows of the flats the gaslight from the kitchens fell upon the scene in long slanting bright blocks of yellow glare.

But as soon as the buckets shot up after that last tremendous wrench of back and shoulder and leg muscles something seemed to snap inside of Harry and he went limp all of a sudden. The buckets thudded to the ground and Harry followed. He lay there writhing, holding his right side.

On one of the porches someone screamed, then fainted. The men rushed from the stairs and picked Harry up. He seemed to be all right again and smiled weakly in shame as they carried him into one of the flats. The men felt him all over.

"It's nothing," he said and got up a little later. "It's nothing, I tell you."

But the next day, when he went to a doctor, he learned he had ruptured himself. The doctor advised an operation, but Harry didn't have the money, so he bought himself a truss and said that it didn't bother him. The whole building talked about it the next day. People started looking toward our porch and Aunt Daisy came inside the flat. There was something hostile in their glances and her being an outsider did not help much.

In the evening, when the men started playing horseshoes, Harry sat on the stairs watching. He had been warned against any form of exercise, and of course lunging forward as you tossed the shoes was out of the question for him. He sat there while the men tossed the shoes in silence and watched the dust clouds settling to the yard. Once he looked up toward our porch, but he saw that Aunt Daisy was not there.

She was crying in her room, with my mother sitting on the bed soothing her. It had been Aunt Daisy who had screamed and fainted. She sobbed out to my mother that now she couldn't sit out on the porch on account of the neighbors, that Milt never took her out or spoke to her any more and she couldn't be expected to sit in the hot flat in the evening when the only place for a breeze was on the porch. My mother didn't answer, but she understood.

So two days later, screwing up her courage, my mother spoke to my father about money for her sister's return fare. She was prepared for rumbling and thunder, she was all set for my father to start shouting and hollering and waited for him to bubble and boil under the collar before his heavy cheeks began quivering in wrath. But nothing of the sort happened.

He went quietly into his bedroom and locked the door behind him. When we heard a ripping of cloth we knew he was slitting the stitches of the mattress to get at his wallet. In a few minutes he came out, handed my mother the money, asked for a needle and thread, and went back into the bedroom, closing the door again. Aunt Daisy, sitting in her own room, was given the money after my father left for the store.

The next day the flat was quiet. Aunt Daisy was going home. My mother made a fine supper, but little was eaten. Before my father returned to the store he said good-by to his sister-in-law and walked out as she was in the middle of thanking him for the railroad fare. She sat at the table, her eyes red, staring over our heads at the windows.

When the time came for her to go she started putting on her hat, the hat with the gray and brown feathers. She looked into the mirror and saw her reddened face, then put more powder on. In the kitchen my mother was drying and redrying her hands on a towel, standing there helplessly. Finally she came into the front room. They said good-by, kissing, and as the two heads bent together, my mother's head of gray touching the black vibrant hair half hidden in the little hat of feathers, my nose began tickling and I stared hard at the shiny doorknob.

Aunt Daisy kissed us all, trying to choke back her sobs. In a corner of the room my sister started crying. Daisy went over and when she kissed Rose both of them began sobbing and hugging each other. My mother blew her nose softly, then put her handkerchief into the pocket of her apron. Finally she said, her voice urging, "The train is leaving right away, you'll miss it."

So Aunt Daisy broke away. She wiped her cheeks with a fine lace handkerchief purchased from the money my mother had given her.

At the door Milt stood waiting. Then Ben put his hat and jacket on and said he was going to the station too. "The bags are heavy, I'll handle one of them."

They swung the door open and carried the grips out into the hall, with Aunt Daisy following, when suddenly she came back into the front room and stood sobbing against my mother's breast. My mother, crying herself, stroked her back soothingly.

Then Aunt Daisy was all set. She wiped her eyes, looked pertly alert and poked her finger at me.

"What did you see? Was I crying?"

I shook my head vigorously.

"There!" she cried happily and strode out after my brothers, who began going down the stairs. We could hear her singing gaily in the hallway, "Tra-la-la-la, tra-la-la-la!" until the door banged.

Then we went to stand at the front windows where we could watch her going up the street, walking between Ben and Milt, stepping jauntily, turning to one then the other, gossiping light-heartedly. It was evident from her stride that she liked to be walking between two big fellows. They went up the gray dusk of the street.

At the corner my brother Milt must have said something to her, for she turned suddenly and waved at us. We waved back, though we knew she could not see us. My sister kept on waving, moving her hand vaguely even after they had turned the corner, while my kid brother pressed his forehead against the glass. The street lamps lit up, and down the block we could hear a splashing sound as a neighbor played his hose against the walk.

"God knows, God knows! . . ." said my mother in the silence, while my sister came forward crying, to feel under the apron for my mother's hand.

FORT DEARBORN*

Edgar Lee Masters

EDGAR LEE MASTERS was a full-time lawyer and a part-time writer for many years. In Chicago, where he had a successful legal practice, he sometimes wrote two or three poems a night. His *Spoon River Anthology* caused a literary furor. Its fame spread rapidly and it soon acquired an international reputation.

During his lifetime Masters wrote many other books of poetry and several novels. His later poems did not match his early ones in power, beauty, or intensity. Here and there, however, one comes across single poems in his later volumes which are as good as any he ever wrote.

Here the old Fort stood
When the river bent southward.
Now because the world pours itself into Chicago
The Lake runs into the river
Past docks and switch-yards,
And under bridges of iron.

Sand dunes stretched along the lake for miles.
There was a great forest in the Loop.
Now Michigan Avenue lies
Between miles of lights,
And the Rialto blazes
Where the wolf howled.

* From *Selected Poems,* by Edgar Lee Masters, published by The Macmillan Co., New York, 1935. Reprinted by special permission of Mrs. E. L. Masters.

In the loneliness of the log-cabin,
Across the river,
The fur-trader played his fiddle
When the snow lay
About the camp of the Potawatamies
In the great forest.
Now to the music of the Kangaroo Hop,
And Ragging the Scale,
And La Seduccion,
The boys and girls are dancing
In a café near Lake Street.

The world is theirs now.
There is neither a past nor a to-morrow,
Save of dancing.
Nor do they know that behind them
In the seed not yet sown
There are eyes which will open upon Chicago,
And feet which will blossom for the dance,
And hands which will reach up,
And push them into the silence
Of the old fiddler.

They threw a flag
Over the coffin of Lieutenant Farnum,
And buried him back of the Fort
In ground where now
The spice mills stand.
And his little squaw with a baby
Sat on the porch grieving,
While the band played.
Then hands pushing the world
Buried a million soldiers, and afterward
Pale multitudes swept through the court house
To gaze for the last time
Upon the shrunken face of Lincoln.
And the fort at thirty-fifth street vanished.

And where the Little Giant lived
They made a park
And put his statue
Upon a column of marble.
Now the glare of the steel mills at South Chicago
Lights the bronze brow of Douglas.
It is his great sorrow
Haunting the Lake at midnight.

When the South was beaten
They were playing
John Brown's Body Lies Mouldering in the Grave,
And Babylon is Fallen and Wake Nicodemus.
Now the boys and girls are dancing
To the Merry Whirl and Hello Frisco
Where they waltzed in crinoline
When the Union was saved.

There was the Marble Terrace
Glory of the seventies!
They wrecked it,
And brought colors and figures
From later Athens and Pompeii,
And put them on walls.
And beneath panels of red and gold,
And shimmering tesseræ,
And tragic masks and comic masks,
And wreaths and bucrania,
Upon mosaic floors
Red-lipped women are dancing
With dark men.
Some sit at tables drinking and watching,
Amorous in an air of French perfumes.
Like ships at midnight
The kingdoms of the world
Know not whither they go nor to what port.
Nor do you, embryo hands,

In the seed not yet sown
Know of the wars to come.

They may fill the sky with armored dragons,
And the waters with iron monsters;
They may build arsenals
Where now upon marble floors
The boys and girls
Are dancing the Alabama Jubilee,
The processional of time is a falling stream,
Through which you thrust your hand.
And between the dancers and the silence forever
There shall be the livers,
Gazing upon the torches they have lighted,
And watching their own which are failing,
And crying for oil,
And finding it not!

CHICAGO ON FIRE*

Alexander Frear

THE Chicago Fire of 1871 was one of the major dis-
asters of the nineteenth century. It was so immense that
it immediately captured the attention of the entire world.
People as far away as Copenhagen and Buenos Aires sent
in relief money; they seemed, even at that distance, to hear
the bells of the frantic fire engines clanging along burning
streets.

Two hundred and fifty bodies were recovered, and hundreds more were never found, because Mrs. O'Leary's cow,
it was said, kicked over a lantern during a parched spell.
Eighteen thousand buildings burned to powdered ash,
among them 1,600 stores, 28 hotels, and 60 major manufacturing establishments. One hundred thousand people
were made homeless, and the property loss mounted to
over $200,000,000, a staggering sum for those days (many
insurance companies folded). While the fire was raging,
30,000 people fled to a cemetery then in Lincoln Park, to
hide behind the cool tombstones which did not remain cool
for very long. Seventy-five thousand men, women, and
children waded into the lake. The heat was so intense that
inhabitants of Holland, Michigan, ninety-five miles across
the water, felt the abnormally hot air currents blowing
toward them from the doomed city. Looting was on a mass
scale. It was said several murders were committed during
the excitement.

The best description I found of the fire was written by a
non-Chicagoan who was visiting the city, a henchman of
Boss Tweed.

* From *Chicago: The Full Story of the Great Fire: Narrative of an Eye
Witness,* by Alexander Frear. New York *World,* October 15, 1871.

ON SUNDAY night, October 8, 1871, I was at the Sherman House. I went there at the request of my sister to see if some of her friends who were expected from Milwaukee had arrived. I had promised to attend to the matter on Saturday, but was prevented by unexpected business. There was a large crowd of strangers and businessmen of the city at the hotel. The corridor and parlors were full of idlers, much as usual. While looking over the register someone said, "There go the fire bells again"; and the remark was made jocosely, "They'll burn the city down if they keep on."

I paid little attention to the conversation, which did not interest me, and having ascertained that the names that I wanted were not on the register, I sauntered in the corridor a while, and meeting Mr. Nixon, the upholsterer on Lake Street, I sat down a moment.

Mr. Nixon made the mistake of pointing out to me a person whom I knew very well by sight, and who lived in Chicago, insisting that it was George Francis Train. And while we were disputing about it my nephew, a young man of eighteen, came up and I appealed to him to identify the person. He then told us that a big fire was burning on the West Side. I asked him if he would mind walking to Ewing Street, where my sister was stopping, and letting her know that her friends were not in town; but he replied that I had better go myself, because the fire was in that vicinity, and he had a friend waiting for him upstairs.

When I came down the wind was blowing fiercely through Clark Street to the river, and I had some difficulty in getting across the Courthouse square. It could not have been ten o'clock, for they were singing in the Methodist church as I passed Follansbee's bank. I noticed the glare of the fire on the West Side as I came along, but thought nothing of it. There were very few people out, and I did not meet with a policeman until I reached Monroe Street. He was walking rapidly towards me, and I asked him if he knew anything about the fire. He looked at me but made no reply, and kept hurrying on. There was a small party of men on the corner of Adams Street. I asked them the same question and one of them said, "It must be a damned big fire this time; you can't put out a high wind with water." The rest of them said nothing, but I thought they looked a little scared.

While I stood there a policeman came up Adams Street on horseback and turned into Clark Street. Some of them halloed to him, but he paid no attention. I kept on, but before I had reached the next street the cinders began to fall thick all around me and it was growing lighter all the time. A great many people were looking out of their windows, and the streets seemed to get full of people suddenly. They were not excited. They stood about in groups listening to the wind that was making a noise very much like the lake on a stormy night.

I went into a Dutch beer saloon to get a cigar, seeing the door half open. The gas was burning, but the persons who kept the place were all in the street. I helped myself to a cigar from an open box that stood on the counter and left a stamp for it; lighting it at the gas burner, I went out without being questioned. While I was holding it up to the jet I noticed for the first time that I was considerably excited myself; my hand shook and I could hear my heart beat. I don't think I was two minutes in the place, but when I came out the cinders were falling like snowflakes in every direction and lit the street, and there was a great hubbub of men and vehicles.

I started to run toward Van Buren Street, but the walks were so crowded with people and the cinders were blown so thickly and fast that I found it was impossible. Besides the wind blew my hat off twice. I took to the middle of the street and found that the crowd coming in the opposite direction was increasing. But it was difficult to see anything clearly on account of the cinders.

Somewhere between Van Buren and Polk Streets I found the crowd jammed into the thoroughfare solidly. There was a four-story brick house on the east side that overlooked the others all around it. A man on top seemed to be gesticulating and shouting to the crowd, but whatever he said was lost in the wind. It was some time before I made out that he was shouting to someone in a window below, and the man below repeated it to the crowd. All I could distinctly hear was "burning on both sides of the river," and just then there was a great pressure in the crowd of the people and a man on horseback forced his way through. He seemed to be a gentleman, and I thought an insurance officer. He had in his hand one of the little red flags switchmen use, which he waved on either side. What he said I could not hear, but it had the effect of producing a panic in the throng.

No sooner did I understand that it was impossible and dangerous to proceed further, and had turned around with the purpose of running to the first bridge, than I saw the light of the fire extending far back in the direction I had come, the flames lighting the houses on the east side of Clark Street as far as I could see. I ran as fast as I could to the Adams Street bridge. Vehicles and people were streaming in from all the streets to the west. I paid little attention to anything, my anxiety to reach my sister's house being very great. With difficulty I got to the bridge, which was beset by teams desiring to cross, and tugs screaming in the stream to get through. There was much confusion, and suddenly a rush of people was made toward me as the bridge began to swing, and I ran to get over. A woman carrying a bureau drawer, and blinded by the sparks, in her desperation struck me with her burden in the breast, breaking the crystal of my watch and stunning me for a moment. It was 1:30 o'clock. While I held the watch in my hand a live coal fell on it as large as a silver half-dollar.

All of Adams Street, reaching to Des Plaines on the West Side, was choked with people. But they were free from the terrible rain of cinders, the wind carrying them in a northeasterly direction across the river. Des Plaines Street was comparatively clear; and on turning into it I lost my hat. Without attempting to recover it I ran as fast as I could in the direction of Ewing Street. My sister's house was out of the line of the fire, but there was no telling at what moment the wind would veer. My brother, who is a lumber merchant, was absent in Sheboygan. The house was occupied by his family, consisting of Mrs. Frear and three children (two girls and boy, all of them under fifteen years of age, the youngest, Johnny, a cripple with rheumatism), and a lodger who was employed as a clerk in Mr. Frear's office. The family were in great consternation. I told Mrs. Frear that I thought there was no present danger as the fire was not burning this side of Jefferson Street, but was being blown swiftly to the east. We were within a block, however, of Jefferson Street, and the heat was intense, and the excitement of the neighbors was very great. I found that she had her clothing and valuables all packed in trunks, which were pulled into the hallway, and she told me that Mr. Wood (the clerk) had gone to get one of Mr. Farwell's trucks to take her things to the warehouse on Wabash Avenue. I tried to dissuade her in vain, and finally, finding she was resolute, I consented to get a coach and take the children to Mrs. Kimball's on Wabash Avenue, she saying she would remain and look after the house until the danger was over.

Fortunately there was not much trouble in getting a coach, and I started as soon after as possible with the three children. The Kimballs were all abed, and I was some time ringing at the door (holding Johnny wrapped in my arms in a rug) before I roused them.

The driver of the coach put his horses to their utmost speed in returning. When we reached the vicinity of Madison Street bridge he threw the door open and said we couldn't get across. The noise of men and vehicles was so great that he had to shout at the top of his voice. We then drove up to Randolph Street, and here we were stopped again, the bridge being open. It seemed that the string of vessels passing through was endless. We were an hour and a half in getting back, I think. The whole of Ewing Street was barricaded with vehicles and household effects. Mrs. Frear was much cooler now that her children were safe. Most of her valuables had been got off, and as it was no longer possible to get a dray up to the house the heavy furniture had to remain. While we were talking Mr. Wood burst into the room and said the fire had reached Wabash Avenue and was sweeping all before it. His appearance as well as his language was terrifying. Nearly blinded by the flying embers, he had dashed water on his head and face, and his matted hair and begrimed skin added to his frightened looks, made him seem like another person.

I begged Mrs. Frear not to alarm herself and ran up to the roof. The house was a two-story-and-a-half frame building, but it joined another which was an addition to a planing-mill. I clambered to the roof of the latter, and was nearly swept off by the wind. As near as I could make out, Wood was right.

Wherever I could see at all the wind blew the burning houses into a mass of live coals that was dazzling. When I returned I found

Mrs. Frear had her waterproof cloak on, and had put her jewelry and money into a satchel and was ready to start. I begged of her to remain, saying that I would see to the safety of the children, but she only answered: "My poor Johnny; my poor, sick Johnny." Mr. Wood and myself then endeavored to get another conveyance. The front steps and the sidewalks were thronged with terror-stricken women, and the street was encumbered with luggage.

The three of us fought· our way through till we reached Mr. McGowan's in Halsted Street, and here we were fortunate enough to get a cab. Wood then went back to the house, and we started for Wabash Avenue, Mr. McGowan driving us himself. I afterwards found out that he had to take us all the way round to Clark Street, on the North Side, to get over the river. But at the time I did not notice our direction until we had crossed the river, being occupied in trying to pacify Mrs. Frear.

We got as far as Washington Street in the avenue when the horse was stopped and McGowan got into an altercation with an officer. I sprang out, and was told that it was useless to go any further for the whole of the avenue was on fire. The roadway was full of people, and the din of voices and the melee of horses rendered unmanageable by the falling embers were terrible. In the confusion it was difficult to get any information; but I was told that the block in which the Kimballs lived (the refuge of Mrs. Frear's children) was burning, and that the people were all out. To add to my distress Mrs. Frear jumped out of the vehicle and started to run in the direction of the fire. Nothing, I am satisfied, saved her from being crushed to death in a mad attempt to find her children but the providential appearance of an acquaintance, who told her that the children were safe at the St. James Hotel.

When we reached the hotel I found it impossible to get her through the crowd without trouble, and so I took her into Soldon & Ward's hair-dressing room in the basement, and went upstairs to look for the children alone. There was a great deal of excitement in the house, but there seemed to be no apprehension of danger from the fire at that distance. The guests and servants of the house were nearly all at the windows or down in the doorways. I found that Mrs. Frear's acquaintance had either intentionally or unintentionally deceived her. The children were not in the house. When I informed her of it she fainted. When she was being taken upstairs to the parlor I found she had lost her satchel. Whether it was left in the cab when she jumped out or was stolen in the house I cannot say. It contained two gold watches, several pins and drops of value, a cameo presented to her by Mrs. Stephen A. Douglas, a medal of honor belonging to her husband (who was an officer in the First Wisconsin Volunteers during the War) and about $200 in bills and currency stamps, besides several trinkets of trifling value. Leaving her in the care of some ladies I then started for John F. V. Farwell's stores on Wabash Avenue, thinking it possible the children were sent there, where their mother's property was.

When I came into Wabash Avenue the full extent of the fire and its danger to the city became for the first time apparent to my mind. I saw the flames distinctly, and, remembering that they were two miles distant when I first saw them, I began to realize the awful nature of the calamity. I spoke to several persons on the street. They seemed to think the flames would be stayed when they reached the durable and massive structures, and that it was only the wooden buildings that caused such a furious burning. The Farwell stores were all closed. The watchman said there had been no goods much less children brought there.

I then ran as fast as I could through Randolph Street to the Sherman House, thinking we might have mistaken the hotel. They had the hose laid on and a party of men were on the roof putting out the cinders. I was told that the place had already been ignited twice. The corridor was a scene of intense excitement. The guests of the house were running about wildly, some of them dragging their trunks to the stairway. Everything was in confusion, and my heart sank within me as I saw that the panic was spreading among those who were the best protected. I looked out of one of the south windows of the house and shall never forget the terrible magnificent sight I saw. The Courthouse Park was filled with people who appeared to be huddled together in a solid mass, helpless and astounded. The whole air was filled with the falling cinders, and it looked like a snowstorm lit by a colored fire. The weird effect of the glare and the scintillating light upon this vast silent concourse was almost frightful. While in the corridor of the Sherman House I encountered my nephew, and he asked me if I wanted to see the fire, saying he had one of George Garrison's horses and only wanted a rubber blanket to throw over him to protect him from the sparks.

I told him about Mrs. Frear but he thought there was no reason to worry. He got a blanket somewhere and we started off in a light wagon for Wabash Avenue, stopping at Wright's, under the Opera House, to get a drink of coffee, which I needed very much. There were several of the firemen of the Little Giant (fire engine company) in there. One of them was bathing his head with whiskey from a flask. They declared that the entire department had given up, over-worked, and that they could do nothing more. While we stood there an Irish girl was brought in with her dress nearly all burnt from her person. It had caught on at the Courthouse steps from a cinder. When we went out a man in his coat sleeves was unhitching the horse; and when we came up he sprung into the wagon, and would have driven off in spite of us if I had not caught the horse by the head. He then sprang out and struck my nephew in the face and ran toward State Street.

We drove as rapidly as we could into Wabash Avenue—the wind sweeping the embers after us in furious waves. We passed a broken-down steamer in the middle of the roadway. The avenue was a scene of desolation. The storm of falling fire seemed to increase every second, and it was as much as we could do to protect ourselves from the burning rain and guide the horse through the flying people and hurrying vehicles. Looking back through Washington Street, toward the Opera House, I saw the smoke and flames pouring out of State Street, from the very point we had just left, and the intervening space was filled with the whirling embers that beat against the houses and covered the roofs and window sills. It seemed like a tornado of fire. To add to the terrors the animals, burnt and infuriated by the cinders, darted through the streets regardless of all human obstacles. Wabash Avenue was burning as far down as Adams Street. The flames from the houses on the west side reached in a diagonal arch quite across the street, and occasionally the wind would lift the great body of flame, detach it entirely from the burning buildings, and hurl it with terrific force far ahead. All the mansions were being emptied with the greatest dis-order and the greatest excitement. Nobody endeavored to stay the flames now.

A mob of men and women, all screaming and shouting, ran about wildly, crossing each other's paths and intercepting each other as if deranged. We tried to force our way along the avenue, which was already littered with costly furniture, some of it burning in the street under the falling sparks, but it was next to impossible. Twice we were accosted by gentlemen with pocketbooks in their hands, and asked to carry away to a place of safety some valuable prop-erty. Much as we may have desired to assist them, it was out of our power. Women came and threw packages into the vehicle, and one man with a boy hanging to him caught the horse and tried to throw us out. I finally got out and endeavored to lead the animal out of the terrible scenes.

When we had gone about a block I saw the Courthouse was on fire, and almost at the same moment someone said the St. James had caught on the roof. I was struck on the arm by a bird cage flung from an upper window, and the moment I released the horse he shied and ran into a burning dray-load of furniture, smashing the wheel of the wagon and throwing my companion out on his shoulder. Fortunately he was only bruised. But the horse, already terrified, started immediately, and I saw him disappear with a leap like that of a panther.

We then hurried on to the St. James Hotel, passing through some of the strangest and saddest scenes it has ever been my mis-fortune to witness. I saw a woman kneeling in the street with a crucifix held up before her and the skirt of her dress burning while she prayed. We had barely passed her before a runaway truck dashed her to the ground. Loads of goods passed us repeatedly that were burning on the trucks, and my nephew says he distinctly saw one man go up to a pile of costly furniture lying in front of an elegant residence and deliberately hold a piece of burning packing board under it until the pile was lit.

When we reached the wholesale stores north of Madison Street the confusion was even worse. These stores were packed full of the most costly merchandise, and to save it at the rate the fire was advancing was plainly impossible. There was no police, and no effort was made to keep off the rabble. A few of the porters and draymen employed by these stores were working manfully, but there were costermongers' wagons, dirt carts, and even coaches backed up and receiving the goods and a villainous crowd of men and boys chaffing each other and tearing open parcels to discover the nature of their contents.

I reached the St. James between two and three o'clock on Monday morning. It was reported to be on fire, but I did not see the flames then. Mrs. Frear had been removed in an insensible state to the house of a friend on the North Side. I could learn of no other particulars.

The house was in a dreadful state of disorder. Women and children were screaming in every direction and baggage being thrown about in the most reckless manner. I now concluded that Mrs. Frear's children had been lost. It was reported that hundreds of people had perished in the flames.

There was a crowd of men and women at the hotel from one of the large boardinghouses in the neighborhood of State and Adams Street, and they said they barely escaped with their lives, leaving everything behind. At this time it seemed to me that the fire would leave nothing. People coming in said the Sherman House was going, and that the Opera House had caught. Finally word was brought that the bridges were burning, and all escape was cut off to the north and west. Then ensued a scene which was beyond description. Men shouted the news and added to the panic. Women, half-dressed and many of them with screaming children, fled out of the building. There was a jam in the doorway, and they struck and clawed each other as if in self-defense. I lost sight of my nephew at this time.

Getting out with the crowd I started and ran round toward the Tremont House. Reaching Dearborn Street, the gust of fire was so strong that I could hardly keep my feet. I ran on down toward the Tremont. Here the same scene was being enacted with tenfold violence. The elevator had got jammed, and the screams of the women on the upper floors were heart-rending. I forced my way upstairs, seeing no fire, and looked into all the open rooms, calling aloud the names of Mrs. Frear's daughters. Women were swarming in the parlors; invalids, brought there for safety, were lying upon the floor. Others were running distracted about, calling upon their husbands. Men, pale and awe-struck and silent, looked on without any means of averting the mischief. All this time the upper part of the house was on fire. The street was choked with people, yelling and moaning with excitement and fright. I looked down upon them from an upper window a moment, and saw far up Dearborn Street the huge flames pouring in from the side streets I had traversed but an hour ago, and it appeared to me that they were impelled with the force of a tremendous blowpipe. Everything that they touched melted.

Presently the smoke began to roll down the stairways, and almost immediately after the men who had been at work on the roof came running down. They made no outcry, but hurried from the house as if for their lives. I went up to the fourth story, looking into every room, and kicking open those that were locked. There were several other men searching in the same manner, but I did not notice them. While up there I obtained a view of the conflagration. It was advancing steadily upon the hotel from two or three points. There was very little smoke; it burned too rapidly, or what there was must have been carried away on the wind. The whole was accompanied by a crackling noise as of an enormous bundle of dry twigs burning, and by explosions that followed each other in quick succession on all sides.

When I was going down I found one of the men dragging an insensible woman downstairs by her shoulders. She was an unusually large woman, and had on a striped satin dress and a great quantity of jewelry, which I supposed she had put upon her person for safety. I assisted him to carry her down, and when she reached the lower story to my surprise she suddenly recovered her consciousness and ran away followed by the man. From the street entrance I could see up Dearborn Street as far as the Portland Block and it was full of people all the distance, swaying and surging under the rain of fire. Around on Lake Street the tumult was worse.

Here for the first time I beheld scenes of violence that made my blood boil. In front of Shay's magnificent dry goods store a man loaded a store truck with silks in defiance of the employees of the place. When he had piled all he could upon the truck someone with a revolver shouted to him not to drive away or he would fire at him, to which he replied, "Fire and be damned!" and the man put the pistol in his pocket again.

Just east of this store there was at least a ton of fancy goods thrown into the street, over which the people and vehicles passed with utter indifference, until they took fire. I saw myself a ragamuffin on the Clark Street bridge, who had been killed by a marble slab thrown from a window, who had white kid gloves on his hands, and whose pockets were stuffed with gold-plated sleeve buttons and on that same bridge I saw an Irish woman leading a goat that was big with young by one arm, while under the other she carried a piece of silk.

Lake Street was rich with treasure, and hordes of thieves forced their way into the stores and flung out the merchandise to their fellows in the street, who received it without disgrace, and fought over it openly. I went through the street to Wabash Avenue, and here the thoroughfare was utterly choked with all manner of goods and people. Everybody that had been forced from the other end of the town by the advancing fire had brought some article with him, and as further progress was delayed if not completely stopped by the river, the bridges of which were also choked, most of them, in their panic, abandoned their burdens, so that the street and sidewalks presented the most astonishing wreck. Valuable oil paintings, books, pet animals, musical instruments, toys, mirrors, and bedding were trampled under foot. Added to this the goods from the stores had been hauled out and taken fire, and the crowd breaking into a liquor establishment were yelling with the fury of demons as they brandished champagne and brandy bottles.

The brutality and horror of the scene made it sickening. A fellow standing on a piano declared that the fire was the friend of the poor man. He wanted everybody to help himself to the best liquor he could get, and continued to yell from the piano until someone as drunk as himself flung a bottle at him and knocked him off it. In this chaos were hundreds of children wailing and crying for their parents. One little girl in particular I saw whose golden hair was loose down her back and caught fire. She ran screaming past me and somebody threw a glass of liquor upon her which flared up and covered her with a blue flame.

It was impossible to get through to the bridge and I was forced to go back toward Randolph Street. There was a strange and new fascination in the scenes that I could not resist. It was now daylight and the fire was raging closely all about me. The Courthouse, the Sherman House, the Tremont House, and the wholesale stores on Wabash Avenue, and the retail stores on Lake Street were burning. The cries of the multitude on the latter streets had now risen to a terrible roar, for the flames were breaking into the river streets. I saw the stores of Mr. Drake, Hamlin, and Farwell burn. They ignited suddenly all over in a manner entirely new to me, just as I have seen paper do that is held to the fire until it is scorched and breaks out in flame. The crowds who were watching them greeted the combustion with terrible yells. In one of the stores—I think it was Hamlin's—there were a number of men at the time on the several floors passing out goods, and when the flames blown over against it enveloped the building, they were lost to sight entirely; nor did I see any effort whatever made to save them, for the heat was so intense that everybody was driven as before a tornado from the vicinity of the buildings.

I now found myself carried by the throng back to near Lake Street, and determined if possible, to get over the river. I managed to accomplish this after a severe struggle and at the risk of my life. The rail of the bridge was broken away, and a number of small boats loaded with goods were passing down the stream. How many people were pushed over into the water I cannot tell. I saw one man stumble under a load of clothing and disappear, nor did the occupants of the boats pay the slightest attention to him nor to the crowd overhead, except to guard against anybody falling into their vessels.

Once over the river I felt safe. It seemed to me highly improbable that the fire would leap the stream, which at this point is the widest. Alas, those who were there told me that the flames of the burning storehouses on Water Street were blown into the windows of the other side, and that before the houses that line the south side were half consumed those on the other side were crackling and flaming with intensity. I went through North Water Street, meeting with a frantic multitude teeming from each of the bridges, and by a tiresome detour got round to the West Side. When I arrived at my sister's house I found my nephew there, who informed me that Mrs. Frear had been taken to a private house in Huron Street, and was perfectly safe and well cared for. I was wet and scorched and bedraggled. My clothes were burnt full of holes on my arms and shoulders and back. I asked Wood to make some coffee, which he promised to do, and I fell down in the hallway and went to sleep. I could not have lain there half an hour when Wood awoke me, saying the fire was sweeping everything before it in the direction of Lincoln Park, and that Mrs. Frear must be moved again.

We both started out then and walked and ran as fast as we could in the direction of the North Side. It was about 8:30 o'clock. We could see across the river at the cross streets that where yesterday was a populous city was now a mass of smoking ruins. All the way round we encountered thousands of people, but the excitement had given way to a terrible grief and scenes of desolation.

Des Plaines and the northern part of Jefferson Street were piled up twelve and fifteen feet high with goods. Luckily Wood knew where to find Mrs. Frear, and he arrived at the house just in time to get her into a baker's wagon, which Wood and I pulled for half a mile. She was in terrible condition, being hysterical, and when we were in Des Plaines Street again there came an omnibus, loaded with frightened children, through Lake Street. They were crying and screaming, and Mrs. Frear heard them and began to screech at the top of her voice. The man who was driving the omnibus stopped and yelled after us to know where we were taking that woman. It was impossible to get the wagon through the street on account of the goods, and so we were forced to go half a mile farther out of our way.

Once at home a number of her neighbors came to her assistance, and about four o'clock in the afternoon word came from the Kimballs that the children were all safe out at Riverside. I spent the greater part of the day in searching for her property without avail. I have lost nothing myself by the fire but what I can recover, but on Monday afternoon I went to bed with a sick headache and a fever, which were the result of mental excitement rather than physical exposure.

THE COLUMBIAN EXPOSITION OF 1893*

Lloyd Lewis and Henry Justin Smith

THE Columbian Exposition of 1893, celebrating the four-hundredth anniversary of the landing of Christopher Columbus on the soil of the New World, had a lengthy history. Many cities put in their bids to Washington for the event; but because of the aggressiveness of the Chicago committee, which pointed out the hometown's strategic rail location, etc., the plum fell to Chicago.

When the exposition opened, it was at once evident that here was the greatest, most stupendous world's fair ever held on earth. A wise building committee had given the country's best architects free rein. In the opinion of many present-day architects, it still remains on the books as the greatest world's fair ever held. Over five hundred different brochures and illustrated volumes were published about it. Some historians think it kept the panic of 1893 away from Chicago's doors for over four months.

ON a cold and cloudy day in January, 1891, a dozen or more architects stood on the bleak beach about seven miles south of the heart of Chicago. They watched the gray rollers come in and gazed dubiously at a vast tract of snow-covered sand, broken by ridges and by ragged patches of wild oak.

A noted Boston architect, muffled against the blasts, climbed on a pier and called down to the leader of the party:

* From *Chicago: The History of Its Reputation,* by Lloyd Lewis and Henry Justin Smith. Copyright, 1929, by Harcourt, Brace & Co., Inc.

"Do you mean to say that you really propose opening a Fair here by '93?"

"Yes," replied this leader, "we intend to."

"It can't be done," said the Bostonian.

"That point," retorted the other, "is settled."

The gentleman who declared it settled tells the story himself, almost literally as above. It is taken from the reminiscences of Daniel H. Burnham, who missed few of the problems and none of the glory of the World's Columbian Exposition. On that January day he had assembled for the first time in Chicago the group of great artists in design who had joined the seemingly impossible enterprise of "opening a Fair here by '93." When he said it was settled, it was. The site looked hopeless; the difficulties were appalling; the time too short. All the elements were present for a typical Chicago problem. But to the skeptic Mr. Burnham returned what was, at that time at least, a typical Chicago answer.

About a year later this tall, round-faced, mustached gentleman with a square chin in which lurked a dimple, showed another and larger group of visitors what was doing in Jackson Park. This was a crowd of about a hundred overcoated, silk-hatted, scrutinizing, and self-important representatives of all the states. The National Commission had come to see how this Fair of "theirs" was getting on. Having been feted no end by Chicago politicians and citizens, having heard and returned vast quantities of oratory, they had got down to business.

Director of Construction Burnham, supported by his staff and smiling officials of the Chicago end of the management, was delighted to show the legislative gentlemen about. He led them along miles of plank, laid upon the treacherous sands and squashing ominously in the February mud. He pointed out how a canal, a lagoon, a "wooded island," and other features of that memorable landscaping were taking form. With gestures of his long arms he indicated great, ghostly skeleton shapes grouped after a careful pattern, yet so enormous that they seemed like mountains upraised passionately by Nature herself.

The visitors saw "floors as broad and as wide as truck farms. They saw arching domes, netted with threads of steel, so far up in the cold fog that the moving workmen seemed like flies crawling on a ceiling. There were broad avenues heaped high with construction material and flanked on either side by towering walls of new timber."

There loomed before the amazed Congressmen, continued this reporter, "a behemoth-structure covering some thirty-two acres. The Capitol building at Washington if set down on the floor of this monster [the Manufactures Building] would be something like a peppermint drop in a frosted cake." The thing was actually coming to pass. And it was astoundingly larger, more complex, and more prophetic of beauty than anybody—that is, any Congressman—had fancied it.

Mr. Burnham was at that time in mid-career, with a record of Chicago masterpieces which made him and his associates the natural leaders in the World's Fair construction. He and his partner, John W. Root, had joined their slim fortunes less than two years after the great fire, when Burnham was twenty-six years old and Root four years younger. They began in a little room, stove-heated, for which they paid $20 a month rent. Profiting by the frantic rush to rebuild the city, and pulling through the hard times of '73 somehow, the young partners found themselves in clover with the arrival of the prosperous eighties. Burnham was the business-getter of the firm; Root inclined to stick to the designing room. Their reputation reached the East, yet they chose to give their talents mainly to the West.

Soon arrived the era of skyscrapers. Burnham and Root designed the first very tall building—the Montauk Block, a "monster" of ten stories. It was the first building in the country set upon "spread foundations," of concrete and railroad rails. They followed this with such achievements as the Rookery and the first section (sixteen stories) of the enormous Monadnock Block. Two other pioneering architects—W. L. B. Jenney and William Holabird, heads respectively of Jenney and Mundie and Holabird and Roche—had the glory of using steel-frame construction for the first time in history. Jenney designed the Home Insurance Building, partly a steel skeleton. Then Holabird created the Tacoma, with metal skeleton throughout. The "curtain of stone" was developed. A Minneapolis man, L. S. Buffington, had already patented a similar idea, but Chicago got real results, thus blazing the way once more. Naturally, Burnham and Root adopted and enlarged the process, and their enterprise, stopping little short of the clouds, made a success of the twenty-one story Masonic Temple.

It was, then, two of the ablest and best advertised Chicago architects, and two men, moreover, of comparative youth, who were selected to see that the World's Fair was built according to the vast general plan. But Root never had a chance to put his fiery soul into it. His death early in 1891 left Burnham to bear the burdens and reap the glory. It also brought into the picture several men, such as Charles H. McKim and Charles B. Atwood, for whom the opportunities might not have been so great had Root lived.

Burnham, sorrowing, went ahead bravely with the work of organizing, harmonizing, crushing through prejudices. He chose an able assistant, Ernest R. Graham. He fought and won a battle with the large and hardheaded group of Chicago businessmen composing the building and grounds committee, persuaded them to give up the idea of competitive designs and to adopt his plan of inviting a selected list of architects. He then picked the architects—four from the East and six from the West—and began to convert them. For some of the Easterners needed converting. They were skeptical about the time available. They were skeptical as to whether the money would be raised. They were "very busy." However, Burnham, using his combination of humor and exhortation, captured them all.

In the meantime a civic patriot and beauty-lover named James W. Ellsworth, of the World's Fair Board, scored a good one by persuading Frederick W. Olmstead, the great landscape-designer, to tackle Jackson Park, with an eye not only to the immediate purpose but also to permanent beauty. Olmstead was dubious. He had planned Washington Park, and he knew Jackson. "You can have fifteen million and a free hand," Ellsworth is reported to have promised, though Lyman J. Gage, president of the Chicago board, was pulling his beard. Olmstead agreed, and, glorying as they all did sooner or later in the miracle-making of those two years, set to work to change a waste of sand, where little would grow and floods were frequent, into something finer than the Luxembourg. His expert assistant caused whole acres of sand to be sliced from the surface, and carloads of loam were dumped there; nearby lakes were searched for beautiful plants and ferns; flowering shrubs were carried miles to beautify lagoons and the "wooded island."

Soon came Augustus St. Gaudens, enlisted under the Burnham colors. A reserved and somewhat eccentric genius, taciturn in crowds, he was, nevertheless, with Burnham to excite him, a powerful helper and suggester. Moreover, he brought into the effort such sculptors as Frederick MacMonnies, Daniel C. French, Paul Bartlett, Karl Bitter, and many others; all, like Chicago's own sculptor, Lorado Taft, glad to get St. Gaudens' ideas and to refer delicate questions of taste to him. Working happily with the forces of art, too, was Frank D. Millet as "director of color." His engagement followed a small collision between Burnham and the previous "director of color," who, because of a decision made without him, held himself slighted.

"I told him," relates Mr. Burnham, "that I saw it differently. He then said he would get out, and he did."

Director Burnham did not have to be "hard-boiled" with his troupe of architects. They were all too much thrilled over the prospect of being able, *at last,* to design great buildings after their heart's desire and practically regardless of cost. Before many months had passed, they had become so inspired by Burnham's appeal for teamwork, and by the grandeur of the whole dream (and, incidentally, such choice lunches had they enjoyed at Chicago's swaggerest restaurant, Kinsley's), that they were even ready to modify their designs where necessary. Difficulties of policy and of taste vanished before this spirit, in those meetings which were referred to as the most notable gatherings of artists for centuries. Inspirations popped out; such as the one that all the buildings should be white, and the decision to give them a uniform cornice-height. Perhaps greater than all, for many of these intense and historically-minded men, was the realization that what was really being accomplished was a new epoch in American architecture—the epoch of the classical, replacing the Romansque as well as other less worthy motives in design.*

These were the chief architects, with the buildings originally assigned to them:

Richard W. Hunt, New York: Administration Building
McKim, Mead and White, New York: Agriculture
George B. Post, New York: Manufactures and Liberal Arts
Peabody and Stearns, Boston: Machinery
Van Brunt and Howe, Kansas City: Electricity
Jenney and Mundie, Chicago: Horticulture
Henry Ives Cobb, Chicago: Fisheries
S. S. Beman, Chicago: Mines and Mining
Adler and Sullivan, Chicago: Transportation
Burling and Whitehouse, Chicago: Venetian Village (not built)

These individuals and firms accepted responsibility for the principal structures, only a few out of the hundreds that were to stand within the grounds. But much of the designing eventually fell into the hands of the gentle, casual Charles B. Atwood, a being so little known, comparatively, and with so little "front," that Mr. Burnham came near not engaging him at all. It was Atwood who, in an emergency caused by the illness of another architect, produced in haste, and with the fire of a positive inspiration, the outlines of the Art Palace. It alone, of the major buildings, survived '93. Opinions of its beauty have but gained warmth during a generation. That building which once housed $1,000,000 worth of the world's art is now to be Chicago's Industrial Museum, owing to the generosity of Julius Rosenwald.

Building the World's Fair, as Mr. Burnham saw it, "consisted of reclaiming nearly seven hundred acres of ground, only a small part of which was improved, the remainder being in a state of nature and covered with water or wild-oak ridges. In twenty months this must be converted into a site suitable for an exposition of the industries and the entertainment of representatives of all the nations of the world. On its stately terraces a dozen palaces were to be

* See *The Story of Architecture in America,* by Thomas Tallmadge; W. W. Norton & Co.

built—all of great extent and of high architectural importance—
these to be supported by two hundred other structures. Great canals, basins, lagoons and islands were to be constructed. The
standard of the entire work was to be kept up to a degree of ex-
cellence which should place it on a level with the monuments of
other ages."

In a passage summing up what was done, Mr. Burham wrote:
"During the storms of summer, through frosts of winter, all day,
all night, week in and week out, for two years the little band of
American boys ran the race for victory with Father Time, and won
it. Without looking for or expecting compensation at all equal to
the services they rendered, without jealousy, with eager willingness,
these men were ever to be found. They showed what to me is the
greatest heroism, forbearance and constant helpfulness."

Yet there was another kind of heroism being shown, as the
buildings rose, were clothed with walls and roofs, were plastered
with "staff" and painted with jets of white paint blown through
hose. There were heroes fighting the cold and the perils; there
were men like sailors climbing among the girders; there were fore-
men and subordinate artists and whatnot who should have had a
medal apiece. Not that they were always cheerful. There were
strikes galore, and near-rebellion. But the work went on.

The winter task of 1891-1892 was severe; that of 1892-1893
even worse. In cold weather few bleaker spots can be found
than a sandy beach along Lake Michigan. The advance troops of
this World's Fair army had to flounder in icy bogs, dig in earth
hardened by frost, and in milder weather face virtual quicksands.
Horses sank leg-deep in the mud; vehicles bringing lumber, or
hauling the soil and plants needed by Mr. Olmstead, had to have
temporary plank-roads. There came heavy snowstorms, when the
weight of drifts crushed in glass skylights, or even roofs. There
were thaws and cold rains when volumes of water started leaks
here and there, or almost threatened to wash the smaller buildings
into the lake.

And then, driven at such speed and working often on details of
construction far from customary—so many bold ideas were being

tried out—the seven thousand or more workmen faced a constant risk of accident. That casualty record was high, as seen today; though at the time it seemed "low—considering." During 1891 over seven hundred accidents to workmen were recorded. Eighteen died.

Other armies of men, engaged in the city-wide work of preparation, were toiling on railroad and streetcar improvements. Still others were hurling together flimsy hotels or rooming-houses.

Chicago of '92 worked as it never had worked since the days following the great fire. . . .

II

Seen down the slope of years, the World's Columbian Exposition still forces the belief that, in many ways, it was the most wonderful thing of its time. It became the ruling passion of statesmen as well as architects, of religionists as well as artisans, of merchants, painters, engineers, musicians, soldiers, orators, and dukes. Its appeal reached the secret workshops of the makers of delicate fabrics, of exquisite jewelry. Not only the most civilized, but some of the most barbaric, peoples of the earth were moved to have a share in this "show."

Only the other day an explorer from Africa told how an old chieftain whom he had just seen in his wilderness remembered the name of Chicago—and not because of its murders, but because of "your World's Fair."

Useless to try a resurrection of that image of beauty! There are stored away, in libraries or elsewhere, large folios of paintings and photographs. Go and see them! . . . But the real colors, the multiform activity, murmurs of fountains, tramp of the multitudes, all the sparkle and thunder of the throng, are gone. Sound-recording was not yet adequate; the movies were invented too late.

We have to look back upon the Fair critically, seeing in it a world-impulse, a culmination of dreams—dreams not typically Chicagoan. Destiny brought to this young city an explosion of idealism, produced a miracle, and then ordered the miracle to disappear, leaving the sand-wastes to a new future. Paul Bourget wrote in farewell to the exposition, "The White City must disappear, while the Black City, which will endure forever, is only at its commencement." Yet in one respect, in city planning, the World's Fair left its impress upon Chicago. As the sociologist Charles Zueblin saw it, "For the first time in American history a complete city, equipped with all the public utilities caring for a temporary population of thousands, was built as a unit on a single architectural scale. Unique in being an epitome of what we had done and a prophecy of what we could do if content with nothing but the best . . . it was a miniature of an ideal city; a symbol of regeneration."

Along with the beauties of this ideal city came the loud carnivals, the bands of fakirs and "three-shell" men, the salacious dancers, the hordes of harpies, to all of which people who took the Fair as a circus had looked forward. The visitors who wanted a "hot time" were not disappointed. Yet many of them must have been most impressed, after all, by the grandeur of the picture—and by Chicago's grit. They knew about the fund-raising valor of men like Lyman J. Gage, Marshall Field, largest single subscriber for stock, Franklin MacVeagh, and others.

At one time, after Congress had set $5,000,000 as the figure Chicago should raise, it was found that New York could furnish $10,000,000. Very well, Chicago would meet the ante; it did so, through sale of stock to middle-class folks, and by bond issues. The Chicagoans, through their local board of directors, had to "carry the weight of governmental suspicion, hesitation, and indifference," wrote one of the leaders. "The only anxiety of Congress was to escape expense." The local corporation, standing in ill-defined relationship to the National Commission, was forced sometimes to defy, and sometimes to yield to, that large and unwieldy body; a multiplicity of committees, a mass of overlapping authority, and all the jealousies; stupidities, and balkinesses of which overorganized human beings are capable, cropped out during the months of high pressure. Finally, the famous Chicago climate—truly wonderful four or five months of the year—outdid the eccentricities of people wearing titles and medals, and made it seem, during one winter, at least, as though the Fair would never open at all. Storms, cold spells, "wet spells," deluge from the skies, hell underfoot, challenged the gritty men who had sworn to "put it over."

When on May 1, 1893, the great invading army of Middle Westerners, supplemented by people from many states, poured into the grounds, they saw an Administration Building with an exquisite dome higher than that of the Capitol at Washington, and in front of this the MacMonnies fountain, with its graceful rowing maidens —acclaimed by St. Gaudens and others as the masterpiece of masterpieces. They saw other fountains, one on each side of the MacMonnies, then the lustrous Grand Basin, with its peristyle at the eastern end, and the Liberty statue upraised, but shrouded, waiting to admire itself in the mirror of the basin. There were the vast creamy flanks of Machinery Hall, Agriculture Hall, the Manufactures and Mining Buildings; to the northwest, the Wooded Island, the dome of the Arts Palace, and a city of structures in which the classic motive faded out among bold and varied conceptions expressed in State buildings.

It was a chill and misty spring morning. All during the early hours anxious people watched the clouds. The crowds came under umbrellas. "Average people" they, accustomed to going afoot, to getting wet, to "pickup" meals. There were almost as many lunch-baskets as umbrellas. Father, mother, and the children were prepared for a gorgeous picnic.

President Grover Cleveland was riding toward the grounds in one of twenty-three carriages, drawn by high-steppers. At his side sat President Thomas W. Palmer, of the National Commission, and President Higinbotham, of the Chicago Board, one time farm boy and dry-goods clerk, now a partner of Marshall Field—gray-bearded, alert, with the face of a scholar and artist. In other carriages, members of Cleveland's Cabinet, World's Fair Directors, Governor Altgeld, General Miles, the Duke and Duchess of Veragua —Mrs. Potter Palmer sitting grandly at the latter's side—the Marquis de Barbales, Don Cristobal Colon y Aquilera and his Doña, other Spaniards—cheered by the crowds, five years later to be at war with them.

And in the very last carriage, lifting his gala hat to those multitudes who knew him far better than any of the others, Carter H. Harrison the elder. He was a happy mayor. Four terms he had served, and then given way to the inevitable; but now he stood elected by a few hundred votes to be that commanding figure, the World's Fair Mayor.

The jingling, bowing, and somewhat haughty procession passed through the Midway Plaisance, where the variegated nationals, the freaks, bevies of fakirs, waiters, dancers, and the like, hailed nobility and officials as they passed. The Algerians were ready to greet them with their yell, "which," as a writer put it, "for penetrating power exceeded anything ever heard in a political meeting." Donkey-boys flattened themselves to earth. Tom-toms were beaten. Four lions of the Hagenbeck show had been trained to roar horrifically while the president passed; and doubtless they did.

Meantime the delighted crowd had been assembling in the Court of Honor, facing the platform erected on the east front of the Administration Building. They had come again, in numbers three times greater than on the day of dedication, drawn by the powerful magnets of curiosity, civic pride, and adulation of celebrities, to see and hear what little they could. The Court of Honor could hold them all, but the space near the platform could not. That standing room was a stretch of mud, all around the silent MacMonnies fountain and far back along both sides of the darkly glistening basin. It is said that between four and five hundred thousand men, women, and children were massed somehow in the area.

At first they spread out harmlessly to the eastward; but as the party of dignitaries mounted the platform there was a rush in their direction by the scrambling thousands, splashing through the mud, brandishing folded umbrellas—for the sun had come out—elbowing, fighting, shouting. Choristers essayed a "Columbian Hymn." Their voices were all but lost in the clamor of the half-panicky mob. President Cleveland and the Spanish nobles sat gazing in amazement upon what was happening below. The luckiest spectators were those who had climbed ropes to the pinnacles of Machinery Hall, or had perched upon the dome of the Agriculture building.

All during the hymn, the spectacle down on the mud-flat was

like a scene from Doré. The huskies pressing toward the platform elbowed women aside; they broke through the defense of
Columbian Guards. Strong husbands lifted their wives up shoulder-
high, so that they could breathe. Crying children were held aloft.
Women with torn clothes climbed to the press-stand and tried to
clamber over the railing; reporters dragged to safety some who
were fainting.

A blind minister rose to pray. He could not be heard for the
terrific yells from the fighting "audience," yells of "Stand still!"
"Get back; you're killing those women!" "For God's sake—" Police crashed through to places where women, and men too, lay
underfoot, unconscious, and lugged them away on stretchers or
wheeled ambulances. Somewhere in the crowd Jane Addams—not
among those in carriages—felt her purse seized by a pickpocket. A
staff officer of the Columbian Guard thrust his sword between the
"dip's" legs, tripped him, and hauled him off to the brig.

After all this, when records were made, there were listed only
seventeen who had fainted and none with bad injuries.

Director-General Davis rose by the table on which stood, in a
purple plush casket, an electric key to be pushed by President
Cleveland. "It only remains for you, Mr. President . . . commen-
surate in dignity with what the world expects. . . . When you
touch this magic key, the ponderous machinery will start. . . ."

President Cleveland, fifty-six years old, but powerful, ruddy, with
a chest like a barrel, laid aside a silk hat a little the worse for
wear, and rose bowing.

His voice had such volume that many could hear him who so
far had not heard a word. The rest caught it in snatches:

Stupendous results of American enterprise . . . Magnificent evidence of American skill and intelligence . . . Greetings we extend to
those of foreign lands . . . Popular education . . . Stimulation of
best impulses . . . Proud national destiny . . . We have built these
splendid edifices . . . Exalted mission . . . Human enlightenment
. . . Brotherhood of nations . . . The machinery that gives life to
this vast exposition is now set in motion. . . .

He touched the key. It was almost exactly noon.

The Stars and Stripes fluttered up the mast in the center of the plaza, the red flag of Castile up another mast, and the white initialed banner of Ferdinand and Isabella up another. On all sides, on the tall domes and cornices of the buildings, flags furled for hours now broke out. From the MacMonnies fountain and its companions the white water gushed. The shroud fell from the Liberty statue, and it glittered in the sun to cries of "Ah-h-h!"

With all this rose the rumble of machinery set off by the electric spark; from the lake came the booming of guns from warships, starting flights of gulls from their beach coverts.

The curtain was up on the glorious spectacle. But just as sometimes a piece in the orchestra thrusts an ominous motif into an opening chorus, there appeared in the newspapers of that afternoon dispatches from Wall Street saying: "The day was one of great depression and considerable excitement. The bearish feeling was very pronounced. Repeated raids were made on leading shares. . . ."

POEMS

Gwendolyn Brooks

HERE are three moving poems by one of America's most gifted poets. Miss Brooks lives on the South Side. She is the author of *A Street in Bronzeville;* and *Annie Allen,* a second book of poems, which won a Pulitzer Prize.

OF De WITT WILLIAMS ON HIS WAY TO LINCOLN CEMETERY*

He was born in Alabama.
He was bred in Illinois.
He was nothing but a
Plain black boy.

Swing low swing low sweet sweet chariot.
Nothing but a plain black boy.

Drive him past the Pool Hall.
Drive him past the Show.
Blind within his casket,
But maybe he will know.

Down through Forty-seventh Street:
Underneath the L,
And—Northwest Corner, Prairie,
That he loved so well.

* From *A Street in Bronzeville,* by Gwendolyn Brooks. Copyright, 1945, by Gwendolyn Brooks Blakely. Reprinted by permission of Harper & Bros.

Don't forget the Dance Halls—
Warwick and Savoy,
Where he picked his women, where
He drank his liquid joy.

Born in Alabama.
Bred in Illinois.
He was nothing but a
Plain black boy.

Swing low swing low sweet sweet chariot.
Nothing but a plain black boy.

THE VACANT LOT*

Mrs. Coley's three-flat brick
Isn't here any more.
All done with seeing her fat little form
Burst out of the basement door;
And with seeing her African son-in-law
(Rightful heir to the throne)
With his great white strong cold squares of teeth
And his little eyes of stone;
And with seeing the squat fat daughter
Letting in the men
When majesty has gone for the day—
And letting them out again.

THE OLD-MARRIEDS*

But in the crowding darkness not a word did they say.
Though the pretty-coated birds had piped so lightly all the day.
And he had seen the lovers in the little side streets.
And she had heard the morning stories clogged with sweets.
It was quite a time for loving. It was midnight. It was May.
But in the crowding darkness not a word did they say.

* From *A Street in Bronzeville*.

MR. AND MRS. FIX-IT*

Ring Lardner

RING LARDNER was born in Niles, Michigan. As a young man, he worked on a Chicago newspaper for several years. He followed the baseball teams on the road, reporting their games and listening to the hotel and locker-room lingo of the players. He died in 1933.

Lardner's influence has been deeply felt in American literature. Deceptively simple in design and writing, his stories sometimes disclose cracks in American life over which the population keeps wheeling merrily along. Often the surface of his work is very funny and to many people he is essentially a humorist.

The best piece written on Lardner I know of is the one in F. Scott Fitzgerald's posthumous volume of notes and memoirs, *Crack-up*. It is a poignant, unforgettable portrait of a wonderful, wise, and sad man.

THEY'RE certainly a live bunch in this town. We ain't only been here three days and had calls already from people representin' four different organizations—the Chamber of Commerce, Kiwanis, and I forget who else. They wanted to know if we was comfortable and did we like the town and is they anything they can do for us and what to be sure and see.

And they all asked how we happened to come here instead of goin' somewheres else. I guess they keep a record of everybody's reasons for comin' so as they can get a line on what features tourists is most attracted by. Then they play up them features in next year's booster advertisin'.

Well, I told them we was perfectly comfortable and we like the town fine and they's nothin' nobody can do for us right now and we'll be sure and see all the things we ought to see. But when they asked me how did we happen to come here, I said it was just a kind of a accident, because the real reason makes too long a story.

My wife has been kiddin' me about my friends ever since we was married. She says that judgin' by the ones I've introduced her to, they ain't nobody in the world got a rummier bunch of friends than me. I'll admit that the most of them ain't, well, what you might call hot; they're different somehow than when I first hung around with them. They seem to be lost without a brass rail to rest their dogs on. But of course they're old friends and I can't give 'em the air.

We have 'em to the house for dinner every little w'ile, they and their wives, and what my missus objects to is because they don't none of them play bridge or mahjongg or do the crossword puzzles or sing or dance or even talk, but just set there and wait for somebody to pour 'em a fresh drink.

As I say, my wife kids me about 'em and they ain't really nothin' I can offer in their defense. That don't mean, though, that the shoe is all on one foot. Because w'ile the majority of her friends may not be quite as dumb as mine, just the same they's a few she's picked out who I'd of had to be under the ether to allow anybody to introduce 'em to me in the first place.

Like the Crandalls, for instance. Mrs. Crandall come from my wife's home town and they didn't hardly know each other there, but they met again in a store in Chi and it went from bad to worse till finally Ada asked the dame and her husband to the house.

Well, the husband turns out to be the fella that win the war, w'ile it seems that Mrs. Crandall was in Atlantic City once and some movin' picture company was makin' a picture there and they took a scene of what was supposed to be society people walkin' up and down the Boardwalk and Mrs. Crandall was in the picture and people that seen it when it come out, they all said that from the way she screened, why if she wanted to go into business, she could make Gloria Swanson look like Mrs. Gump.

Now it ain't only took me a few words to tell you these things, but when the Crandalls tells their story themselves, they don't hardly get started by midnight and no chance of them goin' home till they're through even when you drop 'em a hint that they're springin' it on you for the hundred and twelfth time.

That's the Crandalls, and another of the wife's friends is the Thayers. Thayer is what you might call a all-around handy man. He can mimic pretty near all the birds and beasts and fishes, he can yodel, he can play a ocarena, or he can recite Kipling or Robert H. Service, or he can do card tricks, and strike a light without no matches, and tie all the different knots.

And besides that, he can make a complete radio outfit and set it up, and take pictures as good as the best professional photographers and a whole lot better. He collects autographs. And he never had a sick day in his life.

Mrs. Thayer gets a headache playin' bridge, so it's mahjongg or rhum when she's around. She used to be a teacher of elocution and she still gives readin's if you coax her, or if you don't, and her hair is such a awful nuisance that she would get it cut in a minute only all her friends tells her it would be criminal to spoil that head of hair. And when she talks to her husband, she always talks baby talk, maybe because somebody has told her that she'd be single if he wasn't childish.

And then Ada has got still another pal, a dame named Peggy Flood who is hospital mad and ain't happy unless she is just goin' under the knife or just been there. She's had everything removed that the doctors knew the name of and now they're probin' her for new giblets.

Well, I wouldn't mind if they cut her up into alphabet soup if they'd only do such a good job of it that they couldn't put her together again, but she always comes through O. K. and she spends the intermissions at our place, describin' what all they done or what they're plannin' to do next.

But the cat's nightgown is Tom Stevens and his wife. There's the team that wins the Olympics! And they're Ada's team, not mine.

Ada met Belle Stevens on the elevated. Ada was invited to a party out on the North Side and didn't know exactly where to get off and Mrs. Stevens seen her talkin' to the guard and horned in and asked her what was it she wanted to know and Ada told her, and Mrs. Stevens said she was goin' to get off the same station Ada wanted to get off, so they got off together.

Mrs. Stevens insisted on goin' right along to the address where Ada was goin' because she said Ada was bound to get lost if she wasn't familiar with the neighborhood.

Well, Ada thought it was mighty nice of her to do so much for a stranger. Mrs. Stevens said she was glad to because she didn't know what would of happened to her lots of times if strangers hadn't been nice and helped her out.

She asked Ada where she lived and Ada told her on the South Side and Mrs. Stevens said she was sure we'd like it better on the North Side if we'd leave her pick out a place for us, so Ada told her we had a year's lease that we had just signed and couldn't break it, so then Mrs. Stevens said her husband had studied law and he claimed they wasn't no lease that you couldn't break and some evening she would bring him out to call on us and he'd tell us how to break our lease.

Well, Ada had to say sure, come on out, though we was perfectly satisfied with our apartment and didn't no more want to break the lease then each other's jaw. Maybe not as much. Anyway, the very next night, they showed up, Belle and Tom, and when they'd gone, I give 'em the nickname—Mr. and Mrs. Fix-It.

After the introductions, Stevens made some remark about what a cozy little place we had and then he asked if I would mind tellin' what rent we paid. So I told him a hundred and a quarter a month. So he said, of course, that was too much and no wonder we wanted to break the lease. Then I said we was satisfied and didn't want to break it and he said I must be kiddin' and if I would show him the lease he would see what loopholes they was in it.

Well, the lease was right there in a drawer in the table, but I told him it was in my safety deposit box at the bank. I ain't got

no safety deposit box and no more use for one than Judge Landis
has for the deef and dumb alphabet.

Stevens said the lease was probably just a regular lease and if it
was, they wouldn't be no trouble gettin' out of it, and meanw'ile
him and his wife would see if they couldn't find us a place in
the same buildin' with them.

And he was pretty sure they could even if the owner had to
give some other tenant the air, because he, the owner, would do
anything in the world for Stevens.

So I said yes, but suppose we want to stay where we are. So
he said I looked like a man with better judgment than that and if
I would just leave everything to him he would fix it so's we could
move within a month. I kind of laughed and thought that would
be the end of it.

He wanted to see the whole apartment so I showed him around
and when we come to the bathroom he noticed my safety razor
on the shelf. He said, "So you use one of them things," and I
said, "Yes," and he asked me how I liked it, and I said I liked
it fine and he said that must be because I hadn't never used a regular razor.

He said a regular razor was the only thing to use if a man
wanted to look good. So I asked him if he used a regular razor
and he said he did, so I said, "Well, if you look good, I don't
want to."

But that didn't stop him and he said if I would meet him downtown the next day he would take me to the place where he
bought all his razors and help me pick some out for myself. I
told him I was goin' to be tied up, so just to give me the name
and address of the place and I would drop in there when I had
time.

But, no, that wouldn't do; he'd have to go along with me and
introduce me to the proprietor because the proprietor was a great
pal of his and would do anything in the world for him, and if
the proprietor vouched for the razors, I could be sure I was gettin'
the best razors money could buy. I told him again I was goin' to
be tied up and I managed to get him on some other subject.

Meanw'ile, Mrs. Stevens wanted to know where Ada had bought

the dress she was wearin' and how much had it cost and Ada told her and Mrs. Stevens said it was a crime. She would meet Ada downtown tomorrow morning and take her to the shop where she bought her clothes and help her choose some dresses that really was dresses.

So Ada told her she didn't have no money to spend on dresses right then, and besides, the shop Mrs. Stevens mentioned was too high priced. But it seems the dame that run the shop was just like a sister to Mrs. Stevens and give her and her friends a big reduction and not only that, but they wasn't no hurry about payin'.

Well, Ada thanked her just the same, but didn't need nothin' new just at present; maybe later on she would take advantage of Mrs. Stevens' kind offer. Yes, but right now they was some models in stock that would be just beautiful on Ada and they might be gone later on. They was nothin' for it but Ada had to make a date with her; she wasn't obliged to buy nothin', but it would be silly not to go and look at the stuff that was in the joint and get acquainted with the dame that run it.

Well, Ada kept the date and bought three dresses she didn't want and they's only one of them she's had the nerve to wear. They cost her a hundred dollars a smash and I'd hate to think what the price would of been if Mrs. Stevens and the owner of the shop wasn't so much like sisters.

I was sure I hadn't made no date with Stevens, but just the same he called me up the next night to ask why I hadn't met him. And a couple of days later I got three new razors in the mail along with a bill and a note from the store sayin' that these was three specially fine razors that had been picked out for me by Thomas J. Stevens.

I don't know yet why I paid for the razors and kept 'em. I ain't used 'em and never intended to. Though I've been tempted a few times to test their edge on Stevens' neck.

That same week, Mrs. Stevens called up and asked us to spend Sunday with them and when we got out there, the owner of the buildin' is there, too. And Stevens has told him that I was goin' to give up my apartment on the South Side and wanted him to show me what he had.

I thought this was a little too strong and I said Stevens must of misunderstood me, that I hadn't no fault to find with the place I was in and wasn't plannin' to move, not for a year anyway. You can bet this didn't make no hit with the guy, who was just there on Stevens' say-so that I was a prospective tenant.

Well, it was only about two months ago that this cute little couple come into our life, but I'll bet we seen 'em twenty times at least. They was always invitin' us to their place or invitin' themselves to our place and Ada is one of these here kind of people that just can't say no. Which may be why I and her is married.

Anyway, it begin to seem like us and the Stevenses was livin' together and all one family, with them at the head of it. I never in my life seen anybody as crazy to run other people's business. Honest to heavens, it's a wonder they let us brush our own teeth!

Ada made the remark one night that she wished the ski jumper who was doin' our cookin' would get married and quit so's she wouldn't have to can her. Mrs. Stevens was there and asked Ada if she should try and get her a new cook, but Ada says no, the poor gal might have trouble findin' another job and she felt sorry for her.

Just the same, the next afternoon a Jap come to the apartment and said he was ready to go to work and Mrs. Stevens had sent him. Ada had to tell him the place was already filled.

Another night, Ada complained that her feet was tired. Belle said her feet used to get tired, too, till a friend of hers recommended a chiropodist and she went to him and he done her so much good that she made a regular appointment with him for once every month and paid him a flat sum and no matter how much runnin' around she done, her dogs hadn't fretted her once since this cornhusker started tendin' to 'em.

She wanted to call up the guy at his home right then and there and make a date for Ada and the only way Ada could stop her was by promisin' to go and see him the next time her feet hurt. After that, whenever the two gals met, Belle's first question was "How is your feet?" and the answer was always, "Fine, thanks."

Well, I'm quite a football fan and Ada likes to go, too, when it's a big game and lots of excitement. So we decided we'd see the

Illinois-Chicago game and have a look at this "Red" Grange. I warned Ada not to say nothin' about it to Tom and Belle as I felt like we was entitled to a day off.

But it happened that they was goin' to be a game up at Evanston that day and the Stevenses invited us to see that one with them. So we used the other game as a alibi. And when Tom asked me later on if I'd bought my tickets yet, instead of sayin' yes, I told him the truth and said no.

So then he said:

"I'm glad you ain't, because I and Belle has made up our mind that the Chicago game is the one we ought to see. And we'll all go together. And don't you bother about tickets because I can get better ones than you can as Stagg and I is just like that."

So I left it to him to get the tickets and we might as well of set on the Adams Street bridge. I said to Stevens, I said:

"If these is the seats Mr. Stagg digs up for his old pals, I suppose he leads strangers twenty or thirty miles out in the country and blindfolds 'em and ties 'em to a tree."

Now of course it was the bunk about he and Stagg bein' so close. He may of been introduced to him once, but he ain't the kind of a guy that Stagg would go around holdin' hands with. Just the same, most of the people he bragged about knowin', why it turned out that he really did know 'em; yes, and stood ace high with 'em, too.

Like for instance, I got pinched for speedin' one night and they give me a ticket to show up in the Speeders' court and I told Stevens about it and he says, "Just forget it! I'll call up the judge and have it wiped off the books. He's a mighty good fella and a personal friend of mine."

Well, I didn't want to take no chances so I phoned Stevens the day before I was supposed to appear in court, and I asked him if he'd talked to the judge. He said he had and I asked him if he was sure. So he said, "If you don't believe me, call up the judge yourself." And he give me the judge's number. Sure enough, Stevens had fixed it and when I thanked the judge for his trouble, he said it was a pleasure to do somethin' for a friend of Tom Stevens'.

Now, I know it's silly to not appreciate favors like that and not warm up to people that's always tryin' to help you along, but still a person don't relish bein' treated like they was half-witted and couldn't button their shirt alone. Tom and Belle meant all right, but I and Ada got kind of tired of havin' fault found with everything that belonged to us and everything we done or tried to do.

Besides our apartment bein' no good and our clothes terrible, we learned that my dentist didn't know a bridge from a mustache cup, and the cigarettes I smoked didn't have no taste to them, and the man that bobbed Ada's hair must of been mad at her, and neither of us would ever know what it was to live till we owned a wire-haired fox terrier.

And we found out that the liquor I'd been drinkin' and enjoyin' was a mixture of bath salts and assorted paints, and the car we'd paid seventeen hundred smackers for wasn't nowheres near as much of a car as one that Tom could of got for us for eight hundred on account of knowin' a brother-in-law of a fella that used to go to school with the president of the company's nephew, and that if Ada would take up aesthetic dancin' under a dame Belle knew about, why she'd never have no more trouble with her tonsils.

Nothin' we had or nothin' we talked about gettin' or doin' was worth a damn unless it was recommended or suggested by the Stevenses.

Well, I done a pretty good business this fall and I and Ada had always planned to spend a winter in the South, so one night we figured it out that this was the year we could spare the money and the time and if we didn't go this year we never would. So the next thing was where should we go, and we finally decided on Miami. And we said we wouldn't mention nothin' about it to Tom and Belle till the day we was goin'. We'd pretend we was doin' it out of a clear sky.

But a secret is just as safe with Ada as a police dog tethered with dental floss. It wasn't more than a day or two after we'd had our talk when Tom and Belle sprang the news that they was leavin' for California right after New Year's. And why didn't we go with them.

Well, I didn't say nothin' and Ada said it sounded grand, but it was impossible. Then Stevens said if it was a question of money, to not let that bother us as he would loan it to me and I could pay it back whenever I felt like it. That was more than Ada could stand, so she says we wasn't as poor as people seemed to think and the reason we couldn't go to California was because we was goin' to Miami.

This was such a surprise that it almost struck 'em dumb at first and all Tom could think of to say was that he'd been to Miami himself and it was too crowded and he'd lay off of it if he was us. But the next time we seen 'em they had our trip all arranged.

First, Tom asked me what road we was goin' on and I told him the Big Four. So he asked if we had our reservations and I told him yes.

"Well," he said, "we'll get rid of 'em and I'll fix you up on the C. & E. I. The general passenger agent is a friend of mine and they ain't nothin' he won't do for my friends. He'll see that you're treated right and that you get there in good shape."

So I said:

"I don't want to put you to all that trouble, and besides I don't know nobody connected with the Big Four well enough for them to resent me travelin' on their lines, and as for gettin' there in good shape, even if I have a secret enemy or two on the Big Four, I don't believe they'd endanger the lives of the other passengers just to see that I didn't get there in good shape."

But Stevens insisted on takin' my tickets and sellin' 'em back to the Big Four and gettin' me fixed on the C. & E. I. The berths we'd had on the Big Four was Lower 9 and Lower 10. The berths Tom got us on the C. & E. I. was Lower 7 and Lower 8, which he said was better. I suppose he figured that the nearer you are to the middle of the car, the less chance there is of bein' woke up if your car gets in another train's way.

He wanted to know, too, if I'd made any reservations at a hotel. I showed him a wire I had from the Royal Palm in reply to a wire I'd sent 'em.

"Yes," he says, "but you don't want to stop at the Royal Palm. You wire and tell 'em to cancel that and I'll make arrangements for you at the Flamingo, over at the Beach. Charley Krom, the manager there, was born and raised in the same town I was. He'll take great care of you if he knows you're a friend of mine."

So I asked him if all the guests at the Flamingo was friends of his, and he said of course not; what did I mean?

"Well," I said, "I was just thinkin' that if they ain't, Mr. Krom probably makes life pretty miserable for 'em. What does he do, have the phone girl ring 'em up at all hours of the night, and hide their mail, and shut off their hot water, and put cracker crumbs in their beds?"

That didn't mean nothin' to Stevens and he went right ahead and switched me from one hotel to the other.

While Tom was reorganizin' my program and tellin' me what to eat in Florida, and what bait to use for barracuda and carp, and what time to go bathin' and which foot to stick in the water first, why Belle was makin' Ada return all the stuff she had boughten to wear down there and buy other stuff that Belle picked out for her at joints where Belle was so well known that they only soaked her twice as much as a stranger. She had Ada almost crazy, but I told her to never mind; in just a few more days we'd be where they couldn't get at us.

I suppose you're wonderin' why didn't we quarrel with 'em and break loose from 'em and tell 'em to leave us alone. You'd know why if you knew them. Nothin' we could do would convince 'em that we didn't want their advice and help. And nothin' we could say was a insult.

Well, the night before we was due to leave Chi, the phone rung and I answered it. It was Tom.

"I've got a surprise for you," he says. "I and Belle has give up the California idear. We're goin' to Miami instead, and on account of me knowin' the boys down at the C. & E. I., I've landed a drawin' room on the same train you're takin'. How is that for news?"

"Great!" I said, and I went back and broke it to Ada. For a minute I thought she was goin' to faint. And all night long she moaned and groaned and had hysterics.

So that's how we happened to come to Biloxi.

MILK BOTTLES*

Sherwood Anderson

SHERWOOD ANDERSON is a difficult figure to write about because he meant so much to young writers, especially Chicago writers. *Winesburg, Ohio,* was written in a small room in a Chicago rooming house. Most of his best work was done while he lived in Chicago. He was a catalyst for many, many young writers who, tired of machine-made literature, were fumbling around in the dark for the doorknob. Anderson was always writing of doors, and we younger writers reached out for the knob when he opened the door a crack and showed it to us in the half light.

I think most of us overrated him; but that was not his fault. He saved our literary lives, or directed us, thereby saving us valuable years. Dreiser, Hemingway, and Faulkner never meant so much to beginning writers as did Anderson at one time. I know young people who wrote him letters. I wrote him one when I was holding down a deadening job in Chicago. Anderson answered with a wonderful letter, and I never forgot it. Today, many of us no longer read his novels; but there is still *Winesburg,* and eight or ten really great, great short stories—a more than sufficient production to keep his high fame permanently secure. We all learned from him, and we owe him an immense debt.

Sitting with a girl in the Grand Ticino, a basement Italian restaurant in New York, I once saw Sherwood Anderson a few years before his death. He was quietly eating alone, dressed in a light summer suit. Why didn't I go up to him, tell him how much his work had meant to me? Something held me back. Later, I saw him walk out, still alone.

I LIVED, during that summer, in a large room on the top floor
of an old house on the North Side in Chicago. It was August and
the night was hot. Until after midnight I sat—the sweat trickling
down my back—under a lamp, laboring to feel my way into the
lives of the fanciful people who were trying also to live in the
tale on which I was at work.

It was a hopeless affair.

I became involved in the efforts of the shadowy people and they
in turn became involved in the fact of the hot uncomfortable room,
in the fact that, although it was what the farmers of the Middle
West call "good corn-growing weather," it was plain hell to be
alive in Chicago. Hand in hand the shadowy people of my fanciful
world and myself groped our way through a forest in which the
leaves had all been burned off the trees. The hot ground burned
the shoes off our feet. We were striving to make our way through
the forest and into some cool beautiful city. The fact is, as you
will clearly understand, I was a little off my head.

When I gave up the struggle and got to my feet, the chairs
in the room danced about. They also were running aimlessly
through a burning land and striving to reach some mythical city.
"I'd better get out of here and go for a walk or go jump into
the lake and cool myself off," I thought.

I went down out of my room and into the street. On a lower
floor of the house lived two burlesque actresses who had just come
in from their evening's work and who now sat in their room talking. As I reached the street, something heavy whirled past my
head and broke on the stone pavement. A white liquid spurted over
my clothes, and the voice of one of the actresses could be heard
coming from the one lighted room of the house. "Oh, hell! We
live such damned lives, we do, and we work in such a town! A
dog is better off! And now they are going to take booze away
from us too! I come home from working in that hot theater on a
hot night like this and what do I see—a half-filled bottle of
spoiled milk standing on a window sill! I won't stand it! I got to
smash everything!" she cried.

I walked eastward from my house. From the northwestern end
of the city, great hordes of men, women, and children had come

to spend the night out-of-doors, by the shore of the lake. It was stifling hot there, too, and the air was heavy with a sense of struggle. On a few hundred acres of flat land, that had formerly been a swamp, some two million people were fighting for the peace and quiet of sleep and not getting it. Out of the half darkness, beyond the little strip of park land at the water's edge, the huge empty houses of Chicago's fashionable folk made a grayish-blue blot against the sky. "Thank the gods," I thought, "there are some people who can get out of here, who can go to the mountains or the seashore or to Europe." I stumbled in the half darkness over the legs of a woman who was lying and trying to sleep on the grass. A baby lay beside her and when she sat up it began to cry. I muttered an apology and stepped aside, and as I did so my foot struck a half-filled milk bottle and I knocked it over, the milk running out on the grass. "Oh, I'm sorry. Please forgive me," I cried. "Never mind," the woman answered, "the milk is sour."

He is a tall stoop-shouldered man with prematurely grayed hair and works as a copy writer in an advertising agency in Chicago— an agency where I also have sometimes been employed—and on that night in August I met him, walking with quick eager strides along the shore of the lake and past the tired petulant people. He did not see me at first, and I wondered at the evidence of life in him when everyone else seemed half dead; but a street lamp hanging over a nearby roadway threw its light down upon my face and he pounced. "Here, you, come up to my place!" he cried sharply. "I've got something to show you. I was on my way down to see you. That's where I was going," he lied as he hurried me along.

We went to his apartment on a street leading back from the lake and the park. German, Polish, Italian, and Jewish families, equipped with soiled blankets and the ever-present half-filled bottles of milk, had come prepared to spend the night out-of-doors; but the American families in the crowd were giving up the struggle to find a cool spot and a little stream of them trickled along the sidewalks, going back to hot beds in the hot houses.

It was past one o'clock and my friend's apartment was disorderly as well as hot. He explained that his wife, with their two children, had gone home to visit her mother on a farm near Springfield, Illinois.

We took off our coats and sat down. My friend's thin cheeks were flushed and his eyes shone. "You know—well—you see," he began and then hesitated and laughed like an embarrassed schoolboy. "Well, now," he began again, "I've long been wanting to write something real, something besides advertisements. I suppose I'm silly, but that's the way I am. It's been my dream to write something stirring and big. I suppose it's the dream of a lot of advertising writers, eh? Now look here—don't you go laughing. I think I've done it."

He explained that he had written something concerning Chicago, the capital and heart, as he said, of the whole Central West. He grew angry. "People come here from the East or from farms, or from little holes of towns like I came from, and they think it smart to run Chicago into the ground," he declared. "I thought I'd show 'em up," he added, jumping up and walking nervously about the room.

He handed me many sheets of paper covered with hastily scrawled words, but I protested and asked him to read it aloud. He did, standing with his face turned away from me. There was a quiver in his voice. The thing he had written concerned some mythical town I had never seen. He called it Chicago, but in the same breath he spoke of great streets flaming with color, ghostlike buildings flung up into night skies, and a river, running down a path of gold into the boundless West. It was the city, I told myself, I and the people of my story had been trying to find earlier on that same evening, when because of the heat I went a little off my head and could not work any more. The people of the city he had written about were a cool-headed, brave people, marching forward to some spiritual triumph, the promise of which was inherent in the physical aspects of the town.

Now I am one who, by the careful cultivation of certain traits in my character, have succeeded in building up the more brutal side of my nature, but I cannot knock women and children down in order to get aboard Chicago streetcars, nor can I tell an author to his face that I think his work is rotten.

"You're all right, Ed. You're great. You've knocked out a regular sockdolager of a masterpiece here. Why, you sound as good as Henry Mencken writing about Chicago as the literary center of America, and you've lived in Chicago and he never did. The only thing I can see you've missed is a little something about the stockyards, and you can put that in later," I added, and prepared to depart.

"What's this?" I asked, picking up a half-dozen sheets of paper that lay on the floor by my chair. I read it eagerly. And when I had finished reading it, he stammered and apologized, and then, stepping across the room, jerked the sheets out of my hand and threw them out at an open window. "I wish you hadn't seen that. It's something else I wrote about Chicago," he explained. He was flustered.

"You see, the night was so hot, and down at the office I had to write a condensed-milk advertisement, just as I was sneaking away to come home and work on this other thing, and the street-car was so crowded and the people stank so, and when I finally got home here—the wife being gone—the place was a mess. Well, I couldn't write and I was sore. It's been my chance, you see, the wife and kids being gone and the house being quiet. I went for a walk. I think I went a little off my head. Then I came home and wrote that stuff I've just thrown out of the window."

He grew cheerful again. "Oh, well—it's all right. Writing that fool thing stirred me up and enabled me to write this other stuff, this real stuff I showed you first, about Chicago."

And so I went home and to bed, having in this odd way stumbled upon another bit of the kind of writing that is—for better or worse—really presenting the lives of the people of these towns and cities—sometimes in prose, sometimes in stirring colorful song. It was the kind of thing Mr. Sandburg or Mr. Masters might have done after an evening's walk on a hot night in, say, West Congress Street in Chicago.

The thing I had read of Ed's centered about a half-filled bottle of spoiled milk standing dim in the moonlight on a window sill. There had been a moon earlier on that August evening, a new moon, a thin crescent golden streak in the sky. What had hap-

pened to my friend, the advertising writer, was something like this
—I figured it all out as I lay sleepless in bed after our talk.

I am sure I do not know whether or not it is true that all advertising writers and newspapermen want to do other kinds of writing, but Ed did all right. The August day that had preceded the
hot night had been a hard one for him to get through. All day
he had been wanting to be at home in his quiet apartment producing literature, rather than sitting in an office and writing advertisements. In the late afternoon, when he had thought his desk cleared
for the day, the boss of the copy writers came and ordered him to
write a page advertisement for the magazines on the subject of
condensed milk. "We got a chance to get a new account if we can
knock out some crackerjack stuff in a hurry," he said. "I'm sorry
to have to put it up to you on such a rotten hot day, Ed, but
we're up against it. Let's see if you've got some of the old pep
in you. Get down to hardpan now and knock out something
snappy and unusual before you go home."

Ed had tried. He put away the thoughts he had been having
about the city beautiful—the glowing city of the plains—and got
right down to business. He thought about milk, milk for little
children, the Chicagoans of the future, milk that would produce
a little cream to put in the coffee of advertising writers in the
morning, sweet fresh milk to keep all his brother and sister Chicagoans robust and strong. What Ed really wanted was a long
cool drink of something with a kick in it, but he tried to make
himself think he wanted a drink of milk. He gave himself over to
thoughts of milk, milk condensed and yellow, milk warm from the
cows his father owned when he was a boy—his mind launched a
little boat and he set out on a sea of milk.

Out of it all he got what is called an original advertisement.
The sea of milk on which he sailed became a mountain of cans of
condensed milk, and out of that fancy he got his idea. He made a
crude sketch for a picture showing wide rolling green fields with
white farmhouses. Cows grazed on the green hills, and at one side
of the picture a barefooted boy was driving a herd of Jersey
cows out of the sweet fair land and down a lane into a kind of
funnel at the small end of which was a tin of condensed milk.

Over the picture he put a heading: "The health and freshness of a whole countryside is condensed into one can of Whitney-Wells Condensed Milk." The head copy writer said it was a humdinger.

And then Ed went home. He wanted to begin writing about the city beautiful at once and so didn't go out to dinner, but fished about in the ice chest and found some cold meat out of which he made himself a sandwich. Also, he poured himself a glass of milk, but it was sour. "Oh, damn!" he said, and poured it into the kitchen sink.

As Ed explained to me later, he sat down and tried to begin writing his real stuff at once, but he couldn't seem to get into it. The last hour in the office, the trip home in the hot smelly car, and the taste of the sour milk in his mouth had jangled his nerves. The truth is that Ed has a rather sensitive, finely balanced nature, and it had got mussed up.

He took a walk and tried to think, but his mind wouldn't stay where he wanted it to. Ed is now a man of nearly forty and on that night his mind ran back to his young manhood in the city— and stayed there. Like other boys who had become grown men in Chicago, he had come to the city from a farm at the edge of a prairie town, and like all such town and farm boys, he had come filled with vague dreams.

What things he had hungered to do and be in Chicago! What he had done you can fancy. For one thing he had got himself married and now lived in the apartment on the North Side. To give a real picture of his life during the twelve or fifteen years that had slipped away since he was a young man would involve writing a novel, and that is not my purpose.

Anyway, there he was in his room—come home from his walk—and it was hot and quiet and he could not manage to get into his masterpiece. How still it was in the apartment with the wife and children away! His mind stayed on the subject of his youth in the city.

He remembered a night of his young manhood when he had gone out to walk, just as he did on that August evening. Then his life wasn't complicated by the fact of the wife and children and he lived alone in his room; but something had got on his nerves then, too. On that evening long ago he grew restless in his room and went out to walk. It was summer, and first he went down by the river where ships were being loaded and then to a crowded park where girls and young fellows walked about.

He grew bold and spoke to a woman who sat alone on a park bench. She let him sit beside her and, because it was dark and she was silent, he began to talk. The night had made him sentimental. "Human beings are such hard things to get at. I wish I could get close to someone," he said. "Oh, you go on! What you doing? You ain't trying to kid someone?" asked the woman.

Ed jumped up and walked away. He went into a long street lined with dark silent buildings and then stopped and looked about. What he wanted was to believe that in the apartment buildings were people who lived intense eager lives, who had great dreams, who were capable of great adventures. "They are really only separated from me by the brick walls," was what he told himself on that night.

It was then that the milk-bottle theme first got hold of him. He went into an alleyway to look at the backs of the apartment buildings and, on that evening also, there was a moon. Its light fell upon a long row of half-filled bottles standing on window sills.

Something within him went a little sick and he hurried out of the alleyway and into the street. A man and woman walked past him and stopped before the entrance to one of the buildings. Hoping they might be lovers, he concealed himself in the entrance to another building to listen to their conversation.

The couple turned out to be a man and wife and they were quarreling. Ed heard the woman's voice saying: "You come in here. You can't put that over on me. You say you just want to take a walk, but I know you. You want to go out and blow in some money. What I'd like to know is why you don't loosen up a little for me."

That is the story of what happened to Ed, when, as a young man, he went to walk in the city in the evening, and when he had become a man of forty and went out of his house wanting to dream and to think of a city beautiful, much the same sort of thing happened again. Perhaps the writing of the condensed milk advertisement and the taste of the sour milk he had got out of the icebox had something to do with his mood; but, anyway, milk bottles, like a refrain in a song, got into his brain. They seemed to sit and mock at him from the windows of all the buildings in all the streets, and when he turned to look at people, he met the crowds from the West and the Northwest Sides going to the park and the lake. At the head of each little group of people marched a woman who carried a milk bottle in her hand.

And so, on that August night, Ed went home angry and disturbed, and in anger wrote of his city. Like the burlesque actress in my own house, he wanted to smash something, and, as milk bottles were in his mind, he wanted to smash milk bottles. "I could grasp the neck of a milk bottle. It fits the hand so neatly. I could kill a man or woman with such a thing," he thought desperately.

He wrote, you see, the five or six sheets I had read in that mood and then felt better. And after that he wrote about the ghostlike buildings flung into the sky by the hands of a brave adventurous people and about the river that runs down a path of gold, and into the boundless West.

As you have already concluded, the city he described in his masterpiece was lifeless, but the city he, in a queer way, expressed in what he wrote about the milk bottle could not be forgotten. It frightened you a little, but there it was, and in spite of his anger, or perhaps because of it, a lovely singing quality had got into the thing. In those few scrawled pages the miracle had been worked. I was a fool not to have put the sheets into my pocket. When I went down out of his apartment that evening, I did look for them in a dark alleyway, but they had become lost in a sea of rubbish that had leaked over the tops of a long row of tin ash cans that stood at the foot of a stairway leading from the back doors of the apartments above.

THREE SKETCHES

Ben Hecht

LIKE many Midwest writers (Sandburg, Lloyd Lewis, John Gunther, Meyer Levin, etc.), Ben Hecht worked on the Chicago _Daily News_. He was a police reporter and a feature writer, and in 1921 created a new kind of Chicago journalism with a column which appeared on the back page of that newspaper six times a week.

Hecht's column was very popular, especially with the young people, and many high school and college students began imitating his style.

Read today, most of the pieces which were gathered into a volume called _1001 Afternoons in Chicago_, seem outdated and overly sentimental. But among them several fine vignettes still gleam with a pure, hard light, which is the seal of Hecht's best work. The three pieces printed here are among the best he has done.

Mr. Hecht went on to become a novelist and a successful playwright. For over twenty years he has been a top-flight Hollywood screen writer. Occasionally he has written and produced his own pictures and, invariably, these have been memorable: _The Scoundrel, The Specter of the Rose, Crime Without Passion, Angels Over Broadway_, etc.

DON QUIXOTE AND HIS LAST WINDMILL*

SHERWOOD ANDERSON, the writer, and I were eating lunch in the back room of a saloon. Against the opposite wall sat a red-faced little man with an elaborate mustache and a bald head and happy grin. He sat alone at a tilted round table and played with a plate of soup.

* From _1001 Afternoons in Chicago_, by Ben Hecht, Covici-McGee, Chicago, 1922.

"Say, that old boy over there is trying to wigwag me," said Anderson. "He keeps winking and making signs. Do you know him?"

I looked and said no. The waiter appeared with a box of cigars.

"Mr. Sklarz presents his compliments," said the waiter, smiling.

"Who's Sklarz?" Anderson asked, helping himself to a cigar. The waiter indicated the red-faced little man. "Him," he whispered.

We continued our meal. Both of us watched Mr. Sklarz casually. He seemed to have lost interest in his soup. He sat beaming happily at the walls, a contagious elation about him. We smiled and nodded our thanks for the cigars. Whereupon after a short lapse, the waiter appeared again.

"What'll you have to drink, gentlemen?" the waiter inquired.

"Nothing," said Anderson, knowing I was broke. The waiter raised his continental eyebrows understandingly.

"Mr. Sklarz invites you, gentlemen, to drink his health—at his expense."

"Two glasses," Anderson ordered. They were brought. We raised them in silent toast to the little red-faced man. He arose and bowed as we drank.

"We'll probably have him on our hands now for an hour," Anderson frowned. I feared the same. But Mr. Sklarz reseated himself and, with many head-bowings in our direction, returned to his soup.

"What do you make of our magnanimous friend?" I asked. Anderson shrugged his shoulders.

"He's probably celebrating something," he said. "A queer old boy, isn't he?"

The waiter appeared a third time.

"What'll it be, gentlemen?" he inquired, smiling. "Mr. Sklarz is buying for the house."

For the house. There were some fifteen men eating in the place. Then our friend, despite his unassuming appearance, was evidently a creature of wealth! Well, this was growing interesting. We ordered wine again.

"Ask Mr. Sklarz if he will favor us by joining us at our table for this drink," I told the waiter. The message was delivered. Mr. Sklarz arose and bowed, but sat down again. Anderson and I beckoned in pantomime. Mr. Sklarz arose once more, bowed and hesitated. Then he came over.

As he approached a veritable carnival spirit seemed to deepen around us. The face of this little man with the elaborate black mustache was violent with suppressed good will and mirth. He beamed, bowed, shook hands and sat down. We drank one another's health and, as politely as we could, pressed him to tell us the cause for his celebration and good spirits. He began to talk.

He was a Russian Jew. His name was Sklarz. He had been in the Russian army years ago. In Persia. From a mountain in Persia you could see three great countries. In Turkey he had fought with baggy-trousered soldiers and at night joined them when they played their flutes outside the coffeehouses and sang songs about women and war. Then he had come to America and opened a box factory. He was very prosperous and the factory in which he made boxes grew too small.

So what did he do but take a walk one day to look for a larger factory. And he found a beautiful building just as he wanted. But the building was too beautiful to use for a factory. It should be used for something much nicer. So what did he do then but decide to open a dance hall, a magnificent dance hall, where young men and women of refined, fun-loving temperaments could come to dance and have fun.

"When does this dance hall open?" Anderson asked. Ah, in a little while. There were fittings to buy and put up first. But he would send us special invitations to the opening. In the meantime would we drink his health again? Mr. Sklarz chuckled. The amazing thing was that he wasn't drunk. He was sober.

"So you're celebrating," I said. Yes, he was celebrating. He laughed and leaned over the table toward us. His eyes danced and his elaborate mustache made a grotesque halo for his smile. He didn't want to intrude on us with his story, but in Persia and Turkey and the Urals he had found life very nice. And here in Chicago he had found life also very nice. Life was very nice wherever you went. And Anderson quoted, rather imperfectly, I thought:

> Oh, but life went gaily, gaily
> In the house of Idah Dally;
> There were always throats to sing
> Down the river bank with spring.

Mr. Sklarz beamed.

"Yes, yes," he said, "down the river benk mit spring." And he stood up and bowed and summoned the waiter. "See vat all the gentlemen vant," he ordered, "and give them vat they vant mit my compliments." He laughed, or, rather, chuckled. "I must be going. Excuse me," he exclaimed with a quick little bow. "I have other places to call on. Good-by. Remember me—Sam Sklarz. Be good —and don't forget Sam Sklarz when there are throats to zing down the river benk mit spring."

We watched him walk out. His shoulders seemed to dance, his short legs moved with a sprightly lift.

"A queer old boy," said Anderson. We talked about him for a half-hour and then left the place.

Anderson called me up the next morning to ask if I had read about it in the paper. I told him I had. A clipping on the desk in front of me ran:

Sam Sklarz, forty-six years old and owner of a box factory on the West Side, committed suicide early this morning by jumping into the drainage canal. Financial reverses are believed to have caused him to end his life. According to friends he was on the verge of bankruptcy. His liabilities were $8,000. Yesterday morning Sklarz cashed a check for $700, which represented the remains of his bank account, and disappeared. It is believed that he used the money to pay a few personal debts and then wandered around in a daze until the end. He left no word of explanation behind.

THE THING IN THE DARK*

It has the usual Huron Street ending. Emergency case. Psychopathic hospital. Dunning. But the landlady talked to the police

* From *1001 Afternoons in Chicago*.

sergeant. The landlady was curious. She wanted the police sergeant to tell her something. And the police sergeant, resting his chin on his elbow, leaned forward on his high stool and peered through the partition window at the landlady—and said nothing. Or rather, he said: "Don't know. That's the way with people sometimes. They get afraid."

This man came to Mrs. Balmer's rooming house in Huron Street when it was spring. He was a short, stocky man with a leathery face and little eyes. He identified himself as Joseph Crawford, offered to pay $5 a week for a 12-by-12 room on the third floor at the rear end of the long gloomy hallway and arrived the next day at Mrs. Balmer's faded tenement with an equally faded trunk. Nothing happened.

But when Mrs. Balmer entered the room the following morning to straighten it up she found several innovations. There were four kerosene lamps in the room. They stood on small rickety tables, one in each corner. And there was a new electric-light bulb in the central fixture. Mrs. Balmer took note of these things with a professional eye but said nothing. Idiosyncrasies are to be expected of the amputated folk who seek out lonely tenement bedrooms for a home.

A week later, however, Mrs. Balmer spoke to the man.

"You burn your light all night," said Mrs. Balmer, "and while I have no objection to that, still it runs up the electric-light bill."

The man agreed that this was true and answered that he would pay $1 extra each week for the privilege of continuing to burn the electric light all night.

Nothing happened. Yet Mrs. Balmer, when she had time for such things as contemplation, grew curious about the man in the back room. In fact she transferred her curiosity from the Japanese female impersonator on the second floor and the beautiful and remarkably gowned middle-aged woman on the first floor to this man who kept four kerosene lamps and an electric bulb burning all night on the third floor.

For some time Mrs. Balmer was worried over the thought that

this man was probably an experimenter. He probably fussed around with things as an old crank does sometimes, and he would end by burning down the house or blowing it up—accidentally.

But Mrs. Balmer's fears were removed one evening when she happened to look down the gloomy hallway and notice that this man's door was open. A gay, festive illumination streamed out of the opened doorway and Mrs. Balmer paid a social call. She found her roomer sitting in a chair, reading. Around him blazed four large kerosene lamps. But there was nothing else to notice. His eyes were probably bad, and Mrs. Balmer, after exchanging a few words on the subject of towels, transportation and the weather, said goodnight.

But always after that Mrs. Balmer noticed that the door remained open. Open doors are frequent in rooming houses. People grow lonely and leave the doors of their cubby holes open. There is nothing odd about that. Yet one evening while Mrs. Balmer stood gossiping with this man in the doorway she noticed something about him that disturbed her. She had noticed it first when she looked in the room before saying hello. Mr. Crawford was sitting facing the portieres that covered the folding doors that partitioned the room. The portieres were a very clever ruse of Mrs. Balmer. Behind them were screwed hooks and these hooks functioned as a clothes closet.

Mrs. Balmer noticed that Mr. Crawford, as she talked, kept staring at the portieres and watching them and that he seemed very nervous. The next morning, when she was straightening up the room, Mrs. Balmer looked behind the portieres. An old straw hat, an old coat, a few worn shirts hung from the hooks. There was nothing else but the folding door and this was not only locked but nailed up.

When two months had passed Mrs. Balmer had made a discovery. It had to do with the four kerosene lamps and the extra large electric bulb and the portieres. But it was an irritating discovery, since it made everything more mysterious than ever in the landlady's mind.

She had caught many glimpses of this man in the back room when he wasn't looking. Of evenings he sat with his door opened and his eyes fastened on the portieres. He would sit like that for hours and his leathery face would become gray. His little eyes would widen and his body would hunch up as if he were stiffening. But nothing happened.

Finally, however, Mrs. Balmer began to talk. She didn't like this man Crawford. It made her nervous to catch a glimpse of him in his too-brightly lighted room, sitting hour after hour staring at the portieres—as if there was something behind them, when there was nothing behind them except an old hat and coat and shirt. She looked every morning.

But he paid his rent regularly. He left in the morning regularly and always returned at eight o'clock. He was an ideal roomer—except that there never is an ideal roomer—but Mrs. Balmer couldn't stand his lights and his watching the portieres. It frightened her.

Screams sometimes sound in a rooming house. One night—it was after midnight—Mrs. Balmer woke up. The darkened house seemed filled with noises. A man was screaming.

Mrs. Balmer got dressed and called the janitor. There was no doubt in her mind where the noises came from. Some of the roomers were awake and looking sleepily and frightenedly out of their doorways. Mrs. Balmer and the janitor hurried to the back room on the third floor. It was Crawford screaming.

His door was closed, but it opened when the janitor turned the knob. Mr. Crawford was standing in front of the portieres in the too-brightly lighted room and screaming. His arms, as if overcoming some awful resistance, shot out, and his hands seized the portieres. With the amazing screams still coming from his throat, Mr. Crawford tore crazily at the portieres until they ripped from the rod above the folding door. They came down and the man fell with them. Over him, hanging on the "clothes-closet" hooks, were revealed an old straw hat, an old coat and a worn shirt.

"You see," said Mrs. Balmer to the police sergeant, "he was afraid of something and he couldn't stand the dark. And the portieres always frightened him. But the doctor wasn't able to do anything with him. The doctor says there was some secret about it and that Mr. Crawford went crazy because of this secret. The only thing they found out about him was that he used to be a sailor."

THE GREAT TRAVELER*

Alexander Ginkel has been around the world. A week ago he came to Chicago and, after looking around for a few days, located in one of the less expensive hotels and started to work as a porter in a well-known department store downtown.

A friend said, "There's a man living in my hotel who should make a good story. He's been around the world. Worked in England, Bulgaria, Russia, Siberia, China and everywhere. Was cook on a tramp steamer in the South Seas. A remarkable fellow, really."

In this way I came to call on Ginkel. I found him after work in his room. He was a short man, over thirty, and looked uninteresting. I told him that we should be able to get some sort of story out of his travels and experiences. He nodded.

"Yes," he said, "I've been all around the world."

Then he became silent and looked at me hopefully.

I explained, "People like to read about travelers. They sit at home themselves and wonder what it would be like to travel. You probably had a lot of experiences that would give people a vicarious thrill. I understand you were a cook on a tramp steamer in the South Seas."

"Oh, yes," said Ginkel, "I've been all over. I've been around the world."

We lighted pipes and Ginkel removed a book from a drawer in the dresser. He opened it and I saw it was a book of photographs —mostly pictures taken with a small camera.

"Here are some things you could use," he said. "You wanna look at them."

We went through the pictures together.

"This one here," said Ginkel, "is me in Vladivostok. It was taken on the corner there."

The photograph showed Ginkel dressed just as he was in the

* From *1001 Afternoons in Chicago.*

hotel room, standing near a lamppost on a street corner. There was visible a part of a store window.

"This one is interesting," said Ginkel, warming up. "It was taken in the archipelago. You know where. I forget the name of the town. But it was in the South Seas."

We both studied it for a space. It showed Ginkel standing underneath something that looked like a palm tree. But the tree was slightly out of focus. So were Ginkel's feet.

"It is interesting," said Ginkel, "But it ain't such a good picture. The lower part is kind of blurred, you notice."

We looked through the album in silence for a while. Then Ginkel suddenly remembered something.

"Oh, I almost forgot," he said. "There's one I think you'll like. It was taken in Calcutta. You know where. Here it is."

He pointed proudly toward the end of the book. We studied it through the tobacco smoke. It was a photograph of Ginkel dressed in the same clothes as before and standing under a store awning.

"There was a good light on this," said Ginkel, "and you see how plain it comes out."

Then we continued without comment to study other photographs. There were at least several hundred. They were all of Ginkel. Most of them were blurred and showed odds and ends of backgrounds out of focus, such as trees, streetcars, buildings, telephone poles. There was one that finally aroused Ginkel to comment:

"This would have been a good one, but it got light struck," he said. "It was taken in Bagdad."

When we had exhausted the album Ginkel felt more at ease. He offered me some tobacco from his pouch. I resumed the original line of questioning.

"Did you have any unusual adventures during your travels or did you get any ideas that we could fix up for a story?" I asked.

"Well," said Ginkel, "I was always a camera bug, you know. I guess that's what gave me the bug for traveling. To take pictures, you know. I got a lot more than these, but I ain't mounted them yet."

"Are they like the ones in the book?"

"Not quite so good, most of them," Ginkel answered. "They were taken when I hadn't had much experience."

"You must have been in Russia while the revolution was going on, weren't you?"

"Oh, yes. I got one there." He opened the book again. "Here," he said. "This was in Moscow. I was in Moscow when this was taken."

It was another picture of Ginkel slightly out of focus and standing against a store front. I asked him suddenly who had taken all the pictures.

"Oh, that was easy," he said. "I can always find somebody to do that. I take a picture of them first and then they take one of me. I always give them the one I take of them and keep the one they take of me."

"Did you see any of the revolution, Ginkel?"

"A lot of monkey business," said Ginkel. "I seen some of it. Not much."

The last thing I said was, "You must have come in for a lot of sights. We might fix up a story about that if you could give me a line on them." And the last thing Ginkel said was:

"Oh, yes, I've been around the world."

THE NOMINATION OF LINCOLN*

William E. Barton

ALMOST since its inception, Chicago has been a city in which conventioneers have liked to foregather (Rotary was born here). Large and alive, it has always supplied a suitable background for cloakroom or hotel-room compacts, before the main show moves into the big arena. Perhaps the vastness of the surrounding prairies appeals to the delegates; it challenges them to send their orations rolling out of the halls and upon the illimitable bosom of the plains. Perhaps, also, the city's lively night-life districts in which hard-working politicians far from home can relax after a tough day of orating have had something to do with its choice as a prime political convention town. At any rate, most of the history-making national conventions of both major parties have been held here.

The two most epochal ones, perhaps, were those held in 1860 and 1932. At one of them, when the nation was on the brink of a terrible civil war, a tall, lonely man from Springfield, Illinois, got the nomination. A delegation rode by train to Springfield to inform him of his nomination. At the other, when the nation was on the brink of economic collapse, a man from upstate New York who was to revolutionize the American way of life on many levels, won the nomination. Informed by phone of the balloting score, he flew to the convention in a fast plane to accept it.

THE convention that nominated Lincoln was the first to meet in a building erected especially for its own requirements. No American city at that time had a permanent structure known as a convention hall, or one intended for the particular use of great national gatherings. Up to that time in every city entertaining a national convention, a theater or other hall, erected for local purposes, had been found sufficiently large to house any convention that was held within that municipality. When Chicago invited the Republican convention of 1860, it was with the knowledge that it would be necessary for the city to erect a building adequately to care for the gathering.

If we were to depend entirely upon the press reports concerning "this gigantic structure, the largest audience-room in the United States," as the newspapers of the time truthfully described it, we might possibly exaggerate in our own minds the largeness of the building. If, for instance, it were to be compared with the Coliseum in which the Chicago conventions of recent years have been held, we should discover that the old Wigwam could have been lost almost anywhere inside of the Coliseum. It was just about the size of the Coliseum Annex which now serves for offices, restaurant and other adjunct uses of national conventions. The Wigwam stood at the corner of Lake and Market Streets near the fork of Chicago River. It had a frontage of one hundred and eighty feet on Market Street and a depth of one hundred feet on Lake. Four hundred and sixty-six delegates and about sixty newspaper correspondents were seated upon an elevated platform, which, with a committee room at either end, occupied one entire side of the building. The rest of the structure was open to the public, the ladies and some delegations provided with tickets being seated in the gallery. Chicago announced that the building and the hospitality of the city were equal to taking care of all creation.

Chicago at this time had forty-two hotels, all operated on the American plan. Their rates were from $1.50 to $2.50 per day for board and room, and the hotel proprietors then and ever since were accused of extortion. The number of visitors who came, however, was far beyond the ability of hotels to accommodate; private houses opened their doors, some for pay and others out of hospitality. The Eastern railroads granted a special round-trip rate of $15 from Buffalo, and the Western roads somewhat reluctantly followed their example.

The railroad trains approaching Chicago took what now are known as straw votes among their passengers bound for Chicago. On a Michigan Central train of twelve coaches, Seward had 210 votes against 30 for all other candidates. On a Chicago and Northwestern train Seward had 127 and all others 44. On a Chicago and Rock Island train Seward had 112 and the others totaled 41. On these three trains there appeared not to have been a single vote for Lincoln; but on a Chicago and Milwaukee train Seward had 368, Lincoln 93 and all others 46; while on a New Albany and Salem, Indiana, train Lincoln had 51, Seward 43, and the other candidates totaled 131.

Within the Wigwam on the morning of May sixteenth were crowded fully ten thousand persons. Four years before when the Republican national convention met in Philadelphia, a hall seating two thousand people had been ample for both delegates and spectators. At this convention ten thousand people jammed the Wigwam, and twenty thousand stood with hardly less enthusiasm outside.

The convention assembled at noon on Wednesday, May 16, 1860, Seward's fifty-ninth birthday. It was confidently expected that he would receive the nomination as a birthday present.

Governor Morgan, of New York, Chairman of the National Committee, called the convention to order. David Wilmot, of Pennsylvania, author of the famous Wilmot Proviso, was made temporary chairman and delivered the "keynote" speech. He was not a success as a presiding officer. A good deal of time was consumed discussing the question whether the convention would accept the invitation of the Chicago Board of Trade to take a short excursion on the lake at five o'clock in the afternoon. At two o'clock the convention took recess for three hours and reconvened at five to effect its permanent organization. At the five o'clock session Honorable George Ashmun, of Massachusetts, was elected permanent chairman. He had a good voice, and his rulings were clear and just. His election was a relief after the indecision and feeble presiding of Wilmot. A committee on resolutions was appointed to draft a platform. The convention adjourned until ten o'clock next morning.

The evening appears to have been spent by a considerable number of the delegates in a sail on Lake Michigan, but the politicians were otherwise engaged.

On Thursday morning, the Seward men, all wearing badges, formed a large and picturesque procession in front of the Richmond House, and marched to the Wigwam preceded by a finely uniformed band playing in honor of Seward one of the popular airs of the day, entitled "Oh, Isn't He a Darling." The forenoon of Thursday passed with no very exciting incidents.

On Thursday afternoon the first excitement occurred. The Committee on Platform earnestly desired to present a safe and sane doctrine which would solidify all forces opposed to the Democratic administration. It therefore omitted from the first draft some of the more pronounced utterances of the platform of 1856. Perhaps the most radical of the omitted affirmations was one quoted from the Declaration of Independence declaring that all men were endowed by their Creator with certain inalienable rights, among which were life, liberty and the pursuit of happiness. When the committee presented a platform from which that affirmation had been omitted, Joshua R. Giddings, of Ohio, a white-haired, battle-scarred veteran of the antislavery warfare, arose and moved its reinsertion. The convention voted his amendment down, and Giddings rose and indignantly started to walk out of the Wigwam, but was detained and took a seat in the rear of the room, refraining from participation in the proceedings until the vote was rescinded. A little later George William Curtis, one of the youngest of New York's delegates, rose, and in an earnest and tactful speech renewed Giddings' motion. His amendment prevailed, and Giddings returned placated, and the platform was adopted amid tremendous enthusiasm. Thus the first threatened split was averted.

This result was achieved with a suddenness that surprised the convention, and brought it at an earlier hour than had been expected to the time for nominations.

If printers invariably kept their promises, Abraham Lincoln would not have been president of the United States. If the convention could have got to balloting on Thursday night, William H.

Seward would have been nominated. But the secretary was compelled to announce that the papers necessary for the keeping of the tally were not at hand, but would arrive in a few minutes. The convention was impatient at the delay, and a motion was made by some unknown delegate "that this convention adjourn until ten o'clock tomorrow morning." The motion to adjourn prevailed. If the unnamed delegate who made the motion to adjourn could be identified, he, perhaps animated by no higher motive than restlessness or the desire for a drink, would be entitled to mention as one of the otherwise nameless voices that have uttered the messages of destiny.

The New York delegation was the largest and best organized of the state delegations. It was headed by Thurlow Weed, and had as one of its next most important attractions, a distinguished prize fighter who served as bartender for the Seward interests at the Richmond House. Between these two notable men, the delegates had very nearly all the Republican leadership of New York, except Horace Greeley.

Horace Greeley did not come to the convention of 1860 as a member of the New York delegation. That body was controlled by the Seward interests. Greeley sat in the convention as the substitute for a delegate from Oregon, the state over which as a territory Lincoln had been offered the office of governor.

Greeley came to the Chicago convention as the avowed opponent of Thurlow Weed and William H. Seward. Thurlow Weed was a politician as adroit as America has ever seen. Desiring no office for himself, he greatly desired to say what men should occupy office. He was editor of the Albany *Journal,* and the ablest paragrapher of his generation. During the period when the Whig Party was coming to its end and the Republican Party was in process of formation, Weed and Seward had no more earnest or effective assistant than Horace Greeley, a younger man, who had come into great power as editor of the New York *Tribune.* The *Tribune* had begun with many difficulties attending it; but it grew to be one of the strongest papers in the nation. It was read as few papers are read in rural communities, and it influenced the thought of its readers as few papers then or since have done.

On Saturday evening, November 11, 1854, Greeley wrote to Governor Seward a notable letter, beginning as follows:

Governor Seward:
  The election is over, and its results sufficiently ascertained. It seems to me a fitting time to announce to you the dissolution of the political firm of Seward, Weed and Greeley by the withdrawal of the junior partner—said withdrawal to take effect on the morning after the first Thursday in February next.

When Horace Greeley mailed that letter, he made it possible for Abraham Lincoln to be chosen president six years later.

So Greeley came to the Chicago convention, unrecognized by the New York state delegation, but entitled to a seat, a voice and a vote. He came to defeat Seward. He did not favor Lincoln, though he had heard Lincoln in Chicago in 1847, and met him in Washington in 1848, where his impression was that Lincoln was "a genial, cheerful rather homely man, noticeably tall, and the only Whig from Illinois, not remarkable otherwise."

Greeley came to Chicago with strong expectation of uniting the votes opposed to Seward in support of Edward Bates. But Bates had no possible hope of winning, and Greeley, after midnight of Thursday, sadly faced the fact that if Seward was defeated it must be by another man than Bates. Reluctantly he came to believe that the man who could defeat Seward in the convention without losing the election at the polls was Lincoln.

It was possible for Lincoln to be chosen as the nominee of the Republican convention not because he was believed to be an abler man than Seward, but because Seward by his greater prominence had awakened certain antagonisms which Lincoln by his obscurity had avoided. It must be admitted as we view the matter from its present point of vantage that the hostilities which Seward had aroused were mostly to his credit.

Nevertheless, it was then clearly discerned that Pennsylvania would be hopelessly lost to the Republican Party if Seward were nominated, and Indiana also was more than doubtful. Some of the states which would probably vote against Seward were "October" states, whose national elections were held a month earlier than those of the majority of the states, and whose influence was therefore accounted greater as foreshadowing the probable result of the general election. Seward was defeated because it was so well known just where he stood on the great national issues.

Lincoln was keeping in close touch with the situation. Several men in the convention were keeping him informed. Among them was Mark W. Delahay, of Kansas. Delahay was a Marylander by birth, who had come to Illinois and moved on to Kansas, where he was first a Douglas Democrat, and afterward became a Republican. He is the man who wrote to Lincoln that he thought he could be elected a member of the Kansas delegation, and do something to swing it for Lincoln, but that he could not afford to pay his own expenses to Chicago and back, and to whom Lincoln wrote saying that Lincoln would send him $100 toward his expenses. But Delahay did not succeed in getting on the delegation, and the delegates from Kansas were instructed for Seward. Lincoln wrote to Delahay saying to come with the delegation; "not to stir them up to anger" by too great insistence upon Lincoln, but to come, and Lincoln still would pay the $100. Delahay came to Chicago, and was in frequent communication with Lincoln during the convention. On Thursday afternoon Delahay wired Lincoln that his nomination appeared hopeless, and asked if Lincoln would accept a nomination as vice-president if Seward was chosen as nominee for president. Lincoln replied confidentially that he would accept, provided his friends thought it wise for him to do so.

At 11:40 Thursday night, Horace Greeley, who had been earnestly endeavoring to defeat Seward, telegraphed the New York *Tribune,* "My conclusion from all that I can gather tonight is that the opposition to Governor Seward can not concentrate on any candidate, and that he will be nominated."

Many accounts have been given of what followed. It is certain that William H. Seward would have been nominated if Horace Greeley had not quarreled with Seward and his manager, Thurlow Weed. It is quite certain that Greeley on Thursday night gave up all hope of defeating Seward, but that before morning he had changed his judgment by reason of his faith that Abraham Lincoln not only could defeat Seward in the convention, but also could defeat the Democratic candidate at the polls. Honorable

Addison G. Procter, the sole surviving delegate to the convention, attributes the determining influence to the border-state leaders, notably Cassius M. Clay.

On Friday morning the Seward forces gathered behind their magnificent brass band, and paraded through the streets of Chicago in triumphal procession to the Wigwam. The Lincoln forces, with much less of display, packed the Wigwam with shouters. There were so many Lincoln shouters in the Wigwam that a considerable part of the Seward crowd that had followed the band could not obtain entrance. The story of the disappointment of the Seward men when they returned from their procession and found themselves excluded from the seats for which they held tickets in the galleries of the Wigwam, has been told often, and appears entirely reliable. One incident hitherto unpublished may shed light on the way in which the Lincoln shouters were able to get into the Wigwam ahead of the Seward men, and occupy the seats. There were no reserved and numbered seats, but it was not expected that tickets would be issued in excess of the capacity of the building. On the evening before the nomination, however, Ward Hill Lamon obtained from the printers of the seat tickets a large supply of extra tickets. He set certain young men at work signing these tickets with the names of the officers of the convention. These young men did their part right merrily, and signed tickets nearly all night. In the morning, these tickets were furnished in liberal number to friends of Lincoln, who were clamoring for tickets for their friends. The tickets were given out with the suggestion that it would be well to get in early. Of course, neither Lincoln nor any of his responsible managers knew of this piece of work, which had the effect of crowding out a large fraction of Seward's shouting strength, and giving the space over to the shouters for Lincoln. A brass band upon the street may be considerably less effective than a well-placed company of leather-lunged shouters. But neither they who followed the band nor they who packed the Wigwam knew that already the nomination had very nearly been settled. It had come to be believed by a considerable number of wavering delegates that if Seward should be nominated, he would be defeated; for he could not carry Pennsylvania, Indiana, or perhaps Illinois. Illinois and

Indiana were for Lincoln, and the delegates had been hearing more and more about him, and coming to think more and more favorably for him. When the Pennsylvania delegation came over to Lincoln, the matter was practically settled.

A pamphlet had been circulated among the Pennsylvania men, ostensibly favorable to Cameron as president, but in reality planned to produce a sentiment favorable to his election as vice-president on a ticket with Edward Bates, of Missouri, who was Greeley's candidate. Cameron was certain to be named as the "favorite son" of Pennyslvania, but it was certain that he could not be nominated as president and not likely that he could win the nomination as vice-president. The enthusiastic friends of Lincoln did not hesitate to declare to leading Pennsylvania delegates that if they would be content with a seat in the Cabinet for Cameron, there would be no trouble about arranging the matter, provided Pennsylvania would go for Lincoln. That was welcome news to Pennsylvania. Lincoln had no share in the making of this bargain, but he kept it.

At ten o'clock on Friday morning the Wigwam was jammed, and the crowd outside is said to have reached two blocks away. The New Yorkers prepared to do all necessary cheering for Seward. But the Illinois attendants at the convention were far more numerous. In the matter of lung power the men of the prairies were far and away superior to the New York delegation, because there were more of them.

Nominations began almost immediately. There were then no nominating speeches, such as later have come to thrill and sometimes to weary conventions. Honorable William H. Evarts first obtained the floor, and presented the name of Seward in these words:

"I take the liberty to name as a candidate to be nominated by this convention for the office of president of the United States, William H. Seward."

He was immediately followed by Norman D. Judd, of Illinois, with these words:

"I desire, on behalf of the delegation from Illinois, to put in nomination as a candidate for president of the United States, Abraham Lincoln, of Illinois."

There were other nominations equally brief, and a few seconds.

The only one of these that contained any attempt at oratory was that of Mr. Delano, of Ohio, seconding the nomination of Abraham Lincoln as "a man who can split rails and maul Democrats." That little speech set the convention on fire.

In the balloting now, the roll call of the states is in alphabetical order. It is an impressive sound, the musical names beginning with Alabama, Arkansas, and so on down the alphabet. But in 1860 a geographical order prevailed, beginning with New England and moving westward. There were 465 votes; 233 necessary to choice. On the first ballot Seward had 173½, Lincoln 102, with Cameron, of Pennsylvania, third with 50½. On the second ballot the name of Cameron was withdrawn, and the vote stood, Seward 184½, a gain of 11 votes, and Lincoln 181, a gain of 79. Chase, of Ohio, now stood third with 42½ votes. On the third ballot, Seward had 180, a loss of 4½, while Lincoln had 231½, lacking only 1½ of receiving the number necessary to nominate. Hundreds of people were keeping tally sheets, and it was plainly seen how nearly the third ballot had come to nominating Lincoln. Before the vote was announced, Mr. Carter, of Ohio, sprang upon his chair and announced a change of five votes from Chase to Lincoln. A cannon had been placed on the roof, but the confusion was such that for a moment or two the man in charge could not be made to understand what had happened. When he understood and fired the gun, it could hardly be heard in the Wigwam. The Chicago *Tribune* declared that earth had heard no such tumult since the walls of Jericho fell down.

Other states then hurried to change their votes. There was the familiar "rush to get into the band wagon." When the vote was finally announced, out of 466 votes cast, with 234 necessary to choice, Abraham Lincoln, of Illinois, had 364.

The nomination of Lincoln occurred about half past twelve, and was followed by a number of speeches endorsing the nomination. At about half past one the convention adjourned until five o'clock, at which time it reconvened and nominated Hannibal Hamlin, of Maine, for vice-president. Then the convention gave cheers for the nominees, the platform, and the ladies of Chicago, and adjourned to "meet at the White House on the fourth of March next."

SMITH IS OUT

THE NATIONAL DEMOCRATIC
CONVENTION OF 1932

F. Raymond Daniell
Anne O'Hare McCormick

MOST national political conventions are bitter affairs. There are always the "favorite sons" with their tight coteries of followers who, arriving at the convention hall, go into high gear immediately. Their heroes, of course, are mere pawns in the bigger political game of the show; usually hotel-room deals have already been made before the gavel thumps on the rostrum. But these deals are not hard and fast and the jockeying from the first day on is intense and obdurate. Friendships are sundered and often local political machines are wrecked in an hour.

The Democratic convention of 1932 held in Chicago was a dramatic thing. Every one knew the nomination lay between Alfred Smith and Franklin Roosevelt, two old friends. The result soon became a foregone conclusion, and Al Smith went home without congratulating the winner.

The day after he arrived in New York, mere chance made me a spectator to one of the most poignant little dramas in American political life. On Monday, July 4, 1932, I was sitting in Luchow's Restaurant on Fourteenth Street, New York. For three years I had been struggling to get a foothold in New York as a writer, and only the previous week I had signed a contract with a publisher who was going to bring out my first novel in the fall. With the contract and an advance in my possession, I felt the world was in my pocket. I had been eating in cafeterias or cooking my own meals for years, and I now wanted to splurge. So here I sat in this superb old restaurant with poet and novelist Charles Reznikoff, who was leaving for Hollywood in a few days.

It was a dim, rainy afternoon and the restaurant was almost deserted. Many people had left town during the big holiday and the waiters were standing around idly. As we began attacking our first course, we became aware of a nearby, low-pitched gravelly voice, which had become familiar to millions over the radio and in the newsreels during the past year. Turning our heads toward the back of the restaurant, we saw a small party of men and women eating, surrounded by empty tables. The man who was talking was Alfred E. Smith.

Charlie Reznikoff and I looked at each other. Then we glanced back at the little party in the rear. Al Smith was still talking. He was saying something about his favorite actors or comedians, I forget which. I heard the name George Jessel, only Al Smith said Georgie Jessel. It was obvious that the ex-governor of New York was trying to inject some humor into his sad little party which included his wife; but the meal was going down gloomily. I recognized lean, tight-lipped John F. Curry, then the head of Tammany Hall; he was eating silently. Over at another table Borough President Levey sat eating with his wife. Al Smith waved to Levey and Levey self-consciously waved back, then continued eating.

Though Reznikoff and I did not speak, we were thinking the same thoughts. Only yesterday, at Chicago, this man behind us had been a potential president-elect of the United States of America. Today, sitting here with his wife and a few close friends, he was out. We listened to his gravelly voice, which, as time went on, lost its lift and became petulant and gloomy, a fitting counterpart to the empty restaurant, the rainy afternoon, and his bad break at Chicago.

Halfway through our meal, Al Smith and his party rose. The waiters snapped to that type of reverent attention with which they alert themselves whenever a famous personage enters or leaves the place. The little party passed close to our table and I saw Smith's gloomy, politically battle-scarred face at close range. At that moment it was an eloquent face, telling as it did the story of the biggest defeat of his life.

The three women passed before the three men, Smith and Curry bringing up the rear. As the women and one man went out upon the rainy sidewalk and into the long black chauffeured car that stood waiting at the curb, Curry suddenly put a detaining hand on Al Smith's arm. The head of Tammany Hall with a slight motion indicated he was going to the men's room.

Smith stood there and waited. He stared out at the cheerless rain of Fourteenth Street. He waited while Curry went into the men's room and came out again, adjusting his clothing.

That was all. But in that little drama we saw the final defeat of Alfred E. Smith. If he had gotten the nomination at Chicago, Curry would never have dared to make him wait while he paid that little visit to Luchow's gents' room.

McADOO'S SPEECH STARTS FIREWORKS*

F. Raymond Daniell

THE Democrats, assembled in the great Stadium here at Chicago for their national convention, started their campaign to put Governor Roosevelt in the White House like a medieval army embarking on a holy war.

The moment when his nomination first became certain was as picturesque and dramatic as any convention crowd has witnessed in many years. It was the expression of a paradox, an emotional prairie fire which swept across the delegates, met a backfire from the pro-Smith galleries and blazed on.

William Gibbs McAdoo, gaunt, angular son-in-law of President Wilson, held the match which set it off. The ninety votes of California and Texas were the tinder.

Red-eyed and haggard-looking, the delegates, who had seen the dawn come with no prospect of their deadlock breaking, settled wearily into their seats this evening prepared for another long siege. There had been rumors of defections in the camp of the allies against the New York governor, but nothing definite was known until Mr. McAdoo began to speak.

At the moment when he revealed his purpose of putting Speaker Garner's California vote into the breach for Governor Roosevelt the hall was as silent as a great cathedral during Mass. Then a cheer started on one side of the room from the fringe of the Roosevelt delegates.

It swelled to a roaring, throaty cheer which poured out of the loud-speakers, hung like a bunch of morning glories above the speaker's stand. Men were on their seats cheering, waving their hats and holding up the pine poles to which the standards of their states were fixed. Only the monster floodlights for the motion picture men were burning, and the flag-draped ceiling was as black as the sky on a starless night.

Then the Stars and Stripes began to wave above a dozen delegations at once, not listlessly, not designedly as they had in the stampeding demonstrations for various candidates, but like the colors of a conquering army on the march.

The fire was spreading. It cut a swath across the hall, but it passed by a whole block of standards where the Smith delegations of New Jersey, Massachusetts, Rhode Island and Connecticut were seated. It licked about the standard of New York and conquered it, but passed by John F. Curry, Mayor James J. Walker, John H. McCooey, and all the Tammany leaders.

The California banner with its grizzly bear was waving triumphantly with the national colors. Suddenly a rebel yell split the air, and the delegates from Texas, Speaker Garner's home state, were on their seats waving the standard of their state and above it their Lone Star flag.

From that moment there was no real need of balloting. Everyone knew it was all over but the shouting. Out in the aisles swarmed the half-hysterical delegates. A Texan, who probably won't remember what he did, half ran, half fell through the aisle to the rostrum and surrendered the guidon of Texas to Mr. McAdoo who received it with a grim but satisfied smile.

Like knights raising their petards before their king, the standard-bearers gathered below the tall, straight Mr. McAdoo and held aloft the standards of their states. The surging mob stopped and then moved on around and around the hall and up and down the

two center aisles, black with a phalanx of seated glum-faced followers of the anti-Roosevelt coalition.

Not until the demonstration had almost spent itself did the
backfire become apparent. But in the first lull in the din from the
floor there rolled down from the overcrowded balconies an ominous and sonorous roar of disapproval. The Smith adherents in the
galleries looked upon the defection of California and Texas from
the allied high command as treason. A bullfight crowd, angered at
a gaucherie of a toreador, might have roared as they did.

At Mr. McAdoo's first attempt to continue his explanation of his
vote, interrupted in the middle by the spontaneous response on the
floor, he was drowned out by the roar of disapproval. Thomas J.
Walsh, permanent chairman of the convention, his face red and his
eyes flashing like the eyes of a tiger whose cubs are threatened,
seized his gavel and brought it down with a shattering crash.

It had no effect. Grizzled old veteran that he is, he waited for
the howling mob to catch its breath. In that instant's pause he appealed to their civic pride. The appeal only increased the word-
drowning howls from the balconies.

Senator Walsh appealed to the gallery mob as guests of the convention. Still the bass drone of disapproval rolled down. The chairman paused again. Then he appealed to the Mayor of the city for
the sake of his city's reputation to step in and control the angry
throng. Several moments of booing followed before Mayor Cermak
elbowed his way through the milling delegates on the floor and
stepped before the microphone on the platform.

The booing turned to cheers. Mayor Cermak's Illinois delegation had many adherents of "The Happy Warrior" among its number. He is popular here. But even he could not still the voice of
the mob, which seemed to feel somehow their hero had been
cheated.

As though he realized that only physical exhaustion would end
the hostile demonstration, Mr. McAdoo bent down and placed his
lips close to the microphone.

"I don't care what the galleries think," he began. His next
words were drowned out. He kept right on shouting at the top of

his voice into the microphone, concluding by throwing his hands over his head and shouting in a momentary lull that he was happy to announce that "California casts her forty-four votes for Governor Franklin D. Roosevelt."

"What do the galleries think now?" yelled an excited Texan.

The stampede was on again among the delegates, but it had almost spent itself. Soon the galleries and the delegates grew tired of booing and cheering against each other and subsided to let the clerk continue calling the roll and make official what had been done already.

Young Franklin D. Roosevelt, Jr., the governor's son, was standing on the platform beside the towering Jim Farley, serenely surveying what months of missionary work by him had wrought. His elder brother, James Roosevelt, was down on the floor receiving the congratulations of friends with the nervous excitement of a bridegroom at the church door.

The scenes which followed the formal nomination of New York's governor were but repetitions of the demonstrations which followed Mr. McAdoo's dramatic announcement with only about half as much spontaneity. The mood had passed. They cheered the announcement that the man they had selected to be their nominee in 1932 would be here tomorrow to address them, but they really were very tired after the sleepless ordeal of yesterday.

THE TWO CONVENTIONS: CHICAGO CONTRAST*

Anne O'Hare McCormick

THE most dramatic contrast suggested by the political Olympics in Chicago is not the well-known contrast between the official behavior of Democrats and Republicans (both of whom held their conventions here). They do behave differently, of course. From one convention to the next the signs were shifted in the Stadium, one set of badges was replaced by another, and though the scene was

* Copyright, 1932, by the New York *Times*. Reprinted by special permission of the New York *Times*.

otherwise the same, and the language, ideas and appearance of the delegates were almost indistinguishable, the political climate was completely changed.

A stranger might have supposed that the Republicans were the minority party; they made so little stir and noise, compared to the jostling, crowding, animated Democrats. But even the stranger, comparing these assemblies, would have realized why our parties are of the carry-all type. Each represents incompatibility of opinion and compatibility of temper, a temperamental and emotional congeniality that makes Tammany and Carolina Democrats and Pennsylvania and Idaho Republicans, with nothing else in common, more at home with each other in disagreement than they would be in harmony with the opposite party.

Americans belong to parties for company, rather than by conviction.

We saw one convention attached to a single wire, and the other pulled hither and yon by vocal strings. The first was deserted by the insurgents, which left nothing to argue about except liquor, and the second was threatened by a new kind of political peril, a bolt of the conservatives. New alignments appeared and old leaders disappeared. The more up-to-the-minute became the devices for amplifying sound, the more old-fashioned the oratory. The lapel microphone gives the ear of the universe to the floor delegate who heretofore was only a number in a poll.

Nevertheless, the two conventions were the same two acts of the same old show. The real contrast was between them both and the convention city. If they had intended and designed a scene to reduce them to comic-strip proportions, the parties could not have done better than to meet at this moment, and to gather against the background of Chicago.

As the words of Lincoln and Jefferson echo on the air the Illinois braves call loudly for Len Small and Big Bill Thompson. Squadrons of airplanes zip across the sky to welcome the delegates. Bands and fireworks play along the lakefront, the organ in the new Stadium thunders "How Dry I Am" and "Hail, Hail, the Gang's All Here," parades thump around the aisles, giving the candidate from Texas ten minutes more enthusiasm than the candidate from Maryland.

And on the way to the hall the delegates pass a breadline blocks long. Nearby is a little park where a loud-speaker broadcasts the proceedings. Hungry men stand listless and silent, too impassive even to raise their eyes from the ground, while the waves of speech flow over them.

Chicago is the ideal location for dancing on top of a volcano. Eruptive and exciting, a city of superlatives, it exaggerates all the splendor and squalor of America. The lakefront development is the fabulous façade for some of the darkest slums in the world. Behind the once imposing brownstone fronts of Grand Boulevard lives a solid black city, armed and watchful.

Looping the Loop are other fortified towns. Here the underworld does not bother to hide its face. Where yesterday was Lake Michigan rises another world's fair, rise museums, bridges, arches, audacious outlines of modernist buildings, and on the grassy margins the jobless sleep day and night. One sports a sign: "Don't disturb."

Chicago has a new planetarium, inevitably the first in the United States, the last word in planetariums anywhere. Around the base of the dome the city skyline is cut in silhouette; above it wheel the reflected planets of an artificial firmament. But when the lights are turned on nothing remains of the shadow show save Chicago.

The political conventions are rather like that. Against this background they fade away, insubstantial as the stars of a planetarium. For Chicago is incredible but real. More, it is a kind of live exhibit of all our best and worst. It is real, and it made the party maneuvers even more unreal than usual. To go from the streets into the Stadium, into hotel corridors and into campaign headquarters swarming with barkers and strategists, was like entering a theater where ham actors were rehearsing old-fashioned burlesque.

The delegates themselves felt the unreality. Unlike the professional representatives in Washington, they were fresh from the actual world, and troubled by faint stirrings of a sense of responsibility. But only as individuals they worried; as conventions they developed mass movements and a mass mind swayed by purposes distinct from those of the component members. Thus, the Republican delegates were wetter than the convention as a body. They were almost unanimous in their desire to name a candidate other than Curtis for vice-president. The Democratic majority was less for Roosevelt than against the old party leaders, against the East. The convention dragged its members along almost against their will. It mobilized them into a movement, the movement of an America turning its back on the bright lights of the city and regretfully headed for the old home.

THE EARLY BEGINNINGS
OF BATHHOUSE JOHN*

Lloyd Wendt and
Herman Kogan

IN CHICAGO the tie-up between municipal politics and the underworld is an old, old story. The leaders of the criminal element for the most part have always been strong men, good organizers, valuable vote-swingers. The careers of some of them have been brief, ending in a back alley or at the bottom of the Drainage Canal. Other reigns have been long and fruitful—for the faithful.

Bathhouse John's career was a lengthy one. He was a politician first and last, and he aligned himself with the best vote-getting apparatus of the famous First Ward— the vice element. His was one of the most colorful careers in American politics: among other things, he dabbled in race horses, oratory, popular songwriting and poetry of the barnyard variety. His intimate and partner was Hinky Dink, whose career paralleled his own. Their path crossed that of Yerkes the traction magnate, Big Bill Thompson, Samuel Insull and Cermak, who later took the bullet, down in Florida, intended for Franklin D. Roosevelt.

In *Lords of the Levee,* Lloyd Wendt and Herman Kogan, two very talented Chicago newspapermen, have limned for us that gaudy era when the Levee was wide, wide open.

In this excerpt, we learn how Bathhouse John, one of the big "lords," got his start in Chicago politics.

JOHN JOSEPH COUGHLIN had his roots in the First Ward, and never was a soil more fructuous. There Chicago itself grew up, from a ragged little slab town trestled in a swamp to a blowsy, teeming metropolis that was able, by universal consensus, to burn up in 1871 more ill-gotten damnation than any city since Sodom and Gomorrah. Chicago had a reputation. It was bad, and it was totally ignored by the good citizens who had something better to do than plant lilies in the front yard. Soul and sinew of this ill repute was the First Ward, brilliant with achievement of solid gain by day, red-lighted and lulled by the soft chatter of chips and dice by night.

To this district had come, in 1857, a ruddy, big-chested Irishman named Michael Coughlin. He was a native of County Roscommon, a firm-jawed, benevolent man who had arrived in this country as a boy of thirteen. For some years he had lived in Lake County, Illinois, near Waukegan, then a drab expanse of woods and prairie with a few farmhouses and settlements scattered about. After working for years at varied laboring jobs, Coughlin moved into the rapidly growing city, settling in Connelly's Patch, an Irish district east of the Chicago River, between Adams and Monroe Streets. Here he met Johanna Hanley, a buxom colleen from County Limerick, whom he wed in 1858. Here John, their first son, was born on August 15, 1860.

Despite expenses entailed by the birth of the son, Michael saved enough to buy a grocery at Polk and Wells Streets. He began to prosper mildly, and he and his wife set about devoutly to raise a large family. Two years after John's birth came a dark-eyed son whom they named Joseph. Several years later Mary was born, a birth so difficult for Johanna Coughlin that she died a few days later.

With three youngsters to look after, Michael married Annie Whelan, a neighbor, and she, in the five years preceding the Chicago fire of 1871, bore three children, Michael Jr., George, and Kate. Over this brood the new Mrs. Coughlin ruled efficiently, and John especially was fond of her. The family was typical of Connelly's Patch domesticity. Coughlin, stern and proper, rarely smoked or drank, and in the children's presence never said so much as "damn." He was prudent, industrious and thrifty and on his way toward becoming a well-to-do man when the great fire of 1871 wiped out the store and the family home.

John went into Iroquois County in central Illinois to work on the farm of a relative for several months. By the time he returned to Chicago his father had opened a newer but smaller store at Taylor and Miller Streets. Funds were scarce, and thenceforth the young Coughlin had to earn his spending money and part of his keep. John evidently never regretted this, and in his later political life he made capital of it. Invariably in newspaper stories of later years commemorating the holocaust of 1871, Coughlin was quoted:

"Why, money didn't mean anything to me. I'm glad that fire came along and burned the store. Say, if not for that bonfire I might have been a rich man's son and gone to Yale—and never amounted to nothing!"

When John resumed his classes at the Jones School, at Harrison and Federal Streets, he took a job as assistant to the school janitor. Thus he acquired his first nickname—"Dusty John"—for he usually appeared in class with shirt and trousers grimy and sooty from the coal room. John took no offense at the sobriquet; he was big and agreeable and shyly happy over whatever attention he got. He responded to calls of his playmates with a cheery wave of his hand, a gesture characteristic of him the rest of his life.

Although he was definitely not an honor student, big Johnny Coughlin got along well with his teachers and the other pupils. He liked everybody, and was happy to do things for them. He made friends with towheaded Billy Lorimer, who was to progress to streetcar conductor, then political fixer and grafter, and, finally, United States senator; Joey Friedman, who would later be a saloonkeeper and political aide to Coughlin; and Andy Hoffman, the school's star ballplayer. It was Andy who became to John a symbol of all he himself was not. Andy was lively and quick of speech, and one of the brightest pupils in the school. He had a special ability to get along in the gang. He and big John, who stood a head and a half taller, became close friends, and it was Andy who lured the janitor's helper from his duties, showed him the wonders of the waterfront, took him to theaters and on bicycle trips through Lincoln Park.

This little-man-big-man team was a popular combination in Connelly's Patch. The little fellow did the thinking and planning, the big man lent his presence and took on all comers in combat. Hoffman, indispensable to the team, persuaded his mates in the Phoenix Ball Club, a neighborhood outfit, to permit his cumbersome friend to play with them. After some wrangling young Coughlin was accepted for right field, considered by the club members the least likely spot for action. In addition to that, he batted last. But John was content, and he cheerfully agreed to everything Andy planned for him.

With the members of the Phoenix Club, Johnny Coughlin passed a life of early adolescence in the pattern of the hundreds of other boys who were growing up in the Patch. There were trips to the river docks to watch the windjammers bowl in, laden with lumber, machinery, and bales of goods destined for the wholesale houses on the river's west branch. There were jaunts to Lincoln and Jackson Parks, cross-town journeys to the rapidly developing industrial areas on Goose Island. And sometimes the Phoenix gang went on embarrassed and delicious trips to the environs of the infamous Biler Avenue.

Whenever the Phoenix boys traveled they were certain to have Johnny Coughlin along, for his presence was required as the foundation of a prank favored by Chicago boys in the late seventies. This was brought off when the group boarded a rickety red and yellow horse-drawn car which, despite newspaper shrieks and civic howls, was manned by a single bobtail driver who also served as a conductor. Fares were dropped into a wooden box near the entrance. It was the delight of the Phoenix gang when they went to the baseball fields around Thirty-ninth Street and Wentworth Avenue, to hand several pennies to Big John. These, a fraction of the required five-cent fare, John would hastily deposit in the receptacle and the driver would invariably shout: "Hey, you, not enough!" But he could not very well leave his horse to argue with the ponderous passenger, even if he felt so inclined, and the boys, slapping Johnny's ample back, would yell with laughter. John laughed with

them, shouting to the driver: "Th' papers say there oughta be conductors! Whyn't ya put on conductors if ya think we're cheatin'?"

Johnny Coughlin's fun with the gang was limited, for he was
a big boy and his parents found plenty of jobs for him to do. Andy
Hoffman went on to graduate with highest honors, but John left
the Jones School when he was thirteen years old and in the seventh
grade. For two years he was a student in the Christian Brothers' Industrial School at Federal and Van Buren Streets and when he
was fifteen his education was decreed at an end and he was ready to
go to work.

At fifteen John Coughlin looked a young man of twenty. He
was nearly six feet tall, with powerfully built shoulders and chest,
thick, bull neck, imposing head and jaw, and hard blue eyes. He
worked industriously at all sorts of jobs, once holding three at a
time: butcher's delivery boy, water boy on a railroad gang and
clerk in his father's store. When work was slack he went swimming
in the summer with a neighborhood gang led by Billy Lorimer,
and one winter when he was eighteen he joined a dramatic club
which met in a second-floor hall at Halsted and De Koven Streets.
Good-natured, naïve, content with whatever life offered, Johnny
Coughlin was known as a boy of few bad habits, few possibilities,
and many friends. Until he was nineteen, he was satisfied to work
at the plentiful jobs open to one of brawn, and was happy when he
could save a little money.

Black-haired Joe, his brother, meanwhile had taken to companionship with race-horse jockeys and touts who frequented the downtown saloons. Considerably sharper than John, Joe also made
friends readily, but in addition he made use of them. He got a job
at a race track through such friendly connections, and at seventeen,
looking twenty-three he had developed into a proficient race hand-
icapper. Joe showed up at home flush with money and speaking of
his prominent friends, and John, stirring with a new ambition,
asked his brother if he could get him a job, a real, steady job. Joe
was sure that he could.

Favored spots of Joe and his cronies, next to the saloons, were
the city's bathhouses. To these emporiums of relaxation and cleanli-

ness came prize fighters and jockeys, race-horse trainers and stew bums, politicians and prominent merchants. In them a man could scrub himself in an ample tin-lined tub, steam in a cabinet, take a quick shower, and get a tingling rubdown with salt or sand. Some of the bathhouses were elaborate affairs, equipped with rooms and cots on which a customer could sleep off a cold or a drunk after an hour in the steam room. Finest bathhouse in Chicago was in the Palmer House where, in addition to the wainscoted baths, was a tiny pool in which the clients could swim. The Palmer House baths were famous throughout the country, and drew the patronage of wealthy and powerful men as well as the sporting gentry. A scouring scrub at the Palmer House following a roaring night in the Levee was considered one of the grandest luxuries the nation afforded, and visiting dignitaries often availed themselves of this delightful, if enervating, experience.

The lesser bathhouses were equipped with concrete floors, make-shift showers, and crude bath cabinets, and some, unable to meet the competition of more favored places, were little more than brothels, where the customers if they so desired could receive the ministrations of female attendants.

Racing and fighting men provided the best clientele for the baths, and it was not difficult for Joe Coughlin and his friends to convince the owner of a bathhouse at 205 Clark Street, in the heart of the First Ward, that the employment of Joe's brother would bring him a healthy business.

Big John got the job, and rushed home elated. "Kid," he shouted to Kate, "I got a real job! I'm a rubber in a Turkish bath-house. Now ain't that a real job?"

In the Clark Street bathhouse, Coughlin first laid the founda-tions for the career he would follow in the next fifty years and more. He reveled in the racy talk of jockeys and touts and quickly developed a fanatic interest in horses. He spoke fervently of the day when he himself might own a horse and enter it at Washington Park. The politicians who patronized the place also impressed him mightily. Their pompous demeanor, their ready oratory, their dress, their glib talk of election plots, and their easy spending fascinated the young rubber. The patrons liked hearty Coughlin too, for he soon learned the art of laughing uproariously at every joke and greeting each customer as if he were the most important man in town. And in time young Coughlin learned that the most prominent citizen, shucked down to the skin, is much like everyone else.

"I formed my philosophy," The Bath liked to say in later years, when he had learned the meaning of the word, "while watching and studying the types of people who patronized the bathhouses. Priests, ministers, brokers, politicians and gamblers visited there. I watched, and learned never to quarrel, never to feud. I had the best schooling a young feller could have. I met 'em all, big and little, from La Salle Street to Armour Avenue. You could learn from everyone. Ain't much difference between the big man and the little man. One's lucky, that's all."

A year later Coughlin got a job in the Palmer House baths, reaching the status of head rubber in a few months. Here came the big politicians and businessmen, the congressmen and senators traveling through from Washington, and, on rare occasions, a personage as distinguished as Marshall Field. Coughlin was a favorite with these men; he learned their whims and how to please them. They were rich, and tips were good.

Through a friendship thus formed with John Morris, a popular First Ward saloonkeeper and politician, Coughlin was able to open his own place in 1882. Morris supplemented $800 which Coughlin had religiously saved, and the erstwhile rubber purchased a bathhouse at 143 East Madison Street. At the time it seemed to Coughlin that he had attained the ultimate goal of his whole existence. Waving a receipt, he shouted to the Coughlin family, "I'm my own boss! I got my own bathhouse!" The next day he went to St. John's Church on Eighteenth Street and prayed. Kate lost six pounds hemming dozens of towels for the grand opening.

So successful was this venture that in a few months Coughlin had made enough money to open another bath several blocks west, in the basement of the fashionable, canary-tinted Brevoort Hotel. He was now able to hire a staff of rubbers and attendants, but each morning he appeared promptly at seven o'clock at one of his establishments or the other to greet, with a boisterous jest, those patrons who had slept off all-night jags in the little white cast-iron beds in the locker rooms, or to supervise the service and bustle about, proud and happy in the endless marvel of ownership.

Coughlin was becoming a man of property. He took on more poundage, grew a full mustache and lengthy sideburns, and combed his hair in the high, fashionable pompadour of the time. To his patrons he became known as Bathhouse John and he delighted in the name, just as in his boyhood he felt that his nickname of Dusty John drew him more attention. He set out to get more business. On the walls of his bathhouses and in downtown barbershops he displayed signs reading:

GOOD HEALTH IS PRICELESS
CLEANLINESS GIVES HEALTH
HEALTH IS RICHES—HEALTH IS LIFE
THERE'S HEALTH IN COUGHLIN'S BATHS!

Quite rapidly Coughlin was establishing himself as an aggressive and promising young businessman, with a reputation for honesty. People said of him, "He's not very bright, but once he gives his word you can count on him." He was generous with his earnings, rarely failing to hand a few pennies or more to a beggar on the streets. He liked to accompany such charities with an apt homily. "That man might have been somebody once, might be somebody again," he would say. "It don't pay in this world to think you're better than th' next fellow just because you happen to be on top and he ain't."

His acquaintances among the politicians began to increase. Through Johnny Morris he met Joseph (Chesterfield Joe) Mackin*, the First Ward's dapper Democratic boss, who lived at the Palmer House and often patronized the downtown baths. Mackin

---

* Mackin was a former saloon owner who, by giving an oyster with every beer, introduced in Chicago the saloon free lunch. In 1884 he was sentenced to five years in Joliet Penitentiary in connection with the theft of a ballot box of the Second Precinct, Eighteenth Ward from the county clerk's vault. The original ballots had been removed, and forgeries substituted in the interest of the candidacy of Rudolph Brand for state senator. Brand himself helped expose the plot. By that time Mackin had risen to the position of secretary of the Cook County Democratic central committee.

liked Coughlin's homely philosophy and enthusiasm for people and urged him to become a member of his organization, the First Ward Democratic Club. Coughlin, pleased at the bid, and awed by Mackin's sartorial splendor—Chesterfield Joe habitually wore a Prince Albert coat, striped trousers, silk hat, and a red carnation —promptly joined and became an ardent Mackin man. He was soon appointed Democratic captain of the precinct in which his newest bathhouse was situated. It was an honor he prized, above all others, to his death.

Coughlin loved the loud talk and noisy friendships of politics. He began to develop his own political tenets, based on the "Live and Let Live" theory of Carter Henry Harrison the Elder, four times mayor of Chicago and Democratic hero of the First Ward. Harrison had large First Ward real estate holdings and, like many others of his time, regarded prostitution and gambling, two of the most flourishing industries in the ward, as necessary evils.

Eternally a Democrat, Coughlin proved a vigorous precinct captain for Mackin. To voters less fervent than he about Mackin candidates, Coughlin would declaim as he made his pre-election canvasses in his precinct: "A Republican is a man who wants you t' go t' church every Sunday. A Democrat says if a man wants t' have a glass of beer on Sunday, he can have it. Be Democrats, unless you want t' be tied t' a church, a schoolhouse, or a Sunday school."

A man with such powers of political articulation could not long go unnoticed in the ranks of the First Ward Democrats and by 1883 at a nod from Mackin, Coughlin was put up for his first elective office, the presidency of the First Ward Democratic Club. He was swept in without a murmur of opposition. In this new job it was Coughlin who led the ward cohorts of the Cook County Democratic Marching Club in the heated campaign of 1884. The Bath and his followers, wearing costumes of dark-blue trousers, white hats and white woolen fatigue shirts with the letters C.H.H. on their chests, paraded in Chicago's streets shouting for Grover Cleveland for president and Carter H. Harrison for governor. This first immersion into state and national politics was an exciting experience for young Coughlin. There were fights almost every night in the First Ward as Republican rooters for James G. Blaine, hearkening to the calumny regarding Cleveland's illegitimate child, invaded the precincts in mobs, caroling:

> Ma, Ma, where is Pa?
> He's in the White House. Ha! Ha! Ha!

Indignant Democrats stormed the Republican strongholds, chanting:

> Blaine, Blaine, James G. Blaine,
> Continental liar from the state of Maine!

There were speeches to be made on platforms not only in Chicago but scattered the length of the state. And, touring with the Cook County Marching Club, the handsome Coughlin, now familiarly introduced to all as "Bathhouse John," made an impressive appearance. Coughlin was sorely hurt when Harrison lost to Oglesby, but he found some solace in Cleveland's triumph.

The election over, Coughlin returned to his bathhouses, which continued to prosper. He began to live and dress as befitted a rising politician of the First Ward. He aped the loud checks and raucous colors of the racing crowd, the smooth bowlers and silk hats of the aldermen and gamblers, and added Prince Albert vests, mauve gloves, and tan shoes. Such weird getups attracted considerable attention, which Coughlin innocently attributed to his growing political importance. He began dining in expensive restaurants, at Billy Boyle's where gathered the political and gambler rulers of the city, or at Volegsang's, the Great Northern, or the Sherman House. He rarely drank or gambled, except on the horses, and never made trips to the red-light districts which thrived a brief five minutes' walk from his Brevoort Hotel bathhouse. "I wear good clothes," he told his cronies, "and you can't wear good clothes unless you're clean on th' inside."

Always fascinated by the talk of horses and betting coups, Bathhouse John soon saw his first race. With a ticket given him by his brother, he and a bartender who patronized his bathhouses drove to a running of the American Derby in Washington Park, each June the top social event of the Chicago summer season. The color and excitement of the track stimulated young Coughlin, and he vowed again to own a horse. He visited the track frequently, getting tips from jockey friends of Joe, but betting never more than two dollars on a race. He also handled bets for his friends, who assumed that the brother of one of the best handicappers in the business ought to know where hard-earned money could be placed. Bathhouse John, however, loved racing for its own sake, and in 1885 he withdrew enough savings from the bank to purchase a fine two-year-old. He named her My Queen.

"I'm naming her for Mary," he proudly told his friends.

Mary was Mary Kiley, a sweetheart from childhood whose parents, like Coughlin's, had been among the early settlers in the Patch. The two families had always been friendly, Mary's brothers John and James, owners of a box factory by the river, having been among the first of Coughlin's employers.

It was always assumed by the families that John would wed Mary, for he, in his rare romantic moments, had eyes only for the winsome Kiley girl. But John was shy and slow. On their walks together he delayed all talk of marriage, preferring instead to speak of business, of the political developments, and of the famous men whose hands he had shaken.

Mary listened, and waited patiently. She was proud of John. He was handsome and strong and kind. He had gone a long way, and he was going farther. Politely she corrected his loose grammar, for she was studying to become a schoolteacher, and applauded his accomplishments. Her hopes rose when he told her about My Queen—it was his most romantic gesture.

It was almost a year later, however, that John Coughlin finally proposed marriage. He and Mary were wed on October 20, 1886, in St. John's Church, beginning a union which was to endure for thirty-five years. There was a wedding party in the Kiley house, and then the Coughlins rented a modest apartment on Michigan Avenue and began domestic life without a honeymoon.

For the next few years Johnny Coughlin, prosperous and possessed of many friends, was seemingly content with his lot. He was a cog in the political machine, delivering his precinct regularly according to the direction of the party chieftains. He was a welcome

raconteur in the barrooms, a sprightly figure at the tracks, and
when he took his place in the front rank of the Cook County
Democratic Marching Club parades the newspapers spoke approv-
ingly of his Sandow-like physique. He spent his money freely on
costly suits and frock coats by Meyer Newfield, tailor on La Salle
Street who fashioned wardrobes for the sports of the town. He
bought marble statuary for Mary to set in the hall of their home,
and now and then attended a horse auction to pick a likely yearling.
He was treated with respect, and come campaign time the political
candidates eagerly sought his acquaintance.

Then young Bathhouse grew ambitious. He yearned to sit in the
inner councils of his party, to participate in the plotting and schem-
ing. He dreamed of a new dignity. He had set his goal, he told his
friends—his final goal: a seat in the city council chambers as alderman of the First Ward. When he dared express his hopes to
Mackin and the other elders of the party he was advised, "We're
keeping you in mind, John. You're a comer." He bided his time
and offered only mild protest when others were put up as candidates. Four times he was elected president of the First Ward Democratic Club, and like a good party wheel horse he worked hard in
each election. He grinned and sweated, visited bars, remembered
first names, made more and more friends. "When *you* gonna run
fer alderman, John?" they demanded. "We're for ya!" Coughlin
laughed shyly at the tribute, worked harder than ever, and heark-
ened patiently to the counsel of the party bosses: "Take it easy,
Johnny. Your time will come one of these days. You're young."

This First Ward that Bathhouse John desired to represent—and
slowly he was becoming an expert on its polyglot political population—was the nerve center of a city which at the beginning of
the 1890's was still a roaring, overgrown frontier town. Only fifty
years before had the pioneers sloshed the mud from the harbors,
ditched the Calumet River to reach the port of New Orleans, and
strung great ribbons of steel to hitch up a tough new country to
the spraddling town on the flats at the south tip of Lake Michigan.
In the five decades they had fought pestilence and fire to erect a
city which would dominate the whole new West, from the Gulf

of Mexico to Canada. They had struggled in the mud, defeated Eastern politicians and bankers who wanted their capital elsewhere, and crumpled frontier-town competitors to make Chicago the terminal of a vast, unbroken empire. They had hauled in limestone and lumber which they shaped into big buildings to supplant the huts of their notorious Slab Town. They had sent out business Janizaries to capture the grain and pig trade and chased the great Illinois Central Railroad out of an Indiana terminal into their own front yard. They had built wooden roads, reared elevators, constructed warehouses, knocked together store fronts, and published newspapers and mail-order catalogues. When New York and Boston refused to deal with them, they had gone to Great Britain and Holland for money and they had even hatched a plot to trade with Canada and exclude the United States seaboard entirely until the outmaneuvered East finally came to terms.

They had been too busy fighting and brawling and working to worry much about how the city grew. All they knew or cared was that it was growing: 15,000 one year, 30,000 the next, 45,000 the next. It was going to be a million soon, and too tough and obstreperous for anyone to halt. Into this amazing city had come entrepreneurs, adventurers, carpetbaggers, hairy-chested dock wallopers and construction men, sailors, and card sharps, clerks and barkeepers, gunmen and ministers and solid, hard-handed builders who saw in this juncture of lake, canal and railroads an Eden of opportunity and security. Some had failed in their ventures and had continued westward; others stayed and became laborers or millionaires, worked hard for their money or entered politics.

Within the limits of the First Ward itself, one of the thirty-five into which the city was divided, was concentrated the good and the evil, the power and weaknesses of this lush new empire. Its leading economic groups, as noted in the federal census of 1890, were businessmen and vice. In an area bounded by the Chicago River, Lake Michigan, Twelfth and Canal Streets, wealth and a vigorous culture complacently rubbed shoulders with corrupt power and viciousness. Here the leading ministers exhorted their frock-coated congregations in handsome church edifices, while around the corners the barrel-house bartenders advised their patrons. Here were luxurious Michigan Avenue mansions and the hopeless hovels of Clark Street. Near the center of the ward the magnificent Monadnock Building and the new Masonic Temple reared skyward and nearby the gin mills, miserable cribs and dime hotels tilted on rickety stilts.

To the southwest was the ward's Little Cheyenne, Biler Avenue and the notorious Levee, habitat of the bums and thugs, thieves and gaudy prostitutes, crowded into a district from Wabash Avenue to the south branch of the Chicago River and south from Adams Street for more than a mile. Little Cheyenne had been named for the town in Wyoming, known as the wickedest in the nation while the Northern Pacific Railroad was being built. (Later when the Wyoming community grew large enough to have a respectable neighborhood of its own, the decent citizens there retaliated by calling its vice district Chicago.) Biler Avenue, locale of some of the fiercest dives in the country, was officially Pacific Avenue but received its more familiar name from the din of Rock Island and Lake Shore railroad boiler shops in the vicinity.

The Levee included not only South State Street but Clark Street and Plymouth Court as well. On these streets were the hop joints, concert saloons and brothels, from the twenty-five-cent bagnios to the more expensive houses operated by Carrie Watson, Mae Clark, Ike Bloom, Freddie Train and others. Off Dearborn Street, in the heart of the city, was Gamblers' Alley and nearby, on Randolph Street, from Clark to State Streets, was the infamous Hairtrigger Block, lined with gambling houses of every description. And at Clark and Monroe Streets stood The Store, the extensive establishment of Michael Cassius (King Mike) McDonald, the city's gambling and political boss.

Throughout the ward were endless stretches of lesser saloons and dice and faro houses from which by night issued the pimps, piffers and pickpockets to prey upon citizens and visitors. Dime museums and concert halls, peep shows and bucket shops were interspersed among the newly built wholesale houses and commission offices. To the north and west, along the river, were great shipping wharves on which the lake boats discharged their limestone, coal and lumber, and the grain boats from Europe loaded their bins. Near them were the railroad freight houses and huge red and yellow elevators. To the east, in the center of the ward, were the office buildings and the great department stores, the fine hotels and splendid restaurants and theaters, surrounding a solemn, marble-pillared city hall.

The population of this polyglot district got on well together. The businessmen who lived clear of the ruck, on the fringes of the ward or out of it altogether, cared little how it was governed so long as the price of privilege was not too high. The bums and foreign laboring element were equally unconcerned. It was the saloon men, the keepers of brothels, the gamblers and the numerous denizens of the underworld who took the most practical interest in the ward's politics for they were at the constant mercy of the police and they had to elect, buy and hire politicians to protect them.

For years these elements in the First Ward and in any part of the city where gambling thrived had found their protector and overlord in King Mike McDonald. Portly and plug-hatted, McDonald was the Boss Croker of a Chicago Tammany. Reputedly the first to utter, "There's a sucker born every minute," he made splendid use of his matchless axiom. As a youth recently arrived from Ireland he had been a candy butcher on railroad trains, in which job he defrauded purchasers by selling half-filled boxes of sweets, fake prize packages and glass jewelry. After he moved northward from New Orleans in the late 1850's, he engaged in varied gambling enterprises. When the Civil War started, he readily organized an Irish regiment in Chicago, and, although he was its self-styled colonel, he never left the city for the duration of the conflict.

His gambling career was climaxed in 1875 by the opening of The Store, where he not only offered all types of gaming but where he also did business with Chicago's political rulers. He controlled mayors, senators, and congressmen. He purchased a newspaper, the *Globe,* through which he frequently influenced elections. He was treasurer of the Lake Street Elevated Railroad Company to which his gambling associates referred derisively as "Mike's upstairs railroad." King Mike was a man of great wealth, undisputed power and a friend of the perennial mayor, Carter H. Harrison, even if in each of his campaigns Harrison had disavowed any connections with the boss. In the 1880's the party of Jefferson and Jackson in Chicago was popularly referred to as "Mike McDonald's Democrats."

Toward 1890, however, King Mike McDonald grown rich and careless and preoccupied with unhappy domestic affairs, was beginning to slip. There were those who sought his power, particularly the gamblers Harry (Prince Hal) Varnell, John Condon and George Hankins, whose Garfield Park race track was having trouble with the authorities—difficulties King Mike could not, or would not erase. Prince Hal was an experienced politician himself, and almost as wealthy as King Mike. His gambling house at 119 North Clark Street was a Chicago show place. A four-storied building, equipped at a cost of $80,000, it had Mexican onyx wainscoting on the barroom walls, a floor of Roman mosaic, and a huge bar of genuine mahogany. Neither the saloon nor the gaming rooms upstairs ever closed. Varnell had dabbled in Illinois politics for years, and in 1880 he had served as warden of the Cook County insane asylum. He promptly transformed the place into a country club for politicians, and several of the county commissioners lived there. Parties and dances were held almost every night, and rare foods and wines were served. For this lavish spending of public funds Varnell served a year in Joliet Penitentiary, but upon his release he promptly reassumed his place as a leader among the gambling fraternity.

Varnell, however, was not sufficiently powerful to challenge King Mike openly. He, Condon and Hankins clung to their chief. They agreed to his choices for aldermanic candidates. They even enlisted his aid in financing Garfield Park. But they awaited the day when they might seize his trembling scepter.

Yet McDonald, despite the reports of his growing lack of influence, gave no immediate sign that his political reign was over. Twice he rejected Joe Mackin's suggestion that Bathhouse John Coughlin be put up for alderman, and with the regulars of the Democratic party threw his support to men like Nicholas (Nicky)

Cremer, a cigar maker, in 1890, and to Johnny Morris, the saloon-keeper, in 1891.

Neither Cremer nor Morris, especially the former, were proving effectual in the council in behalf of the Varnell-Hankins interests, nor were they particularly pleasing to McDonald. When Nicky failed to stop the determined efforts of the Republican mayor, Hempstead Washburne, to close the Garfield Park track, Prince Hal was prepared to act. He took note of reports that some of the First Ward regulars, led by John Coughlin's school chums, were irked by Cremer's upstage manners and were determined to obtain the nomination for Bathhouse John. This little push, which included Jake Zimmerman, Henry Carroll, Ben Barnett and Freddie Train, the latter a brothel owner who had once worked beside Coughlin in the Palmer House baths, subscribed to the sentiments expressed by Joey Friedman, the saloonkeeper.

"Nicky's no good," Joey told the others. "He thinks he's too smart for us fellas. We're going to look around for someone else. Me, I'm for Johnny Coughlin. He's a good talker, he's got a good reputation, he's president of th' club, an' everybody likes him."

While Friedman sought the approval of the regular party chiefs, and Coughlin's friends did yeoman work for their candidate about the saloons, Varnell decided that the young bathhouse owner would be a good man to back. He knew that Bathhouse John adored horses and horse racing. Here, then, was a likely politician to help him fight to keep Garfield Park track open. Coughlin, Varnell noted, was popular with the saloonkeepers, who made up most of the political working force in Chicago at the time. To become alderman, especially in the First Ward, a man needed the support of the saloonkeepers and this Coughlin seemed to have, notably that of John Linedecker, the First Ward committeeman who owned a popular saloon at Harrison and State Streets.

If there was any doubt in Varnell's mind as to the unsuitability of Cremer and the need of an enthusiastic horse fan on his side in the city hall, it was dispelled December 3, 1891, when the council passed an ordinance directed at Garfield Park, one which would prevent the track from reopening for the spring and summer season. The die was cast. For Varnell it was to be Coughlin and after some earnest talking Prince Hal persuaded Hankins and the others of the race crowd to back his choice. By this time even Mike McDonald was ready to admit Cremer's utter lack of party responsibility—there were rumors that the grand jury was soon to look into boodle matters and that Cremer was one of those who would be scotched. In their gatherings at Billy Boyle's, Varnell and his associates urged and talked until finally such comparatively unenthusiastic ones as Sol van Praag, a former state representative, and Billy (The Clock) Skakel, a Civil War veteran, gambling-house proprietor and bucket-shop operator, decided to help elect Coughlin. Skakel even agreed to contribute $700 to the campaign fund. At the same time Friedman, Carroll, and other cronies of Bathhouse John had organized most of the precincts for Coughlin, and this preparation, plus the approval of McDonald and the support of the Garfield Park gang, was virtual assurance of a victory at the nominating convention.

Once it was determined that Coughlin would be the party's candidate in the spring elections, he was accepted more readily into the inner councils of the Democrats who met at luncheon daily in Billy Boyle's chophouse, just off Gambler's Alley. Here the leaders of the party gathered to exchange political gossip, engineer plans and make and unmake minor party chiefs as they chewed on Billy Boyle's lamb chops and hung beef, and sipped his excellent coffee.

This famed eating place was the favored haunt of King Mike McDonald, who twice weekly ordered Billy's chef to prepare for him huge helpings of salt pork with truffles. He would sit at a corner table, stuffing himself with food, and talking with such men as A. S. Trude, a brilliant criminal lawyer and strategist of the Cook County Democrats; Gray Tom Gallagher, Curt Gunn, Sam Doll, Congressman William (Billy) Mason, Teddy Frieberger, all of them important in politics, the gambling or saloon businesses; Frieberger was a power in the brothel district.

Boyle's chophouse was severe in its furnishings, the dark wood-work everlastingly wreathed with blue tobacco smoke and the rime of deep-fat cookery. Billy ruled his guests with a heavy hand. He wanted a dignified conversation, heavy eating, and no drinking. If he disapproved of a customer, he hauled out his special menu card, à la carte, and presented it to the unwelcome visitor with a snarl. It read: Pigs' feet, an order, $4.30; Ham and eggs, $4.40; Rum omelet, $4.50; Raw oysters, $5.40; French peas, $1.25; Potatoes, $1.10; Coffee, fifty cents. Once when two Negroes entered, Billy handed them the special menu, at which they gazed without flinching. They ordered a full meal, paid a check of $32, and, to Boyle's astonished gurgling, bought two black cigars at $1 each. Then, puffing grandly, they stalked out.

It was in this restaurant that the famous scheme for electing John M. Palmer, the first Democratic United States senator from Illinois since Stephen A. Douglas, had been concocted. For sixty-three days, early in 1890, the 101 Democratic members of the Illinois Assembly, who had been pledged to Palmer at a meeting of their leaders held in Boyle's loft, persistently cast their votes for Palmer, while leaders among their Republican and Farmers' Alliance opponents struggled, took sick, died, and eventually lost their battle. Hero of this affair was Charles (Big Sandy) Walters, a First Ward peanut-stand proprietor, who as Democratic sergeant-at-arms of the House repeatedly saved the day for his party by carrying to the chambers on his back ailing Democrats whose votes were needed.

In Billy Boyle's place Coughlin now strengthened rudimentary acquaintanceships. He grew more friendly with Johnny Condon, another of the triumvirate ruling the Garfield Park gang, and he had long conferences with Hankins, Varnell, van Praag and Skakel. He lunched with Friedman and Freddie Train, and sat and talked occasionally with McDonald, who seemingly had overcome his earlier aversion to the bathhouse owner. Two of Billy Boyle's habitués eventually became Coughlin's close and valuable friends. One was Trude, who would in future provide useful advice on political strategy, and the other Congressman Mason, earthy and practical.

"Never take anything big," Mason advised young Coughlin. "Stick to the little stuff. It's safer."

At home when Coughlin finally confided to Mary that he was going to sit on the city council, she began industriously to prepare him for the honor. Her daily assaults upon his grammar were intensified. When her husband had finished his usual breakfast of thick slices of ham and a half-dozen fried eggs Mary carefully surveyed him, scraped the traces of yolk from his cravat, or forbade his departure until he had changed his vest.

"John," she'd tell him, "if you're going to be an alderman you must talk and act like one."

Mary was proud of her rising young husband. She slipped out secretly and bought him a gift, a big porcelain spittoon. This she carried to a nearby art school, where she inquired of the director: "Could one of your girls decorate it with some pretty flowers? Some red and blue ones? Mr. Coughlin is very fond of flowers."

"You're gettin' th' ax!" was the warning shouted to Cremer by his hirelings as the boom for Coughlin gained momentum. Desperately Cremer attempted to stem the drive. But the meetings of the First Ward Democratic Club had been turned into campaign rallies for John Coughlin, and Cremer was thwarted in every step he took. At one of these meetings, soon after Coughlin's cronies and the Garfield Park crowd had joined forces, Cremer was booed heartily when he tried to make a speech and he left in a huff.

But Nicky was not finished. Realizing that most of the delegates to the forthcoming ward convention could be instructed to vote for Coughlin, Cremer directed his helpers to circulate about the ward buying up as many proxies as possible, exchanging $10 for the signatures of bona fide delegates who would be relieved of the necessity of attending themselves. This was a corporation method new to politics and was destined to fail.

Cremer and his boys came to the convention armed with proxies, which were duly presented to Tom McNally, a Coughlin wellwisher who was chairman of the meeting. McNally twisted the proxies into a compact bundle and shoved them into his pocket. When the meeting started and the name of the first absent delegate was called, one of Cremer's followers arose and announced, "I represent this man."

"Where are your credentials?" demanded McNally.

"The chair has the credentials, all properly signed. The chair has 'em!" shouted Cremer.

"Th' chair don't know what you are talkin' about," was McNally's bland reply. "Let's get on with th' meetin'."

This was repeated several times and the ensuing rumpus nearly broke up the convention. Cremer and his followers were thrown into the street. They stood outside and howled until the police chased them away. Then the Cremerites, noted a *Tribune* reporter, went off to the Levee where they got drunk and told the bartenders and the prostitutes their troubles.

Inside, the convention proceeded in routine and dignified fashion. The votes were taken, counted, and the result, decided upon weeks earlier, was announced:

Bathhouse John Coughlin would be the Democratic party candidate for the city council.

THE SECOND
TUNNEY-DEMPSEY FIGHT

John Kieran, James R. Harrison, and James P. Dawson

THE second Tunney-Dempsey fight was a long time in the making. Many cities wanted the big event but canny Tex Rickard chose Chicago. He must have known that it was going to be the last colossal-gate fight in fistic history, and he wanted a good setting for it; he threw everything in the way of superpromotion into it. Some people sitting in the last rows of Soldier Field never did get to know what was happening.

When Tunney and Dempsey arrived in Chicago to set up training camps things began to boil. Dempsey looked so good that some of the heavy bettors went for him, though no ex-heavyweight champ in history had ever regained his crown. As the weeks of preparation passed, the hysteria mounted. There were more newspaper reporters in town than during a national political convention. Stories about the two stars' training programs were sent all over the world. If Dempsey strained an arm muscle or Tunney jabbed his finger with a fork at lunch it was the hottest news.

The night before the big fight the city seemed to have gone stark crazy. The lobbies of all the Loop hotels were surging with humanity. A big dry federal army mobilized under Mr. E. C. Yellowley was on the scene, but its efforts to dampen enthusiasms proved futile. For three days the trains had been rolling in, increasing the pandemonium in the Windy City. The New York Central ran fifteen extra sections of the Twentieth Century, hooked ten more to the Broadway Limited. The Pullman Company reported it was the first time in history that every *private car* in the service had been placed in rolling operation. The Pennsylvania delivered thirty-five extra trains. The B & O ran specials from New York, Philadelphia, Pittsburgh, Washington, Akron, Youngstown, Cleveland. The Sante Fe ran extras from Los Angeles. All air flights were booked solid and the passenger planes kept dropping on the airfields like crows. People were already being killed in auto accidents arriving for the fight. Two legal attempts to stop the contest (one initiated by a taxpayer who sued on the grounds that the "fight was a low and vulgar exhibition") were quashed at the last minute. On the last day 145,000 miles of AP wires were leased for 1,200 newspapers. Someone figured out that Gene Tunney would have to serve 2,737 solid years as a private in the Marine Corps to earn what he would get for thirty minutes of actual fighting (ten rounds).

On the opening night, in Soldier Field at the lakefront, 120,000 buns were readied, together with 30,000 bottles of pop, four tons of hot dogs, one ton of hamburger, and thousands of straw cushions which proved uncomfortable. Tunney's take was a guaranteed $1,000,000; Dempsey's, $450,000. Estelle Taylor, Dempsey's wife, collapsed in her Chicago hotel suite and became hysterical after listening in on the radio because of the seventh round; she locked herself in the bathroom, then came out and tuned in the radio and listened to the remainder of the fight.

And—but take it away from here. It happened, of course, in Chicago.

TIMID FANS LEARN INSIDE FIGHT FACTS *

John Kieran

EVERYTHING is in readiness for the big battle along the lakefront here tomorrow. This is a momentous occasion. Two pugilists are to meet before the biggest fight crowd of all time and share the biggest purse in the history of the manly art of self-defense. The heavyweight championship of the world is at stake. This is no time for temporizing. The cry is for action and plenty of it.

With the opportunity of a lifetime staring them in the face, thousands of fight fans who have joined the wild whirl along Michigan Avenue have become timorous. They are hedging. They are backing and filling, shadow-boxing with the chance to win a "nest egg," a modest competence, or an "immense fortune," at one delightful swoop.

The problem is to name the winner of the heavyweight championship bout and back that opinion with current coin of the realm. It doesn't seem difficult. There are only two possible choices, Tunney and Dempsey. One must be right. There is only one chance for a man to go wrong. How much simpler this is than baseball, for instance, where a man must choose one club from a field of eight, or racing, where a man has one horse running for his money and sometimes eighteen running against it.

And yet the fight fans are timorous. Some say: "Tunney will win if—" Others say: "Dempsey will knock him out provided—"

There should be no shilly-shallying in a case like this. It is too important. There are 170,290-odd seats in the big arena. The gate receipts will be $2,500,000 or thereabouts. There will be perhaps 150,000 spectators on hand and untold millions listening to radio returns all around the world. Tunney will be, perhaps, the first man in history to become a millionaire by the simple process of going through a thirty-minute physical drill. Dempsey is attempting a feat which has never been accomplished, the winning back of a heavyweight championship crown.

The fighters are not hedging, nor are they timorous. "Let me at him," says Jack Dempsey, "I will knock him in two directions at once, over and down." "I defeated him easily last year," says Tunney; "this time I shall knock him out."

One of them must be wrong, but which one? Is it possible to predict in advance just what will happen in the ring tomorrow night at Soldier Field? Certainly it is, if proper judgment is called into play. Somewhere in this story the persistent reader will find a paragraph which contains the true story—and in advance. It is quite simple.

Before the greatest crowd ever to witness a fight since the caveman grappled with the dinosaur, Gene Tunney will retain his heavyweight crown at Soldier Field here tomorrow night by outpointing Jack Dempsey before 150,000 more or less delirious spectators. It will be a repetition of the Sesquicentennial battle, only more so. Dempsey will be outclassed from the first bell to the end of the bout.

Before the contenders shake hands in the center of the ring tomorrow evening some two hundred specials and excursion trains will have brought thousands of fight fans to the big battle along the lakefront, and these ardent pursuers of sights pugilistic will see Jack Dempsey, the great Manassa Mauler, knock out Gene Tunney, the alleged manly marine, in the third round of the scheduled ten-round bout. It will be evident from the start that Tunney never was a real champion and that Dempsey was not himself in the Philadelphia ring just a year ago.

Tex Rickard's coterie of millionaires, political lights and state officials grouped around the ring will see again the Dempsey who battered down Willard, the Dempsey who annihilated Carpentier, the Dempsey who slaughtered Firpo, the Wild Bull of the Argentine. The sight of the Terror of Toledo bounding over the comeback trail to the championship will thrill even the blasé correspondents in the press row. Tom Wignail of The London *Daily Mail* will say, "Fancy that," or words to that effect.

That's just what will happen. In the third round William Harrison Dempsey will land a right to the body, followed by a left to the jaw, as Tunney sinks to the canvas. A man in the 313th row with a $5 seat will say to his neighbor, "What's going on? Can you see anything?" and his neighbor will answer: "Certainly. On the left I can see Lake Michigan. Behind me I can see the Field Museum. On the right I can see the buildings on Michigan Avenue. But I can't see anything in front of me except a collection of overcoats and felt hats. I feel as though I were spending the night in the clothing department of a big store."

Without fear or favor, it can be prophesied that the fight will go as stated. Tom Meighan, Harold Lloyd, Buster Keaton and other movie stars in the select ringside sections will see Tunney pop that left at the bewildered Dempsey all through the earlier rounds. Weary and worn and cut and bruised, game but gory, Dempsey will get weaker and weaker.

The crowd will yell for a knockout—the cry of the pack—and, casting his usual caution to the wind, Gene will put over the finishing blow in the center of the great arena, which has 170,290 seats, many of which will be occupied. The end will come in the seventh round and Jack Dempsey will have the most expensive attack of sleeping sickness on record. Gene Tunney will prove himself a real champion with a bright future as a multimillionaire.

Everything connected with the staging of the big battle of Chicago will be on a gigantic scale. It will take a force of ten thousand ushers, gatemen, special policemen and other officials to handle the enormous crowd. There will be thousands of volunteer firemen in the aisles to see that the concrete stadium doesn't burn down. There will be denizens of Cicero, Ill., in the $5 sections and at least one merchant from Cape Town, South Africa, in a ringside seat when Dempsey is declared the winner on a foul in the sixth round.

The merchant from Cape Town, South Africa, will not see the foul but the denizens of Cicero, Ill., some seven hundred feet or more from the ring and blocked off from all sight of the encounter, will go home and describe the illegal blow in detail for years to come. The five hundred sports writers in the press section will flash the words around the world: "Dempsey regains championship on a foul. Sixth round."

Over the air, in the greatest radio hook-up ever looped for any athletic event, will go the blow-by-blow details of the bout and its unfortunate ending. Radio listeners in the lonely hills of Tennessee, on the plains of the Dakotas, in Cuba, in Europe, Asia, Oceania and Ethiopia will hear the voice of the announcer at the ringside in Chicago saying:

"This is the ninth round of the heavyweight championship fight between Gene Tunney and Jack Dempsey at Soldier Field, Chicago, Illinois. Dempsey may not last long now. He has taken a terrific battering all the way through. He isn't the old Dempsey. Tunney has peppered him—there goes another left to his syn-

thetic nose—another—another—Dempsey is short with a right—
he rushes in—no, Tunney rushes—pardon me, it was Dempsey
after all—Tunney lands a—hey, wait a minute—somebody is down
—it's Jack Tunney—do wait a minute, it's Gene—Dempsey—foul
—somebody say foul—yes—folks, this is the most exciting—Tunney wins on a foul! Yes, sir. A foul in the ninth round. Tunney wins!
Oh, Gene, Gene, just a moment and I'll have the champion here
to say a word. This is being broadcast by Stations ABC, DEF, GHI,
JKL, MNO, PQR, STU, VWX, YZ&. Here's the champion
now. Mumble—Grumph—Grmph—Tcha—Woof. That was Gene
Tunney, folks. We are signing off. Good night."

Yes, indeed. It will be a great fight but the crowd will be dissatisfied when the draw decision is handed down. Tunney's clever-
ness will be offset by Dempsey's aggressiveness. Tunney will be
lighter on his feet but Dempsey will be heavier with his fists.
The crowd which will contribute something like $2,500,000 in
cash for the evening's entertainment will file out of the great stadium singing one slogan: "Never again." Shades of John L. Sullivan, Jim Corbett, Bob Fitzsimmons and Jim Jeffries. A draw, bah!

As a matter of fact, what will really happen is this: After all
the preparations, the open letters, the rush of visitors for the fight
with no hotel accommodations, the discussions over the referee and
the bandages for the hands, a heavy rain will drench the whole
city and force a post—no, that would be too cruel. Don't mention
it.

GREATEST RING SPECTACLE *

James R. Harrison

OUT of the welter and turmoil and clamor of the "fight of the
ages," one clear face stands out—that tonight Tex Rickard un-
veiled the most beautiful picture in the history of sports here or
elsewhere.

One hundred and fifty thousand persons watched in the darkness

* Copyright, 1927, by the New York *Times*. Reprinted by special permission
of the New York *Times*.

—the greatest of all boxing crowds by about 35,000. It would fill more than two Yankee Stadiums and almost two Yale Bowls; it would pack the Polo Grounds to capacity and leave 100,000 on the outside.

The total receipts were put at $2,800,000.

Governors and Mayors and United States Senators and millionaires lent the right tone to the occasion and millions listened to the story of the fight as it went out "on the air."

Yet the facts and figures do not seem particularly important as compared to the sheer beauty of a picture that only an artist could paint. This may or may not have been "the fight of the ages," but it most certainly was the "sight of the ages."

The veil of darkness over it all; the rippling sea of humanity stretching out as far as the eye could see; the Doric columns of Soldier Field glowing a soft white along the upper battlements of the arena; and finally the ring itself, where two men fought it out with their fists in a pool of white light—these were the high spots of an unforgettable spectacle.

It was a picture that should have been seen from the air, from the cockpit of an airplane, where the lights and shadows and the black and whites of the panorama could have been viewed in their proper perspective.

The ingredients of the picture were striking. A long, low oval stadium of classic lines, filled to its utmost rim. A gently sloping bank of humanity that seemed to stretch to the horizon, and in the center of the canvas a twenty-foot ring bathed in the fierce light that beats about a throne.

The vastness of the spectacle was its most impressive quality. It filled the eye and staggered the senses. We have seen the Yale Bowl jammed with people, and last November we saw the same Soldier Field at the Army-Navy game, but this was the crowd of crowds and the spectacle of spectacles, lacking only the natural beauty of Poughkeepsie and New London.

Even though he did not sell all of his 163,000 seats, Tex Rickard reached a long-cherished goal in his career as an impresario. The 90,000 of Boyle's Thirty Acres and the 115,000 of the

Sesquicentennial were left far behind as Chicago and its influx of fight fans poured through the portals of this sports temple.

There they sat, shoulder to shoulder, from the ring up to the top rim where American flags rippled in a brisk western wind. Not that the stadium was full. The cheaper $5 seats, a few city blocks to the north and south, were sparsely settled, proving that you may lead a boxing fan to water but you can't make him drink. And tonight Rickard reached the limit in distances. His $5 patrons were seven hundred or more feet from the ring, which at the Yankee Stadium would locate him somewhere beyond the center-field fence.

As the citizens flocked through the gates half of them were armed with binoculars, opera glasses and telescopes. Here and there one could see some shrewd lads who had brought portable radios with them. They were the $5 boys, who were going to listen even if they did not see.

The weather man was not fooling when he said fair and warmer, for that was a perfect forecast. The fans brought light coats with them, but they were hardly necessary, especially around the ring, where the heat of the bright lights was very noticeable.

The afternoon was gray and overcast and twilight showed a drab, threatening sky and mist which foreboded rain. At 8:30 o'clock a few drops of rain fell, causing veterans of the Sesqui to shudder, but the menace passed as quickly as it had come. . . .

The most inconspicuous man at the ringside was probably the most important of the 150,000 spectators. He was Graham MacNamee, who talked to more people over the radio than any other man in history. His story went to some 50,000,000 listeners all over the world—a record-breaking hookup that was in keeping with the other angles of this unprecedented and stupendous sporting event.

John Righeimer, Chairman of the Illinois Boxing Commission, was an early visitor at the ringside. Asked who would referee the main bout, he remarked mysteriously, "Wait and see."

The front ringside aisles were all cluttered up with celebrities and policemen and the notables had to push through a plebeian throng to get to their seats. Rickard had a picked squad of ushers to take care of the select throng, especially the 107 front-row seats, where the cream of the cream was concentrated.

Genius of a high order was displayed by Mr. Rickard in cramming two newspapermen into a space that nature intended for only one. Compared to the experts at the bout, sardines live in the great open spaces.

Floodlights on the top of the arena battlements illuminated the scene, while the fans were waiting for the first preliminary fighters to appear. At that moment there were empty spaces in many sections and it did not look as if Mr. Rickard would have a sellout.

The twilight was gray and forbidding and a west wind was rippling the American flags on the heights of the arena. However, a local weather sharp remarked that a west wind does not mean rain while it is cool. . . .

Every once in a while a flashlight would explode and the experts jumped nervously, fearing that another Chicago gang war had broken out.

Mr. Stillman, the head usher, came along and begged the correspondents in the second row to "move along a couple of inches, boys, and let this writer in." This request was greeted with loud and unfeeling laughter.

The movie boys and photographers were parked on lofty crows'-nests to the north of the ring. The movie perch was covered with a canvas awning in case of rain.

Doug Fairbanks leaped lightly over three cops, vaulted a railing and landed in his seat at 8:32 P.M. He was followed a minute later by Charlie Chaplin, who looked rather queer without a trick hat and cane.

When the Mayor of Chicago, William Hale Thompson, appeared the cops executed a "right by army corps" and escorted His Honor to his seat.

Governor Fred Green of Michigan was one of the many state governors present. He did a Lindbergh from Lansing.

The first preliminary bout hadn't gone one minute before the loud cry of the raspberry could be heard in the outlying sections. The boys were tuning up early.

George M. Cohan waltzed in and felt at home right away when he saw all the American flags that decorated the battlements.

David Belasco was a ringside onlooker and he admitted that he had never put on as great a show as this. Flo Ziegfeld was nearby.

Kenesaw Mountain Landis was horribly handicapped. He had no rail to rest his chin on while he gazed at the proceedings.

A courier dashed up to the press section and announced that Charles M. Schwab, Clarence H. Mackay, Otto Kahn and Bernard Baruch were discovered near the ringside.

Harold Lloyd attempted to slink in disguised without eyeglasses, but he was spotted by a scout.

In the Mayor's section was Kendrick of Philadelphia, who helped to put on the Sesquicentennial party a year ago.

"The only thing I'll hand to Chicago is its weather," he said.

The words were hardly out of his mouth when a few drops of rain fell at 8:30. Mr. Kendrick concealed a chuckle with great difficulty.

TUNNEY KEEPS TITLE BY DECISION
AFTER TEN ROUNDS*

James P. Dawson

HIS refusal to observe the boxing rules of the Illinois State Athletic Commission, or his ignorance of the rules, or both, cost Jack Dempsey the chance to regain the world's heavyweight championship here tonight in the ring at Soldier Field.

By the same token this disregard of rules of ring warfare, or this surprising ignorance, saved the title for Gene Tunney, the fighting ex-marine, who has been king of the ring for just a year.

The bout ended with Tunney getting the decision, and the vast majority in the staggering assemblage of 150,000 people, who paid, it is estimated, $2,800,000 to see this great sport spectacle, approved the verdict.

The decision was given by Referee Dave Barry and Judges

George Lytton, wealthy department store owner, and Commodore Sheldon Clark of the Sinclair Oil Company. It was announced as a unanimous decision, but this could not be verified in the excitement attending the finish of the battle. But it should have been unanimous according to all methods of reasoning and boxing scoring, for Tunney won seven of the ten rounds, losing only the third, sixth and seventh, in the last of which Dempsey made his great mistake. It is known that Judge Lytton voted for Tunney.

In that seventh round Dempsey was being peppered and buffeted about on the end of Tunney's left jabs and hooks and sharp though light right crosses, as he had been in every preceding round, with the exception of the third.

In a masterful exhibition of boxing Tunney was evading the attack of his heavier rival and was countering cleanly, superbly, skillfully, accurately the while for half of the round or so.

Then Dempsey, plunging in recklessly, charging bull-like, furiously and with utter contempt for the blows of the champion, since he had tasted of Tunney's best previously, suddenly lashed out a long, wicked left to the jaw with the power of old. This he followed with a right to the jaw, the old "iron mike" as deadly as ever, and quickly drove another left hook to the jaw, under which Tunney toppled like a falling tree, hitting the canvas with a solid thud near Dempsey's corner, his hand reaching blindly for a helping rope which somehow or other refused to be within clutching distance.

Then Dempsey made his mistake, an error which, I believe, cost him the title he values so highly.

The knockdown brought the knockdown timekeeper, Paul Beeler, to his feet automatically, watch in hand, eyes glued to the ticking seconds and he bawled "one" before he looked upon the scene in the ring.

There he saw Dempsey in his own corner, directly above the prostrate, brain-numbed Tunney, sitting there looking foolishly serious, his hand finally resting on the middle ring strand. Beeler's count stopped. Referee Barry never started one.

It is the referee's duty to see to it that a boxer scoring a knockdown goes to the corner farthest from his fallen foe and it is the duty of the knockdown timekeeper to delay the count from the watch until this rule is obeyed. Beeler was simply observing the rule, which Dempsey either forgot to observe or refused to observe.

The challenging ex-champion stood there, arms akimbo on the top ropes of the ring of his own corner, watching his fallen rival, the characteristic Dempsey snarl o'erspreading his countenance, his expression saying more plainly than words: "Get up and I'll knock you down again, this time for keeps."

Dempsey had no eyes for Referee Barry, who was waving frantically for the former titleholder to run to a neutral corner, even as he kept an eye on the fallen Tunney. Instead, Dempsey merely looked down at Tunney squatting there, striving instinctively to regain his feet and waiting for his whirling brain to clear.

Finally, Dempsey took cognizance of the referee's frantic motions. He was galvanized into action and sped hurriedly to a neutral corner, which was furthest removed from the fallen champion.

But three or four, or possibly five precious seconds had elapsed before Dempsey realized at all what he should do. In that fleeting time of the watch Tunney got the advantage. No count was proceeding over him, and quickly his senses were returning. When Referee Barry started counting with Timekeeper Beeler, Tunney was in a state of mental revival where he could keep count with the tolling seconds and did, as his moving lips revealed.

Slowly the count proceeded. It seemed an eternity between each downward sweep of the arm of Referee Barry and the steady pounding of the fist of Timekeeper Beeler.

Seconds are like that in a crisis, and here was one if ever one existed.

Tunney's senses came back to him. He got to his feet with the assistance of the ring ropes and with visible effort at the count of "nine." He was groggy, stung, shaken, his head was whirling as so many other heads have whirled under the Dempsey punch.

But Dempsey was wild in this crisis, a floundering, plodding man-killer, as Tunney, back-pedaling for dear life, took to full flight, beating an orderly, steady retreat with only light counter moves in the face of the plunging, vicious Dempsey, aroused now for the kill.

Dempsey plodded on so futilely and ineffectively that he tired from his own exertions. The former champion stood dead in his tracks in mid-ring and with a smile spreading over his scowling face, motioned disgustedly, daringly, for Tunney to come on and fight.

But Tunney was playing his own game, and it was a winning game. He did not want to expose himself to that deadly Dempsey punch again, and he would not.

Tunney backed steadily away from Dempsey, pecking and tantalizing with left jabs and grazing right hooks or crosses to the face or jaw. Which meant absolutely nothing to Dempsey. He brushed in against Tunney's blows but, in his eagerness, Dempsey was wild.

After motioning Tunney in, Dempsey backed the champion into the ropes near the challenger's corner and lunged forward savagely with a left and right to the jaw. But Tunney clinched under the blows and held Dempsey for dear life. And Dempsey never again got the chance that round to follow his advantage.

As the bell sounded the end of the round Dempsey was warned for striking low with a left for the body. He was hurling his punches in a blind fury, not particularly concerned over where they landed, so long as they did land.

The crowd which witnessed this dramatic fight, and particularly the critical moments of the seventh round, experienced varying emotions at the crisis. Some yelled themselves hoarse. The shrieks of women mingled with the howls of staid old businessmen and the thousands of the purely sporting fraternity clustered about the ringside and extending backward from the battle platform in serried rows of faces.

Society's bluebloods forgot decorum and yelled excitedly. Kings of finance and princes of industry were mingling their yells with those of governors, mayors, representatives in Congress, senators, lawyers, doctors, theater and movie folk and just plain ordinary people.

It was a scene to grip the observer, a situation to send quickening throbs through the pulses of those at the ringside and in the other sections of Chicago's memorial to her dead heroes. Here was a war hero, a ring hero, a champion, on the floor, and everybody was affected.

Out over the ether wastes some 50,000,000 people who listened to the fight broadcast by the National Broadcasting Company over the greatest hookup ever attempted for sport, had not the advantage of those actually watching the contest.

To those countless listeners it was evident that Dempsey was the victim of something, but just what only those who watched were aware. And there were some watching who did not realize the enormous consequences of this colossal mistake, because they were not versed in boxing rules. But it is safe to say that none among the 150,000 watching or among the 50,000,000 listening, will ever forget that particular lapse of time.

Leo P. Flynn, Dempsey's manager, made no effort after the fight to disguise or conceal his feelings or those of Dempsey. In plain words Flynn said that Dempsey had been robbed of victory because of that seventh-round situation.

"The watch in our corner showed fifteen seconds from the time Tunney hit the floor until he got up at the count of nine," Flynn said. "The legal count over a fallen boxer is ten seconds, not fifteen. Dempsey was robbed. That's the way I look at it. But I'm going to appeal to the State Athletic Commission to reverse the decision, as is my privilege. Dempsey will fight him again and will knock him out if Tunney ever can be coaxed into meeting him again, just the way he knocked him out tonight."

In the final analysis, however, Dempsey was hoist on his own petard. The rule compelling a boxer to go to the corner furthest removed from a fallen foe is traceable to Dempsey himself. Its adoption followed the Manassa Mauler's battle in 1923 with the giant Firpo when Dempsey stood directly above the fallen Firpo striking the South American just as soon as his knees left the floor without waiting for Firpo to come erect after a knockdown.

Dempsey was permitted to do this then. His attempt to do it tonight was the most expensive mistake he has ever made in his life.

THE LIFE, TIMES, AND END OF DION O'BANION*

Herbert Asbury

FOR color, nerve, and sheer daring, the roaring twenties in Chicago remain unmatched in American big-time criminal activity. The planks that built the platform upon which the gangsters played their starring roles and walk-on parts were supplied by the Eighteenth Amendment. To hustle whiskey and beer to a thirsty population meant big money for the hustlers—money and competition.

Prohibition ushered in the age of the rub-out. Previously, hoodlums were murdered occasionally if they squealed or double-crossed their pals. But during the roaring twenties, the rub-outs were executed mainly for "business reasons."

Chicago, during that era, resembled a continent overrun by armed dukes and barons turned war lords. The boundaries of principalities were staked out—one mob ran the beer business as far as North Avenue, another took over from there to Diversey, another carried on east of Halsted Street, and so on. Because distant pastures always have looked enticingly green, mobs frequently crossed boundary lines at dawn with beer trucks—and the result was the crackling of submachine-gun fire. Undertaking parlors and casket companies were working full shifts in those days.

O'Banion was one of the big hoods of the era. In describing his life and demise, Herbert Asbury tells us a great deal about an entire epoch.

JOHNNY TORRIO and Al Capone were riding high in the spring of 1924, but great trouble for them was looming on the

* From *Gem of the Prairies,* by Herbert Asbury. Copyright, 1940, by Alfred A. Knopf.

horizon of the underworld, and most of it was to be caused by Dion O'Banion. As a boy, O'Banion sang in the choir of the Holy Name Cathedral and was remarkable for piety and obedience; as a man, he was a swashbuckling, ambidextrous, flower-loving, cheerful murderer, who wore a carnation in his buttonhole and carried three pistols stowed away in special pockets built into his expensive clothing by expert tailors. Chief of Police Morgan Collins characterized O'Banion as "Chicago's archcriminal" and declared that he had killed, or ordered killed, at least twenty-five men. But he was never brought to trial for any of these crimes, for politically he was only less important than Torrio or Capone. He was particularly powerful in the Forty-second and Forty-third Wards on the North Side, and for years he and his gunmen had kept them safely in the Democratic column. So widely was his ability as a vote-getter recognized that a question-and-answer wheeze developed in Chicago: "Who'll carry the Forty-second and Forty-third?" "O'Banion, in his pistol pocket."

As the November, 1924, election approached, Democratic politicians were disturbed by rumors that O'Banion intended to throw his strength to the Republicans. To avert such a calamity, a testimonial dinner was held in October at the Webster Hotel on Lincoln Park West, at which the gang leader was presented with a platinum watch richly encrusted with rubies and diamonds. Who sponsored the dinner and bought the watch was never divulged. Prominent among the guests were Frank Gusenburg, Schemer Drucci, George Bugs Moran, Maxie Eisen, Hymie Weiss; Louie Alterie, who, besides being one of O'Banion's crack gunmen, was president of the Theater and Building Janitors' Union; Jerry O'Conner, gambling-house owner and vice-president of the union; and the union's secretary, Con Shea, notorious labor slugger and racketeer, who had served a term in Sing Sing for the attempted murder of a woman. But also present were Colonel Albert A. Sprague, Chicago's Commissioner of Public Works and Democratic candidate for United States Senator; County Clerk Robert M. Sweitzer; Chief of Detectives Michael Hughes, half a dozen police captains and lieutenants, and many lesser officeholders and politicians. When ordered by Mayor William E. Dever to explain why he had attended the dinner, Chief Hughes said he had understood that the party was to be in honor of Jerry O'Conner. "But when I arrived," he said, "and recognized a number of notorious characters I had thrown into the detective bureau basement a half-dozen times, I knew I had been framed, and withdrew almost at once."

The gang chieftain accepted the platinum watch with pleasure, but whoever put up the money for it did so in vain. For favors expected and received, by slugging, bribery, shooting, kidnapping, and the use of floaters and repeaters, O'Banion delivered both the Forty-second and Forty-third Wards to the Republican ticket, headed by United States Senator Charles S. Deneen and Robert E. Crowe, the latter running for re-election as State's Attorney. Crowe defeated the Democratic nominee, Michael I. Igoe, nearly two to one.

O'Banion was a product of Little Hell, on the North Side near the Sicilian quarter and Death Corner, where tenements swarming with children were interspersed among brothels, disorderly saloons, and immoral cabarets. Throughout his formative years he was surrounded by criminal influences, and under the pressure of environment he soon forgot the moral lessons taught by the priests of the Cathedral. He became a thieving loafer and a member of the Market Street gang, and then a singing waiter in McGovern's Cabaret at Clark and Erie Streets, one of Little Hell's toughest dives. He sang sentimental ballads while picking the pockets of maudlin customers. At this time he was known as Gimpy O'Banion, because his left leg was a trifle shorter than the right, but no one ever called him Gimpy, and lived, after he had become a Big Shot. From robbing drunken revelers, O'Banion turned to highway robbery, burglary, and safecracking. He served three months in the Bridewell in 1909, when he was seventeen years old, for burglary, and three months in 1911 for assault. And that was all the time he ever spent in prison.

When prohibition came upon the land in 1920, O'Banion was well known to the police as a dangerous hoodlum and as chief of one of the most successful criminal gangs Chicago has ever harbored. His followers included such notorious gunmen and bandits as Handsome Dan McCarthy, Bugs Moran, Maxie Eisen, Frank Gusenberg; Vincent Drucci, better known as the Schemer; Two-Gun Louis Alterie, also called the Cowboy Gunman because he owned a ranch in Colorado; Hymie Weiss, who was O'Banion's alter ego and second in command of the gang; and Samuel J. Morton, called Nails, who had won the *Croix de guerre* in France and had returned from the World War a First Lieutenant in the United States Army. Morton died as the result of what his fellow gangsters regarded as despicable treachery; he was thrown and kicked to death while riding a horse in Lincoln Park. A committee of the O'Banion gang, determined to exact vengeance, kidnapped the horse a few days later, led it to the spot where Morton's body had been found, and solemnly "bumped it off," each gangster firing a shot into the animal's head.

Morton, known by the police to have committed several murders, was buried with elaborate religious, fraternal, and military honors, and his funeral was attended by the usual assortment of truckling city, state, county, and Federal officials. "Five thousand Jews," said the *Daily News,* "paid tribute to Morton as the man who had made the West Side safe for his race. As a young man he had organized a defense society to drive 'Jew-baiters' from the West Side." A year after Morton's death a memorial service was planned by his friends, and the printed announcement of the service carried the names of Rabbi Felix A. Levi, the Reverend John L O'Donnell, General Abel Davis, and Captain Ed Maher. It was also announced that Johnny Torrio, Hymie Weiss, Terry Druggan, and other criminals would participate. The principal address was to be delivered by a well-known criminal lawyer, Frank Comerford. The plan was abandoned when General Davis withdrew from the committee; he said it would be a mistake to flaunt Morton's record "in the faces of decent citizens."

O'Banion's income from the liquor traffic, though not nearly so large as that of either Torrio or Capone, was sufficient to make him a very rich man; it was estimated by the police after his death that he had banked almost $1,000,000 a year from this source alone. He supplemented his booze earnings with the proceeds of frequent safe-robberies, payroll holdups, and hijackings. At least two of his exploits were noteworthy even for Chicago. He led his crew of gunmen into West Side railroad yards and stole a hundred thousand dollars' worth of Canadian liquor from a freight car; and in 1924 he carried out the famous robbery of the Sibley warehouse, trucking out 1,750 barrels of bonded whiskey and leaving in their stead as many barrels of water. He was indicted for this, together with ten of his gangsters, four city detectives, and officials of the Sibley Warehouse Company, but no one was convicted. In 1922 O'Banion further augmented his income by buying a half-interest in William E. Schofield's flower shop on North State Street, directly opposite the Cathedral where he had once served as choir boy. As gangland's official florist O'Banion sold thousands of dollars' worth of flowers to the friends and foes of slain gunmen, for underworld etiquette demanded that a killer send expensive floral tributes to the funeral of his victim. Even without the business of the gangsters, ownership of the shop would have brought great prosperity to O'Banion, for he had considerable business ability and possessed a consuming love of flowers. He had a knack of arranging blooms, and unless hampered too much by instructions his floral creations were, in many instances, works of art.

For three years after O'Banion joined Torrio's league of gunmen he appeared to be content with what he could get out of the North Side. But after the taking of Cicero he began to express dissatisfaction; several of his killers had supported Al Capone during the election-day rioting in the suburban city, and he had got nothing out of it but a brief word of thanks. To placate the disgruntled O'Banion, Torrio turned over to him a strip of Cicero territory in which the beer concession was worth about $20,000 a month. O'Banion soon quintupled this business; he canvassed the South and West Sides and persuaded fifty saloonkeepers who had been buying beer from the Sheldon, Saltis-McErlane, and Druggan-Lake gangs to move into Cicero, where they competed with saloons which were supplied by Torrio and Capone. Torrio demanded a share of the new revenue, and in return offered O'Banion an interest in the syndicate's earnings from brothels. But O'Banion refused. Like the O'Donnells, he was not interested in prostitution.

O'Banion also nursed a grievance against Torrio's allies the Genna brothers—Sam, Jim, Pete, Angelo, Tony and Mike, known as the Terrible Gennas, who were the special pets of Diamond Joe Esposito and high in the councils of the Unione Siciliana. The North Side gang chieftain complained that the Gennas were "muscling in" on his territory and flooding the district with bad whiskey which they sold for $3 a gallon. O'Banion had been getting from $6 to $9, but delivering a much better grade of liquor. He demanded that Torrio drive the Gennas back to the West Side, and when Torrio protested that he could not accomplish such a miracle of discipline, the fiery O'Banion angrily threatened to do it himself. This was a task which no one but the North Sider would even have considered, for of all Chicago gunmen the Gennas and their henchmen were the most feared.

Five of the six Genna brothers were typical Sicilian killers—haughty, overbearing, contemptuous, savage, treacherous, and at the same time devoutly religious; they went regularly to church, and carried rosaries and crucifixes in their pistol pockets. The exception was Tony, known in the Italian colony as Tony the Gentleman and Tony the Aristocrat, who studied architecture, built model tenements for his poor countrymen, was a patron of the opera, and lived elegantly in a downtown hotel. He never killed, but he attended all family councils at which murder was planned, and had a voice in all decisions. The qualities that Tony the Gentleman lacked were to be found in ample measure in the Gennas' principal followers—Sam Smoots Amatuma, the dandy of gangland, accomplished musician and double-crosser; Giuseppe Nerone, called the Cavalier, university graduate and teacher of mathematics; and those ferocious murderers John Scalisi and Albert Anselmi, beside whom Frank McErlane was the personification of loving-kindness. It was Scalisi and Anselmi who taught Chicago's gangsters to rub their bullets with garlic, to increase the chances of gangrene.

The Gennas put hundreds of Sicilians and Italians to work cooking corn sugar alcohol in West Side tenements in the vicinity of Taylor Street, using a process which is said to have been invented by their brother-in-law, Harry Spingola, a wealthy lawyer. In less than a year the Genna cookeries and stills were producing thousands of gallons of raw alcohol, which was cut, flavored, colored and sold as brandy, whiskey, or whatever the customer desired in the way of fine liquor. At the peak of their prosperity, early in 1925, the assets of the Gennas, including good will and a three-story warehouse on Taylor Street, were valued at $5,000,000; gross sales amounted to $350,000 a month, of which at least $150,000 was profit. This lucrative business was protected by a police and political hookup arranged by Torrio and Esposito, by which the gangsters paid, monthly, sums which ranged from a small amount in the beginning to nearly $7,000 in April, 1925. Federal agents investigating the Gennas obtained a confession from their office manager, who said that five police captains were on the Genna payroll. He also said that four hundred uniformed police-men, mostly from the Maxwell Street station, besides many plain-clothes officers from Headquarters and the State's Attorney's office, called at the Genna warehouse each month to receive their bribes. In addition, the police received large quantities of alcohol at whole-sale prices.

To show his contempt for the Gennas and to emphasize his dissat-isfaction with Torrio's leadership, O'Banion hijacked a Genna truck loaded with thirty thousand dollars' worth of whiskey. The Gennas immediately polished up their armament and started on the war-path, but were restrained by Torrio and Mike Merlo, president of the Unione Siciliana, an important figure in the Nineteenth Ward, and the most powerful Sicilian or Italian in Chicago. Among his countrymen Merlo's word was law. He was intimately associated with Torrio, Capone, and other Italian and Sicilian gangsters and tolerated much lawlessness, but took no part in gang wars and was strongly opposed to murder. Both he and Torrio believed that peace with O'Banion could be arranged without recourse to the pistol and the shotgun. At that time, incidentally, the machine gun had not yet appeared as an instrument of gang warfare.

But O'Banion refused to listen to Torrio's overtures, and relations between the North Side chieftain and the leaders of the Sicilian gangs were strained throughout the winter of 1923–4, although no shootings occurred. The breaking point was reached in the spring of 1924, when O'Banion double-crossed Torrio and swindled him out of several hundred thousand dollars. In partnership with Torrio and Capone, O'Banion owned the Sieben Brewery on the North Side, one of the largest breweries to operate during prohibition. About the middle of May, 1924, O'Banion called Torrio and Capone into conference and told them he had decided to wind up his affairs and retire to Louis Alterie's ranch in Colorado. To make the story more plausible he intimated that he was afraid of the Gennas. Torrio and Capone bought O'Banion's share of the brewery for a price said to have been half a million dollars, and the property was transferred immediately. O'Banion agreed to assist in the dispatch and protection of one more convoy of beer from the plant and suggested May 19 as the best date for making the shipment.

On the night of May 19 the Sieben Brewery was raided by a strong force of policemen under the command of Chief of Police Morgan Collins and Captain Matthew Zimmer. Thirteen trucks piled high with beer barrels were confiscated, and twenty-eight gangsters and beer-runners arrested, including Torrio, Hymie Weiss, Louis Alterie, and O'Banion. Instead of taking his prisoners to a police station, Chief Collins turned them over to the Federal authorities. When asked why he had thus taken the case out of the hands of the State's Attorney, Chief Collins replied that the United States District Attorney "has promised us prompt cooperation." Johnny Torrio dipped into his well-lined pockets and brought up cash bail for himself and his half-dozen gunmen, but declined to furnish bonds for O'Banion, Weiss, and Alterie, none of whom had the necessary money on hand. They were compelled to await the arrival of Billy Skidmore, a professional bondsman and gambler, whose name is still frequently mentioned in connection with the Chicago underworld.

As soon as the police appeared at the brewery, Johnny Torrio suspected treachery. Later he obtained proof that O'Banion had double-crossed him. Through his political connections the North Sider had learned of the raid and had taken advantage of the knowledge to unload his share of the brewery upon Torrio and Capone. O'Banion also knew the prosecution would be handled by the United States District Attorney, and that Torrio's influence did not extend to the Federal court. He was well aware that he might himself be fined, but he anticipated that Torrio, as one of the owners of the brewery and as a second offender—Torrio had been fined $2,000 in 1923 for operating a brewery—would be much more severely punished. In the main, events occurred as O'Banion had expected. He paid no fine himself because he was dead by the time the brewery case came into court, but Torrio, one of eleven defendants who pleaded guilty, was fined $5,000 and sentenced to nine months in jail. He remained free on bail, however, for nearly a year.

Among Johnny Torrio's dominant traits, and accounting in large measure for his greatness as a criminal, were patience and the ability to hold his passions in check. Unquestionably he hated O'Banion as much as he had ever hated anyone, but he went about his business as if nothing had happened, realizing that war with the fierce North Sider would disrupt his system of liquor distribution, and throw gangland into chaos, as, eventually, it did. But O'Banion soon made a bad matter worse. Advised by the shrewd Hymie Weiss to make peace with Torrio and the Gennas, O'Banion said with huge contempt: "Oh, to hell with them Sicilians." This phrase, repeated by O'Banion gunmen as a choice bit of gangland repartee, was really the gangster florist's death warrant, for to Sicilians and Italians alike it was a deadly insult. Several times during the summer of 1924 the murder of O'Banion was planned by Torrio, Capone, and the Gennas, but each time they were stopped by Mike Merlo, who still hoped for a peaceful settlement. But Merlo died on November 8, 1924, to be succeeded by Angelo Genna as president of the Unione Siciliana, and two days later Dion O'Banion lay dead among his flowers.

Merlo's funeral was an imposing ceremony. A hundred thousand dollars' worth of flowers were sent to his home by friends; they filled not only the house but the lawn outside as well. The most impressive of these pieces was a statue of the dead man twelve feet high, made entirely of flowers, and said to have been a recognizable likeness. In the funeral cortege it was carried in a car preceding the hearse. Many of the flowers came from O'Banion's shop; he filled a $10,000 order for Torrio, and an $8,000 order for Al Capone.

Even one of the Gennas, Jim, called at O'Banion's place and paid $750 for a floral tribute. But, as developed later, Genna's visit was really for the purpose of familiarizing himself with the interior of the shop. All day Sunday, November 9, O'Banion and his partner, Schofield, worked hard arranging floral designs and sending them to the Merlo residence. That night, after O'Banion had gone, a man called by telephone and ordered a wreath. He said it would be called for next morning.

About noon on November 10 three men entered O'Banion's flower shop and walked abreast toward the gangster, who was clipping the stems of a bunch of chrysanthemums in the rear of the front room. He was alone in the place except for a Negro porter, mopping the floor in the back room. Over the top of a swinging wicker door, the porter saw O'Banion advance to meet the callers, heard him say: "Hello, boys, you want Merlo's flowers?" and saw him extend a hand in greeting. Ordinarily when O'Banion talked to anyone, particularly to strangers, he kept one hand in a pistol pocket. But this time he was off guard; his right hand was outstretched, and the left, holding a pair of shears, was at his side. The center man of the three simply grasped O'Banion's hand and suddenly jerked him forward, and before the gangster could recover his equilibrium and snatch a pistol, the men on either side of him had fired five bullets into his body, and a sixth—the grace shot to make death certain—into his head.

The Negro porter said that two of O'Banion's murderers were Italians, and that the third might have been a Greek or a Jew, but he could give no better description of their appearance. The police were never able to obtain sufficient evidence even to justify an arrest, and the crime is still officially unsolved. But O'Banion's gunmen learned, to their own satisfaction at least, that the killing was planned by Torrio and Capone, and that the man who seized O'Banion's hand was Mike Genna. The death shots were fired by John Scalisi and Albert Anselmi, each of whom received $10,000 in cash and a $3,000 diamond ring. Scalisi sent his ring to his sweetheart in Sicily.

The funeral of O'Banion was the gaudiest of all gangland's burials. His casket cost $10,000, and was shipped from Philadelphia

to Chicago in a special express car. Forty thousand persons viewed
the body as it "lay in state," as the *Tribune* put it, in an undertaker's
chapel. The funeral procession was a mile long, led by three bands
and a police escort from Stickney, Chief Collins having refused to
allow Chicago policemen to participate in the ceremonies. Twenty-
five trucks and cars were required to carry the flowers. Ten thousand persons followed the hearse, and ten thousand more waited
at the grave. Cardinal Mundelein had refused to allow funeral services to be held over the dead gangster, but at Mount Carmel Cemetery a priest who had known O'Banion since childhood recited a
litany, a Hail Mary, and the Lord's Prayer. The gangster was
buried in unconsecrated ground, but five months after his death the
body was disinterred and reburied in a plot which had been bought
by Mrs. O'Banion. It was thus placed in consecrated ground, a circumstance which led Captain John Stege, an honest policeman
who fought the gangsters with great vigor, to remark:

"O'Banion was a thief and a murderer, but look at him now,
buried eighty feet from a bishop."

REMEMBER THE BLACK SOX?*

John Lardner

DIRECTLY after the end of World War I, in 1918, when
the soldiers began returning from France, sports zoomed
into high at home, as though the doughboys wanted to
quickly forget the muddy trenches of Normandy, the army
food, and the sergeants' commands. Baseball rocketed to
the top of the popularity list. A year later the national
pastime was all but wrecked.

The anguish among the juvenile population of the country was deep and almost traumatic. In Chicago, the base
of the sellout, the kids of the city wandered about in a
daze for weeks. They simply could not believe that their
hero, the supergreat White Sox aggregation, was a team
riddled with crooks. On street corners and in sand lots
the kids' hearts hung at half-mast.

Of course baseball did not die; its roots went too deep
into the national life. When purged, the game grew more
popular than ever. But the shadow cast by the "Black Sox"
scandal hovered for years over the big stadia of the land.

CHICAGO	CINCINNATI
J. Collins, r.f.	Rath, 2b.
E. Collins, 2b.	Daubert, 1b.
Weaver, 3b.	Groh, 3b.
Jackson, l.f.	Roush, c.f.
Felsch, c.f.	Duncan, l.f.
Gandil, 1b.	Kopf, ss.
Risberg, ss.	Neale, r.f.
Schalk, c.	Wingo, c.
Cicotte, p.	Ruether, p.

* From *The Saturday Evening Post,* 1938. Reprinted by special permission
of John Lardner.

THE first of October, 1919, was the Fourth of July all over again in Cincinnati. Most of the big stores were closed for the day. Flags draped the business section of town, and newsboys yelled themselves hoarse. Sen. Warren Gamaliel Harding and party had the bridal suite at the Sinton Hotel. Barney Oldfield held court at the Gibson.

Tickets? You could still get a block of three for a hundred bucks from that operative over there in the corner of the lobby, if you liked to do business with Sitting Bull on a strictly Custer basis. The face value of a block was $16.50—first, second and sixth games, Cincinnati at home.

Everybody who was anybody would be at the ball game that afternoon. Anybody who was everybody would do the best he could. They were setting up direct-wire connection, follow it play-by-play on the scoreboard, getcher official line-up here, getcher autograph picture of Eddie Roush!

Big-league baseball had boomed in its first season after the World War. Every year the magnates cleared their throats and said, "Baseball, the national pastime, has enjoyed a banner year," and this time, in the autumn of 1919, they never spoke a truer word. The fever was soaring. Lotteries or pools, selling tickets on total scores for the week, had done a million-dollar business from Oregon to Virginia since May. Batting averages were familiar to the country, and players heroic, as they never had been before.

And now, at the end of the bobtailed—140 games—but lively season, the fans were sitting down, unglutted, to a World Series that was a World Series. Or, rather, to an exhibition of skill and science by the greatest ball club of all time, complete with human foils. For the White Sox, of Chicago, were like John L. Sullivan in the days when the Strong Boy toured the country offering $100 to the local volunteer who could go three rounds with him. Cincinnati, the critics said, would last five rounds anyway—the series was five games out of nine. The Reds were simply the survivors of a National League dogfight. But the Sox—

Take the testimony of an expert witness, Edward Trowbridge Collins.

"They were the best," says Eddie, their captain and second baseman. "There never was a ball club like that one, in more ways than one. I hate to say it, but they were better than the Athletics I played with from 1910 through 1914.

"Offensively, from top to bottom, there wasn't a breather for an opposing pitcher in the line-up; and when it came to pitchers, Cicotte, Williams, Kerr and Faber were tops as pitchers in the American League at the time—all on one club."

Shano Collins or Nemo Liebold in right field; your witness, Eddie Collins, the peer of Lajoie, Hornsby and Gehringer, second base; Buck Weaver, natural ballplayer of natural ballplayers, third base; Shoeless Joe Jackson, forerunner of Ruth, left field; Hap Felsch, great thrower and dangerous hitter, center field; Chick Gandil, a slick genius, first base; Swede Risberg, sure-handed fielder and tidy batsman, shortstop; Ray Schalk, the fastest and smartest catcher of his generation, behind the plate; and Cicotte, Williams, Kerr.

The Reds were just a pretty good team, and their best friends did not claim more for them at the time. The Redlegs who survive today—Greasy Neale, for one, whose brain, working on the side line of the Yale Bowl every fall, can be heard to purr like a dynamo as far away as Bridgeport—will not contradict you when you classify them as the short-enders of the century. On paper, they were 5 to 1.

But October first brought high carnival to Cincinnati just the same. Thirty-one thousand squeezed into the grandstand and bleachers, and hundreds of thousands stood outside by the scoreboards.

This was the first postwar World Series, the crowning glory of baseball's renaissance, and it was Shineball Eddie Cicotte pitching for the White Sox—the greatest right-hander, next to Walter Johnson, in the game.

Cicotte's second pitch of the day hit the batter, Maurice Rath, Red second baseman, in the small of the back. It wasn't the first pitch, as generally believed. The first was a called strike.

In the last half of the fourth inning, Cicotte took the mound with the score 1 to 1 and looked nervously around at his fielders. Something about his manner had been puzzling the inmates of the press box from the start, from the time he hit Rath. Now they muttered, "What the hell?" Those men behind Eddie Cicotte could field their positions in their sleep.

Then boff! boff! boff! A run was in, and there were Reds on second and third. Dutch Ruether, Cincinnati pitcher, came to the place. He whaled a terrific triple between Felsch and Jackson. A few minutes later, five Red runs were in, and Cicotte was out. Kid Gleason, tough, gray little manager of the White Sox, was on the playing field, yanking his arms around, crazy with rage and grief. The Reds won the ball game 9 to 1, as the Sox batsmen, each a sharpshooter, waved gently at Ruether's delivery.

Cincinnati went solidly nuts that night. But some of the folks from out of town—ballplayers who watched from the grandstand, certain Chicago baseball writers, and a small percentage of Chicago fans—were mumbling and shaking their heads. This wasn't any part of the ball club they'd been seeing.

Kid Gleason went into conference that night with his employer, the Old Roman, Charles A. Comiskey. And up in a double room at the Sinton Hotel, where the telephone rang every sixty seconds, a fellow called Bennett, from Des Moines, became very irritable.

"This thing is beginning to smell," he said to his roommate, a fellow from New York. "The dogs in the street know it."

If, by dogs in the street, Mr. Bennett meant smart gamblers, he was absolutely correct. But the country at large didn't know for another twelve months that the fix was in—the biggest, sloppiest, crudest fix of a sporting event that ever was known to man. It was a makeshift job; compounded in equal parts of bluff and welsh and cold gall, with no contributor or agent-contributor knowing what the man next to him was up to, and very seldom bothering to find out.

The Series was fixed on the strength of a fake telegram, with the help of a pair of go-betweens who lost their shirts on it. Three-quarters of the bounty money was withheld from the players who threw the Series. Arnold Rothstein, widely accused of being the Judas-in-chief of the stratagem, could sit back and deny the charge blandly and securely, because, after coming up and telling him what they were going to do and insuring him a handsome betting profit, the fixers went through with the thing without him.

It was a haphazard business, all right, comical in some of its aspects, but it nearly wrecked baseball for all eternity. Those who followed its unraveling in 1920 remember that it touched off a rash of scandal rumors that spread across the face of the game like measles. A hundred players and half a dozen ball clubs were involved in stories of sister plots. Baseball was said to be crooked as sin from top to bottom.

And people didn't take their baseball lightly in those days. They threw themselves wholeheartedly into the game when the war ended, so much so that the sudden pull-up, the revelation of crookedness, was a real and ugly shock. It got under their skins. You heard of no lynchings, but Buck Herzog, the old Giant infielder, on an exhibition tour of the West in the late fall of 1920, was slashed with a knife by an unidentified fan who yelled, "That's for you, you crooked such-and-such!"

Buck's name had been mentioned by error in a newspaper rumor of a minor unpleasantness in New York that John J. McGraw had ironed out ruthlessly a few years before. Buck was innocent as a newborn pigeon, but rumors were rumors, and the national temper was high.

"Too high," says Mr. Herzog, looking back. "I never want to see the like again."

It's a fact that some of the White Sox, after the scandal hearings, were unwilling to leave the courtroom for fear of mobs.

Well, that was the business that nearly forestalled the careers of Joe DiMaggio, Jerome H. Dean, Carl Hubbell, Lou Gehrig, Mickey Cochrane, William (Terrible) Terry and Paul Waner. The public came within a whisker's width of never seeing another box score, never heckling another umpire, never warming another hot stove. It was close—too close for comfort. And though the baseball magnates of today like to think of 1919 as a tightly sealed chapter, and though the Hall of Fame at Cooperstown is closed, actually if not officially, to Joe Jackson, Buck Weaver and Eddie Cicotte— well, we're wallowing in baseball luxury now. We can afford to

look back at the abyss after the long years of hard, steady climbing.

To a loosely knit group of technicians on the fringe of baseball,
the news of the scandal, when it broke, was no complete surprise. It took the country by storm, but Jack Doyle remembers that
there were rumors of something off-key several days before the
Series began, which means a full year before the story became public property.

"You couldn't miss it, if you were doing important betting," says
Mr. Doyle, Broadway's price maker. "The thing had an odor. I
saw smart guys take even money on the Sox who should have been
asking five to one. Those Sox, may they rest in peace, should have
been the shortest-priced favorites that ever started a World Series."

The Series was scheduled to open on the first of October. On
September 29 in Boston, well-known professionals began to grab
all the 4-to-1 money they could lay their hands on, and backed the
price down to even money. Similar movements started simultaneously in Pittsburgh, New York, St. Louis, Des Moines and Philadelphia. The Red wave seemed senseless, but Nat Evans and Nick
the Greek were not senseless fellows when it came to laying their
funds on the line. Nor were Rachel Brown and Sport Sullivan and
Joe Gedeon.

The fix had been clumsy. It's small wonder that sharp-eared
characters like Nicholas Dandolos were "wised up and kicking the
market to hell," in the subsequent bitter words of Abe Attell. They
were even wised up in Wall Street, where bets of $1,000 were
placed on Cincinnati at even money.

The Series began with Cicotte's strange defeat. It grew stranger.
In the second game, Lefty Claude Williams—"the best control
pitcher in this league," said Gleason—yielded three walks and two
hits in the fourth inning, for three runs. The Reds picked up another
run in the sixth. The final score was 4 to 2.

"The game was given to Cincinnati on a platter," said Gleason.
It was a thing any manager might say under the circumstances, and
when Wee Dickie Kerr, former bantamweight prize fighter, shut

out the Reds in the third game, the fans of Chicago took heart. But the small-time professionals of the city were going around hotel lobbies with sheaves of folding money in their hands, offering 5 to 2 on Cincinnati, begging to be covered. The market was dead, for the moment.

Eddie Cicotte's second start, in the fourth game of the Series, produced an eerie development. Cicotte, a good fielding pitcher, managed to turn in two errors before three men were out. For one, he made an atrociously bad throw to Chick Gandil on first. The other came after Pat Duncan, young Red outfielder, had reached second. Larry Kopf singled into Joe Jackson's territory. Joe's great arm rifled the ball ahead of the runner, toward home. Cicotte made the technically proper play—when he saw that Duncan was not going to try to score, he intercepted the throw, apparently to make sure that Kopf would not try to take two bases while the ball was going all the way to the plate. But instead of completing the interception, Cicotte's gloved hand batted the ball to the grandstand. Duncan scored. Then Kopf did, too, on Greasy Neale's double off Cicotte. The Sox supporters were not alone in expressing their chagrin over Cicotte's performance when the Reds won, 2 to 0.

"In all his life he never pulled two like that before," said Gleason to reporters.

On October 7, trailing by four games to one, the Sox rallied behind a failing Kerr and won the hard way, in the tenth inning, on hits by Weaver and Gandil. Cincinnati businessmen lost $60,000 in bets that day.

The Sox won again behind Cicotte, next afternoon. And then, on October 9, with Chicago fans yelling for a stretch finish, and the Reds seemingly on the run, the greatest ball team on earth collapsed like a parasol. The generous Williams gave up three runs before two were out in the first inning. In Chicago's half of the first in this game, with Liebold and Eddie Collins on base, and no one out, Weaver and Felsch went down in order, on two swinging strike-outs. And the mighty Jackson finished the inning by fouling out.

"If they'd shut their eyes, they couldn't 'a' done it," said Kid

Gleason. The Kid seemed to have aged ten years in nine days. The furrows in his face were deeper, and his feet moved with a drag.

Rumors soared like kites in the breeze off Lake Michigan on October 10, the day after the Series ended. They were rumors strong enough to demand public attention. Charles A. Comiskey offered a reward of $20,000 for "a single clue" to evidence that his "boys" had been to the tank. No clues were forthcoming, and the rumors subsided. Chicago did not know that Commy was hiring private detectives to carry on the investigation undercover, or that the pay checks of eight White Sox players were held up— Jackson, Cicotte, Williams, Gandil, Felsch, Weaver, Risberg, and the utility infielder and pinch hitter, Fred McMullin.

Christy Mathewson spoke of the rumors at the time. He said it was ridiculous to question the honesty of the Series. To be sure, Matty was a National League booster and the recently retired manager of the Cincinnati club (1918), and talk of a fix was hard for him to stomach.

His arguments were irrefutable:

1. Too many players would have to be approached and bribed. One man can't throw a Series. 2. A manager can't throw a Series. The team will hustle in spite of him. 3. A pitcher can't do it. He would be yanked at the first sign of weakness. 4. You can't fix several players on one club and be sure your secret is safe. 5. No player would want to risk everything—his career, his future, his income—for a bundle of quick cash.

"And besides," said Matty, summing up, "it's just unthinkable, generally."

It was unthinkable, all right, and the way they worked it, it was grotesque. The dizziest wonder of all is that the whole house of marked cards did not topple about the ears of Sleepy Bill Burns and Billy Maharg and Abe Attell and Bennett, of Des Moines, and the boys on the field, long before Jake Daubert planted his shoe on first base for the final put-out of the Series.

Before we examine the gamblers and their methods, though, let's have a look at the boys on the field. Unthinkable, said Matty. But this was a ball club unique in baseball history. Eddie Collins tells you it was the greatest club of all time and the greatest trouble club.

"That's what made its greatness so hard to understand," Eddie says. "As a rule, the chief requirement for a great team is harmony and cooperation on and off the field. That was an important thing about Connie Mack's teams. The White Sox? They were night and day to the Athletics. They seethed with discord and bitterness. Time after time they were close to open fighting with fists among themselves. And still they won going away."

It was a team of cliques, conspiracies, headaches and fights. Collins and Chick Gandil, playing side by side in the infield, hadn't been on speaking terms since 1917, following a queer episode in which Gandil raised a pool among the players to reward the members of another club which had helped them win the pennant. Ray Schalk, the catcher, spoke to only three of the pitchers between games, Faber, Kerr and Lowdermilk.

Gandil was known around the league as a gambler and a trouble-maker. Cicotte used to say, "Chick was raised with low characters. He ain't got no ethics." Ethics or not, Chick had a strong influence over Cicotte and the happy-go-lucky Jackson.

Was the ball club underpaid? That's the excuse which many critics give for what happened in 1919. Commy was a powerful, upright man, a baseball pioneer, but his best friends could not call him a lavish spender—not with the hired help. The salaries of the "takers," or Black Sox, excepting McMullin, the utility man, ranged from $5,000 to $10,000. Jackson got a little more, $12,000. And they were the stars of the team—some of them the stars of all baseball.

This was before a fellow named Ruth revolutionized the game and nudged the wage scale upward with the blows of his mighty bat. Few ballplayers had five-figure incomes prior to 1920. But Commy's scale was lower than most, and his players were better than any. It's not hard to understand that the prospect of making the equivalent of a year's salary—"all in one whack, all green," as Jackson said—would dazzle the boys.

Throwing a ball game—"It's easy," said Cicotte later. "Gee, how easy! And you can make it look good." There was a lot of talk like that in the summer of 1919, among some of the players, especially in the later months, when it became obvious that the Sox were a shoo-in for the pennant. The talk was mostly in hotel rooms. One of the hotels was the Ansonia, in New York. They were talking there one day, Gandil and Cicotte, and a couple of outsiders were with them—a former ballplayer and a former fighter.

Sleepy Bill Burns had pitched here and there in both major leagues, with the White Sox and the Reds among other clubs. He moved from team to team, not sticking long with any. Bill had a habit of going to sleep on the bench, which won him his nickname. He was a guy who had been around. He admitted it. Billy Maharg, from Philadelphia, was an old-time lightweight who had fought some of the good ones, including Freddie Welsh.

Gandil and Cicotte and Burns and Maharg sat talking in the hotel room, with the door shut and the window open and a hot breeze and the smell of asphalt sifting in. Presently Burns and Maharg went away. A couple of days later, Sleepy Bill went out to the race track. They were running at Jamaica then.

"Where's Rothstein?" he asked of a fellow he knew.

"Over on the rail."

Bill went over. Arnold Rothstein, the "real-estate operator" and sportsman, a pale-faced pouter pigeon of a man, said, "Hello."

"The Series can be fixed," said Bill. "It's ripe. But it'll take financing. They'd want a hundred grand."

Rothstein shook his head.

"They'll do business," urged Burns. "It's strictly an investment."

"No, not me," said Rothstein. "It's not the money. It's the details. It's too risky. It can't be done."

Burns took "no" for an answer. At least, he swears up and down that he did, and Rothstein's intimates of the time swear he did, and while one man's oath is another man's succotash, the thing is altogether logical. For Rothstein had his ear to the ground. He knew the mood and temper of some of the White Sox. One way or another, he thought, the fix would be in, and there was no sense in tying up money that could otherwise be bet. This thought occurred later to other minds, to the mortification of the White Sox who threw the Series. The bank-rolling of the scheme—the pay-off—was a department which gripped the interest of almost nobody. Rothstein used to say, in the years that followed, that he never made a nickel betting on the Series of 1919, but people close to him put the figure now at closer to $60,000.

It was Abe Attell who next tuned in on the eloquence of Sleepy Bill Burns. Bill was eloquent still, but a trifle discouraged, and even shocked, by the nearsighted reluctance of business leaders to invest in a sure-fire scheme. Bill was like Fulton, peddling his steamboat. It seemed to him sometimes that he had been born too soon. These were backward times.

But Abe Attell gave him hope. Abe was another fellow who had been around. One of the greatest small fighters of all time—former featherweight champion of the world, a miracle of speed, skill and science—he had taken to living by his wits when he left the ring. Abe's wits were in first-class condition. "I think maybe Rothstein has changed his mind," he said.

That was good enough for Burns.

It was at the Sinton, a couple of days before the Series began, and not until then, that Attell showed Burns, Maharg and Gandil "proof" that Rothstein was financing the deal. The proof was a telegram signed with Rothstein's name. It was all the proof that Gandil, now ringmaster of the players' side of the circus and chief go-between, ever saw. Would the boys be paid off? Chick didn't know, and he didn't much care. He had money. He was betting it. And so, it seemed to Attell and Bennett, was everybody else. Bennett, Des Moines gambler, was working with Abe, digging up money and getting it down at the best odds possible, but the best odds were none too good by the morning of October 1. It was most annoying. Those thieves in Boston, New York, Pittsburgh, St. Louis and elsewhere were butchering the price. Even dumb ballplayers around the leagues were on the line for Cincinnati and getting rich.

"Kind of an open secret, eh, pal?" said Mr. Attell.

"It smells," grumbled Mr. Bennett.

"Well, keep punching," said Abe. "Get it down."

The ballplayers, tipped off by Gandil that the promised fee was $100,000 to be paid in installments of $20,000 after each of the five losing games and split among them, were getting restless and uneasy in their hotel rooms and around the clubhouse. Cicotte's nerves were close to breaking.

"You can't bluff me," he told Burns, Maharg and Gandil. "I got to have $10,000, and have it now."

He got it after the first game, which he lost. But he and the rest of the boys were drifting around in a heavy mist.

"We didn't know nothin'," says Joe Jackson. "Not a thing."

Burns and Maharg, calling at Attell's room on the morning of the second game, got $10,000 for Cicotte, and no more. Eddie said later that he found the money half hidden under his pillow— two or three $1,000 bills and several hundreds in the pile.

A total of $25,000 was paid up, divided among three players. The rest say they never touched a dime, and the facts seem to bear them out. The pay-off department, as noted above, was not popular with any of the gamblers involved in the deal. It was office work, drudgery, giving no scope to the soaring qualities of the intellect.

And out on the ball field, the Sox went blindly through their paces. They were cutting their own throats on the strength of a fake telegram, and they were doing a thorough job. The fix of the Series was a hit-or-miss business by the gamblers, who seemed to be making up the plot as they went along, but the players' work was well done.

Cicotte lobbed the ball to the plate "so you could read the trademark on it." Williams, "the best control pitcher in the league," gave out passes like a drunken press agent. Risberg's foot missed the bag by twelve inches on an easy double-play ball. Felsch played his position for Neale as though Greasy, a long hitter, were a crippled schoolgirl.

"It's too terrible to watch," shuddered Gleason, on the bench.

But the lighthearted Joe Jackson, now confused and shaken, could not pass up all that appetizing Cincinnati pitching. Joe was the leading batsman of the series, with .375. He hit the only home run. And when he walked to the plate, he carried his lucky hairpins with him. Hairpins were always lucky for Joe. He took them along up there even when he knew that Lady Luck had gone to Cain's Warehouse for the duration of the Series.

Burns and Maharg were moaning in close harmony with the players. Thinking that the third game was also in the bag for Cincinnati, they had lost all their funds betting against Dickie Kerr. And they felt they had reason enough to do so.

"If we can't win for Cicotte and Williams," Gandil had said a few days before, "we're not gonna win for no busher."

The sixth game, won by Chicago the hard way, was a betting counterstroke. Cincinnati businessmen, supporting their home team heavily by now, were milked at odds which favored the Reds. On the last game, when the White Sox seemed to be coming back, a group of Texas oil men admitted later that they were taken for $82,000. Gambling experts all over the country were sitting in on the game by then, and business was good.

The Series ended, and the boys went home to hunt, fish, and loaf—and to grumble and chew their nails, for there was trouble about the delivery of those Series pay checks, and friends in Chicago wrote some of them that Commy's detectives were up to their noses in hot scents.

As the winter wore on, Gandil made a fuss—for publication— about his next season's salary, and dropped quietly from the club. When the scandal broke, the following September, Chick was in a hospital in Lufkin, Texas, having his appendix removed. He lost this spare part the same day, September 28, that Eddie Cicotte lost his nerve and talked to the grand jury of Cook County.

The White Sox, racked by internecine strife, nobody talking to anybody, were still a good enough ball club at this time to be fighting with Cleveland for the pennant—one game behind, three games to go. Comiskey, with his world breaking about him, sent seven copies of one telegram to seven men:

You and each of you are hereby notified of your indefinite suspension as a member of the Chicago American League baseball club.

Your suspension is brought about by information which has just come to me directly involving each of you in the baseball scandal now being investigated by the present Grand Jury of Cook County resulting from the World Series of 1919.

If you are innocent of all wrongdoing, you and each of you will be reinstated; if you are guilty, you will be retired from organized baseball for the rest of your lives if I can accomplish it.

Until there is a finality to this investigation, it is due the public that I take this action, even though it cost Chicago the pennant.

Actually, the information had not "just come" to Commy. It was all in his hands when the scandal suddenly went off in scattered pops, like a string of firecrackers. The grand jury had subpoenaed Bill Burns, Abe Attell, Arnold Rothstein and others on September 24. Billy Maharg had told his side of the case to Jimmy Isaminger, Philadelphia's alert baseball writer, and the story was circulated nationally. There was nothing for Commy to do but break up his ball club, and, in fairness to him, it should be said that he did a thorough and relentless job of it. Offers from Col. Jake Ruppert and other club owners of "your choice of players" were rejected with thanks. Cleveland clinched the pennant.

In a queer set of semiformal talks with the grand jury, Cicotte, Jackson, Williams and Felsch told their stories. The shock hit the baseball public between the eyes, but the hearing fathered two phrases which promptly became paid-up members of the American language. There is nothing bogus about the origin of these phrases; just a little juggling. Three local writers and a news-service man were on hand when a kid stepped out of a group of kids and said to Jackson, just leaving the confessional:

"It ain't true, is it, Joe?"

"Yes, boys, I'm afraid it is," said Shoeless Joseph.

The authenticity of this incident seems pretty well established by the fact that four different men mentioned it in four different stories within three hours of the time that Jackson left the hearing. The capsule, cross-section version of the kid's remark was, "Say it ain't true, Joe," and if he didn't actually put it that way, he leaves himself open to a charge of untidy rhetoric.

As for Cicotte, Eddie "did it for the wife and kiddies" three times in the presence of the court stenographer, who took his words down in shorthand.

The grand jury and prosecuting staff of Cook County were seriously seeking indictments for conspiracy against the eight Sox. The magnates weren't. Not when they thought it over. They would handle this thing in their own way. They did.

There is a Napoleonic bee in the bonnet of nearly every baseball magnate, owing, probably, to the fact that he has the power of buy-and-sell over his employees; the power—it has been called unconstitutional—of auctioneering in terms of men, of black-listing and suspending without hearing, of writing and signing contracts which guarantee the rights of the owner, but not the chattel.

It would prick the vanity of many a club owner today to see his affairs—baseball affairs—settled in a court of law. Commy and his colleagues wanted to keep this thing in the lodge. They had their own way of dealing with it—more effective and ruthless, when you consider the facts, than any judgment a criminal court could pass.

The trial of the eight Sox, in July and August, 1921, was a little on the hollow side. The signed confessions taken by the grand jury the year before had "disappeared"—certain of the magnates advancing the theory, which would have been funnier in dialect, that Rothstein had made a secret trip to Chicago and bribed an aide of the district attorney's to burn them.

These confessions were the backbone of the case for conspiracy, although Sleepy Bill Burns testified for twelve hours, and went to sleep in the box before he had finished. The night of the acquittal, the Sox held a celebration party at an Italian restaurant near the Loop. The jurors held a celebration party in the same restaurant the same night. There was no prearrangement about this joint revel, and though their private rooms adjoined, the two parties kept sternly to themselves.

Then the magnates went to work. Kid Gleason had taken the stand in defense of his players in the "kangaroo" court, but when the state acquitted them the Kid turned cold as steel. He had little vitality left in his small, tough body after 1921, but all there was of it he directed against the men who had sold him out. He never spoke to one of them again.

The retrial of the Black Sox by baseball's own tribunal was a star-chamber affair. The decision was foregone, and the action swift. The eight men—Gandil, Cicotte, Jackson, Felsch, Weaver, Risberg, Williams and McMullin—were barred from the game for life. This meant organized baseball, which meant everything but

the frayed fringes of the professional game—semipro ball, sand-
lot ball, twilight-league ball. Within a few months, most of the
outlaws were skimming those fringes for what they could find.

The boys, all of them, pleaded their innocence for years afterward, to anyone who would listen. Eddie Cicotte came back from
the semipro honky-tonk to Detroit, to argue his case on street corners. Joe Jackson buttonholed patrons in his barbecue hutch in
South Carolina. Hap Felsch harangued the customers at his Milwaukee beer parlor.

It's obvious today that some of them, fix or no fix, were never
paid money to throw a game. That all of them are serving life
sentences without trial. That, with one or two exceptions, none
of them belongs in the same league with Arnold, Tarquin, Cesare
Borgia or Guy Fawkes.

If they never did anything else, the outlawed Sox—black or
white, take your pick—were responsible for the presence of that
snow-haloed, hawk-faced gentleman who hung over the edge of his
field box at the world series, chewing the brim of his hat. Judge
Kenesaw Mountain Landis once fined the Standard Oil Company
$29,000,000, a tidy assessment. When the scandals broke in 1920,
there was a cry for a high commissioner to replace the three-man
commission at the head of baseball, and the judge was elected,
and if you hear eight strong voices joined some evening in the
strains of We Made Him What He is Today, those are the outlaws
serenading Judge Landis.

There's another matter which calls the Sox of 1919 to mind
these days. Up in Cooperstown, New York, where Abner Double-
day experimented with balls and bats some nine-and-ninety years
ago, there is a Hall of Fame.

The names of great ballplayers have been or will be inscribed
there—Ruth, Cobb, Wagner, Johnson, Mathewson, Speaker,
Young, Lajoie and Alexander. Which of the Black Sox, on playing merit alone, deserve mention in the same breath? Well, Jackson, Weaver and Cicotte, by general agreement among the people,
especially the ballplayers, who saw them in action. There is no

ruling which says that the baseball writers cannot vote the Sox to the Hall, if they feel in their hearts that they belong there. There never will be a ruling until some outlaw collects enough votes to qualify him for the holy tablets, and the magnates hope very earnestly that no such emergency will arise.

The Spalding Guide, the voice of the magnate, said editorially in 1921:

The gambler has done his worst again. He is the respecter of no game. He would as quickly buy the youth in the lot as the professional in the arena, if he could. He has tried both. He will try again. The honest ballplayer need have no fear of any gambler. There are thousands and thousands of honest ballplayers. There is another small group—they were ballplayers once—to be immured in the Chamber of Oblivion. There let them rest.

That seems to be official.

FIRST DAYS AT HULL HOUSE*

Jane Addams

DRIVING south on Halsted Street in your car or on a trolley, you pass a group of modest brick houses near Polk Street. In 1889 two young girls moved into one of them, with very little capital but with a great deal of hope. One of them, Jane Addams, went on to become one of the great women of the world. Almost singlehanded, she revolutionized American metropolitan social service. Her fame soon spread beyond the confines of Chicago as her work and writings became internationally known. Most of the world's great stopped off at Hull House whenever they visited Chicago.

Today Hull House still carries on at the old stand. You don't hear much about it because its founders are dead and because it has been with us so long. But as you pass it in your car or on the trolley, you feel you are looking at a monument to a great woman, a great ideal.

THE next January found Miss Starr and myself in Chicago, searching for a neighborhood in which we might put our plans into execution. In our eagerness to win friends for the new undertaking, we utilized every opportunity to set forth the meaning of the settlement as it had been embodied in Toynbee Hall, although in those days we made no appeal for money, meaning to start with our own slender resources. From the very first the plan received courteous attention, and the discussion, while often skeptical, was always friendly. Professor Swing wrote a commendatory column in the *Evening Journal,* and our early speeches were reported quite out of proportion to their worth. I recall a spirited evening at the home of Mrs. Wilmarth, which was attended by that renowned scholar, Thomas Davidson, and by a young Englishman who was a member of the then new Fabian society and to whom a peculiar glamor was attached because he had scoured knives all summer in a camp of high-minded philosophers in the Adirondacks. Our new little plan met with criticism, not to say disapproval, from Mr. Davidson, who, as nearly as I can remember, called it "one of those unnatural attempts to understand life through cooperative living."

It was in vain we asserted that the collective living was not an essential part of the plan, that we would always scrupulously pay our own expenses, and that at any moment we might decide to scatter through the neighborhood and to live in separate tenements; he still contended that the fascination for most of those volunteering residence would lie in the collective-living aspect of the Settlement. His contention was, of course, essentially sound; there is a constant tendency for the residents to "lose themselves in the cave of their own companionship," as the Toynbee Hall phrase goes, but on the other hand, it is doubtless true that the very companionship, the give and take of colleagues, is what tends to keep the Settlement normal and in touch with "the world of things as they are." I am happy to say that we never resented this nor any other difference of opinion, and that fifteen years later Professor Davidson handsomely acknowledged that the advantages of a group far outweighed the weaknesses he had early pointed out. He was at that later moment sharing with a group of young men, on the East Side of New York, his ripest conclusions in philosophy and was much touched by their intelligent interest and absorbed devotion. I think that time has also justified our early contention that the mere foothold of a house, easily accessible, ample in space, hospitable and tolerant in spirit, situated in the midst of the large foreign colonies which so easily isolate themselves in American cities, would be in itself a serviceable thing for Chicago. I am not so sure that we succeeded in our endeavors "to make social intercourse express the growing sense of the economic unity of society and to add the social function to democracy." But Hull House was soberly opened on the theory that the dependence of classes on each other is reciprocal; and that as the social relation is essentially a reciprocal relation, it gives a form of expression that has peculiar value.

In our search for a vicinity in which to settle we went about with the officers of the compulsory education department, with city missionaries and with the newspaper reporters whom I recall as a much older set of men than one ordinarily associates with that profession, or perhaps I was only sent out with the older ones on what they must all have considered a quixotic mission. One Sunday afternoon in the late winter a reporter took me to visit a so-called anarchist Sunday school, several of which were to be found on the northwest side of the city. The young man in charge was of the German student type, and his face flushed with enthusiasm as he led the children singing one of Koerner's poems. The newspaperman, who did not understand German, asked me what abominable stuff they were singing, but he seemed dissatisfied with my translation of the simple words and darkly intimated that they were "deep ones," and had probably "fooled" me. When I replied that Koerner was an ardent German poet whose songs inspired his countrymen to resist the aggressions of Napoleon, and that his bound poems were found in the most respectable libraries, he looked at me rather askance and I then and there had my first intimation that to treat a Chicago man, who is called an anarchist, as you would treat any other citizen, is to lay yourself open to deep suspicion.

Another Sunday afternoon in the early spring, on the way to a Bohemian mission in the carriage of one of its founders, we passed a fine old house standing well back from the street, surrounded on three sides by a broad piazza which was supported by wooden pillars of exceptionally pure Corinthian design and proportion. I was so attracted by the house that I set forth to visit it the very next day, but though I searched for it then and for several days after, I could not find it, and at length I most reluctantly gave up the search.

Three weeks later, with the advice of several of the oldest residents of Chicago, including the ex-mayor of the city, Colonel Mason, who had from the first been a warm friend to our plans, we decided upon a location somewhere near the junction of Blue Island Avenue, Halsted Street, and Harrison Street. I was surprised and overjoyed on the very first day of our search for quarters to come upon the hospitable old house, the quest for which I had so recently abandoned. The house was of course rented, the lower part of it used for offices and storerooms in connection with a factory that stood back of it. However, after some difficulties were overcome, it proved to be possible to sublet the second floor and what had been the large drawing room on the first floor.

The house had passed through many changes since it had been built in 1856 for the homestead of one of Chicago's pioneer citizens, Mr. Charles J. Hull, and although battered by its vicissitudes, was essentially sound. Before it had been occupied by the factory, it had sheltered a second-hand furniture store, and at one time the Little Sisters of the Poor had used it for a home for the aged. It had a half-skeptical reputation for a haunted attic, so far respected by the tenants living on the second floor that they always kept a large pitcher full of water on the attic stairs. Their explanation of this custom was so incoherent that I was sure it was a survival of the belief that a ghost could not cross running water, but perhaps that interpretation was only my eagerness for finding folklore.

The fine old house responded kindly to repairs, its wide hall and open fireplaces always insuring it a gracious aspect. Its generous owner, Miss Helen Culver, in the following spring gave us a free leasehold of the entire house. Her kindness has continued through the years until the group of thirteen buildings, which at present comprises our equipment, is built largely upon land which Miss Culver has put at the service of the Settlement which bears Mr. Hull's name. In those days the house stood between an undertaking establishment and a saloon. "Knight, Death, and the Devil," the three were called by a Chicago wit, and yet any mock heroics which might be implied by comparing the Settlement to a knight quickly dropped away under the genuine kindness and hearty welcome extended to us by the families living up and down the street.

We furnished the house as we would have furnished it were it in another part of the city, with the photographs and other impedimenta we had collected in Europe, and with a few bits of family mahogany. While all the new furniture which was bought was enduring in quality, we were careful to keep it in character with the fine old residence. Probably no young matron ever placed her own things in her own house with more pleasure than that with which we first furnished Hull House. We believed that the Settlement may logically bring to its aid all those adjuncts which the cultivated man regards as good and suggestive of the best life of the past.

On the eighteenth of September, 1889, Miss Starr and I moved into it, with Miss Mary Keyser, who began by performing the housework, but who quickly developed into a very important factor in the life of the vicinity as well as in that of the household, and whose death five years later was most sincerely mourned by hundreds of our neighbors. In our enthusiasm over "settling," the first night we forgot not only to lock but to close a side door opening on Polk Street, and were much pleased in the morning to find that we possessed a fine illustration of the honesty and kindliness of our new neighbors.

Our first guest was an interesting young woman who lived in a neighboring tenement, whose widowed mother aided her in the support of the family by scrubbing a downtown theater every night. The mother, of English birth, was well bred and carefully educated, but was in the midst of that bitter struggle which awaits so many strangers in American cities who find that their social position tends to be measured solely by the standards of living they are able to maintain. Our guest has long since married the struggling young lawyer to whom she was then engaged, and he is now leading his profession in an Eastern city. She recalls that month's experience always with a sense of amusement over the fact that the succession of visitors who came to see the new Settlement invariably questioned her most minutely concerning "these people" without once suspecting that they were talking to one who had been identified with the neighborhood from childhood. I at least was able to draw a lesson from the incident, and I never addressed a Chicago audience on the subject of the Settlement and its vicinity without inviting a neighbor to go with me, that I might curb any hasty generalization by the consciousness that I had an auditor who knew the conditions more intimately than I could hope to do.

Halsted Street has grown so familiar during twenty years of residence, that it is difficult to recall its gradual changes—the withdrawal of the more prosperous Irish and Germans, and the slow substitution of Russian Jews, Italians, and Greeks. A description of the street such as I gave in those early addresses still stands in my mind as sympathetic and correct.

Halsted Street is thirty-two miles long, and one of the great thoroughfares of Chicago; Polk Street crosses it midway between the stockyards to the south and the shipbuilding yards on the north branch of the Chicago River. For the six miles between these two industries the street is lined with shops of butchers and grocers, with dingy and gorgeous saloons, and pretentious establishments for the sale of ready-made clothing. Polk Street, running west from Halsted Street, grows rapidly more prosperous; running a mile east to State Street, it grows steadily worse, and crosses a network of vice on the corners of Clark Street and Fifth Avenue. Hull House once stood in the suburbs, but the city has steadily grown up around it and its site now has corners on three or four foreign colonies. Between Halsted Street and the river live about ten thousand Italians—Neapolitans, Sicilians, and Calabrians, with an occasional Lombard or Venetian. To the south on Twelfth Street are many Germans, and side streets are given over almost entirely to Polish and Russian Jews. Still farther south, these Jewish colonies merge into a huge Bohemian colony, so vast that Chicago ranks as the third Bohemian city in the world. To the northwest are many Canadian-French, clannish in spite of their long residence in America, and to the north are Irish and first-generation Americans. On the streets directly west and farther north are well-to-do English-speaking families, many of whom own their houses and have lived in the neighborhood for years; one man is still living in his old farmhouse.

The policy of the public authorities of never taking an initiative,

and always waiting to be urged to do their duty, is obviously fatal
in a neighborhood where there is little initiative among the citizens. The idea underlying our self-government breaks down in
such a ward. The streets are inexpressibly dirty, the number of
schools inadequate, sanitary legislation unenforced, the street lighting bad, the paving miserable and altogether lacking in the alleys
and smaller streets, and the stables foul beyond description. Hundreds of houses are unconnected with the street sewer. The older
and richer inhabitants seem anxious to move away as rapidly as
they can afford it. They make room for newly arrived immigrants
who are densely ignorant of civic duties. This substitution of the
older inhabitants is accomplished industrially also, in the south and
east quarters of the ward. The Jews and Italians do the finishing for
the great clothing manufacturers, formerly done by Americans,
Irish and Germans, who refused to submit to the extremely low
prices to which the sweating system has reduced their successors.
As the design of the sweating system is the elimination of rent
from the manufacture of clothing, the "outside work" is begun
after the clothing leaves the cutter. An unscrupulous contractor regards no basement as too dark, no stable loft too foul, nor rear
shanty too provisional, no tenement room too small for his work-
room, as these conditions imply low rental. Hence these shops
abound in the worst of the foreign districts where the sweater
easily finds his cheap basement and his home finishers.

The houses of the ward, for the most part wooden, were originally built for one family and are now occupied by several. They
are after the type of the inconvenient frame cottages found in the
poorer suburbs twenty years ago. Many of them were built where
they now stand; others were brought thither on rollers, because
their previous sites had been taken for factories. The fewer brick
tenement buildings which are three or four stories high are comparatively new, and there are few large tenements. The little
wooden houses have a temporary aspect, and for this reason, perhaps, the tenement-house legislation in Chicago is totally inadequate. Rear tenements flourish; many houses have no water supply
save the faucet in the back yard, there are no fire escapes, the garbage and ashes are placed in wooden boxes which are fastened to

the street pavements. One of the most discouraging features about the present system of tenement houses is that many are owned by sordid and ignorant immigrants. The theory that wealth brings responsibility, that possession entails at length education and refinement, in these cases fails utterly. The children of an Italian immigrant owner may "shine" shoes in the street, and his wife may pick rags from the street gutter, laboriously sorting them in a dingy court. Wealth may do something for her self-complacency and feeling of consequence; it certainly does nothing for her comfort or her children's improvement nor for the cleanliness of anyone concerned. Another thing that prevents better houses in Chicago is the tentative attitude of the real estate men. Many unsavory conditions are allowed to continue which would be regarded with horror if they were considered permanent. Meanwhile, the wretched conditions persist until at least two generations of children have been born and reared in them.

In every neighborhood where poorer people live, because rents are supposed to be cheaper there, is an element which, although uncertain in the individual, in the aggregate can be counted upon. It is composed of people of former education and opportunity who have cherished ambitions and prospects, but who are caricatures of what they meant to be—"hollow ghosts which blame the living men." There are times in many lives when there is a cessation of energy and loss of power. Men and women of education and refinement come to live in a cheaper neighborhood because they lack the ability to make money, because of ill-health, because of an unfortunate marriage, or for other reasons which do not imply criminality or stupidity. Among them are those who, in spite of untoward circumstances, keep up some sort of intellectual life; those who are "great for books," as their neighbors say. To such the Settlement may be a genuine refuge.

In the very first weeks of our residence Miss Starr started a reading party in George Eliot's *Romola,* which was attended by a group of young women who followed the wonderful tale with unflagging interest. The weekly reading was held in our little upstairs dining room, and two members of the club came to dinner each week, not only that they might be received as guests, but that they might help us wash the dishes afterwards and so make the table ready for the stacks of Florentine photographs.

Our "first resident," as she gayly designated herself, was a charming old lady who gave five consecutive readings from Hawthorne to a most appreciative audience, interspersing the magic tales most delightfully with recollections of the elusive and fascinating author. Years before she had lived at Brook Farm as a pupil of the Ripleys, and she came to us for ten days because she wished to live once more in an atmosphere where "idealism ran high." We thus early found the type of class which through all the years has remained most popular—a combination of a social atmosphere with serious study.

Volunteers to the new undertaking came quickly; a charming young girl conducted a kindergarten in the drawing room, coming regularly every morning from her home in a distant part of the North Side of the city. Although a tablet to her memory has stood upon a mantel shelf in Hull House for five years, we still associate her most vividly with the play of little children, first in her kindergarten and then in her own nursery, which furnished a veritable illustration of Victor Hugo's definition of heaven—"a place where parents are always young and children always little." Her daily presence for the first two years made it quite impossible for us to become too solemn and self-conscious in our strenuous routine, for her mirth and buoyancy were irresistible and her eager desire to share the life of the neighborhood never failed, although it was often put to a severe test. One day at luncheon she gaily recited her futile attempt to impress temperance principles upon the mind of an Italian mother, to whom she had returned a small daughter of five sent to the kindergarten "in quite a horrid state of intoxication" from the wine-soaked bread upon which she had breakfasted. The mother, with the gentle courtesy of a South Italian, listened politely to her graphic portrayal of the untimely end awaiting so immature a wine bibber; but long before the lecture was finished, quite unconscious of the incongruity, she hospitably set forth her best wines, and when her baffled guest refused one after the other, she disappeared, only to quickly return with a small dark glass of whiskey, saying reassuringly, "See, I have brought you the true American drink." The recital ended in seriocomic despair, with the rueful statement that "the impression I probably made upon her darkened mind was, that it is the American custom to breakfast children on bread soaked in whiskey instead of light Italian wine."

That first kindergarten was a constant source of education to us. We were much surprised to find social distinctions even among its lambs, although greatly amused with the neat formulation made by the superior little Italian boy who refused to sit beside uncouth little Angelina because "we eat our macaroni this way,"—imitating the movement of a fork from a plate to his mouth,—"and she eat her macaroni this way," holding his hand high in the air and throwing back his head, that his wide-open mouth might receive an imaginary cascade. Angelina gravely nodded her little head in approval of this distinction between gentry and peasant. "But isn't it astonishing that merely table manners are made such a test all the way along?" was the comment of their democratic teacher. Another memory which refuses to be associated with death, which came to her all too soon, is that of the young girl who organized our first really successful club of boys, holding their fascinated interest by the old chivalric tales, set forth so dramatically and vividly that checkers and jackstraws were abandoned by all the other clubs on Boys' Day, that their members might form a listening fringe to "The Young Heroes."

I met a member of the latter club one day as he flung himself out of the House in the rage by which an emotional boy hopes to keep from shedding tears. "There is no use coming here any more, Prince Roland is dead," he gruffly explained as we passed. We encouraged the younger boys in tournaments and dramatics of all sorts, and we somewhat fatuously believed that boys who were early interested in adventurers or explorers might later want to know the lives of living statesmen and inventors. It is needless to add that the boys quickly responded to such a program, and that the only difficulty lay in finding leaders who were able to carry it out. This difficulty has been with us through all the years of growth and development in the Boys' Club until now, with its five-story building, its splendid equipment of shops, of recreation and study rooms, that group alone is successful which commands the services of a resourceful and devoted leader.

The dozens of younger children who from the first came to Hull House were organized into groups which were not quite classes and not quite clubs. The value of these groups consisted almost entirely in arousing a higher imagination and in giving the children the opportunity which they could not have in the crowded schools, for initiative and for independent social relationships. The public schools then contained little hand work of any sort, so that naturally any instruction which we provided for the children took the direction of this supplementary work. But it required a constant effort that the pressure of poverty itself should not defeat the educational aim. The Italian girls in the sewing classes would count that day lost when they could not carry home a garment, and the insistence that it should be neatly made seemed a superrefinement to those in dire need of clothing.

As these clubs have been continued during the twenty years they have developed classes in the many forms of handicraft which the newer education is so rapidly adapting for the delight of children; but they still keep their essentially social character and still minister to that large number of children who leave school the very week they are fourteen years old, only too eager to close the schoolroom door forever on a tiresome task that is at last well over. It seems to us important that these children shall find themselves permanently attached to a House that offers them evening clubs and classes with their old companions, that merges as easily as possible the school life into the working life and does what it can to find places for the bewildered young things looking for work. A large proportion of the delinquent boys brought into the juvenile court in Chicago are the oldest sons in large families whose wages are needed at home. The grades from which many of them leave school, as the records show, are piteously far from the seventh and eighth where the very first instruction in manual training is given, nor have they been taught any other abiding interest.

In spite of these flourishing clubs for children early established at Hull House, and the fact that our first organized undertaking was a kindergarten, we were very insistent that the Settlement should not be primarily for the children, and that it was absurd to suppose that grown people would not respond to opportunities for education and social life. Our enthusiastic kindergartner herself demonstrated this with an old woman of ninety, who, because she was left alone all day while her daughter cooked in a restaurant, had formed such a persistent habit of picking the plaster off the walls that one landlord after another refused to have her for a tenant. It required but a few weeks' time to teach her to make large paper chains, and gradually she was content to do it all day long, and in the end took quite as much pleasure in adorning the walls as she had formerly taken in demolishing them. Fortunately the landlord had never heard the æsthetic principle that the exposure of basic construction is more desirable than gaudy decoration. In course of time it was discovered that the old woman could speak Gælic, and when one or two grave professors came to see her, the neighborhood was filled with pride that such a wonder lived in their midst. To mitigate life for a woman of ninety was an unfailing refutation of the statement that the Settlement was designed for the young.

On our first New Year's Day at Hull House we invited the older people in the vicinity, sending a carriage for the most feeble and announcing to all of them that we were going to organize an Old Settlers' Party.

Every New Year's Day since, older people in varying numbers have come together at Hull House to relate early hardships, and to take for the moment the place in the community to which their pioneer life entitles them. Many people who were formerly residents of the vicinity, but whom prosperity has carried into more desirable neighborhoods, come back to these meetings and often confess to each other that they have never since found such kindness as in early Chicago when all its citizens came together in mutual enterprises. Many of these pioneers, so like the men and women of my earliest childhood that I always felt comforted by their presence in the house, were very much opposed to "foreigners," whom they held responsible for a depreciation of property and a general lowering of the tone of the neighborhood. Sometimes we had a chance for championship; I recall one old man, fiercely American, who had reproached me because we had so many "foreign views" on our walls, to whom I endeavored to set forth our hope that the pictures might afford a familiar island to the immigrants in a sea of new and strange impressions. The old settler guest, taken off his guard, replied, "I see; they feel as we did when we saw a Yankee notion from down East"—thereby formulating the dim kinship between the pioneer and the immigrant, both "buffeting the waves of a new development." The older settlers as well as their children throughout the years have given genuine help to our various enterprises for neighborhood improvement, and from their own memories of earlier hardships have made many shrewd suggestions for alleviating the difficulties of that first sharp struggle with untoward conditions.

In those early days we were often asked why we had come to live on Halsted Street when we could afford to live somewhere else. I remember one man who used to shake his head and say it was "the strangest thing he had met in his experience," but who was finally convinced that it was "not strange but natural." In time it came to seem natural to all of us that the Settlement should be there. If it is natural to feed the hungry and care for the sick, it is certainly natural to give pleasure to the young, comfort to the aged, and to minister to the deep-seated craving for social intercourse that all men feel. Whoever does it is rewarded by something which, if not gratitude, is at least spontaneous and vital and lacks that irksome sense of obligation with which a substantial benefit is too often acknowledged.

In addition to the neighbors who responded to the receptions and classes, we found those who were too battered and oppressed to care for them. To these, however, was left that susceptibility to the bare offices of humanity which raises such offices into a bond of fellowship.

From the first it seemed understood that we were ready to perform the humblest neighborhood services. We were asked to wash the newborn babies, and to prepare the dead for burial, to nurse the sick, and to "mind the children."

Occasionally these neighborly offices unexpectedly uncovered ugly human traits. For six weeks after an operation we kept in one of our three bedrooms a forlorn little baby who, because he was born with a cleft palate, was most unwelcome even to his mother, and we were horrified when he died of neglect a week after he was returned to his home; a little Italian bride of fifteen sought shelter with us one November evening, to escape her husband who had beaten her every night for a week when he returned home from work, because she had lost her wedding ring; two of us officiated quite alone at the birth of an illegitimate child because the doctor was late in arriving, and none of the honest Irish matrons would "touch the likes of her"; we ministered at the deathbed of a young man, who during a long illness of tuberculosis had received so many bottles of whiskey through the mistaken kindness of his friends, that the cumulative effect produced wild periods of exultation, in one of which he died.

We were also early impressed with the curious isolation of many of the immigrants; an Italian woman once expressed her pleasure in the red roses that she saw at one of our receptions in surprise that they had been "brought so fresh all the way from Italy." She would not believe for an instant that they had been grown in America. She said that she had lived in Chicago for six years and had never seen any roses, whereas in Italy she had seen them every summer in great profusion. During all that time, of course, the woman had lived within ten blocks of a florist's window; she had not been more than a five-cent car ride away from the public parks; but she had never dreamed of faring forth for herself, and no one had taken her. Her conception of America had been the untidy street in which she lived and had made her long struggle to adapt herself to American ways.

But in spite of some untoward experiences, we were constantly impressed with the uniform kindness and courtesy we received. Perhaps these first days laid the simple human foundations which are certainly essential for continuous living among the poor: first, genuine preference for residence in an industrial quarter to any other part of the city, because it is interesting and makes the human appeal; and second, the conviction, in the words of Canon Barnett, that the things which make men alike are finer and better than the things that keep them apart, and that these basic likenesses, if they are properly accentuated, easily transcend the less essential differences of race, language, creed and tradition.

Perhaps even in those first days we made a beginning toward that object which was afterwards stated in our charter: "To provide a center for a higher civic and social life; to institute and maintain educational and philanthropic enterprises, and to investigate and improve the conditions in the industrial districts of Chicago."

THE LOEB-LEOPOLD CASE*

Clarence Darrow

NO ONE who lived in Chicago during the 1920's will ever
forget the excitement generated by the Loeb-Leopold case.
It rivaled, or surpassed, the ferment caused by the Lindbergh case in the East. It was a brand new type of murder
case and for the first time psychoanalysts, or "alienists,"
as they were called, descended upon an American courtroom en masse.

There was no hysteria but at all hours of the day and
night everybody seemed to be talking about the murderers
of Bobby Franks. When the trial began, the newspapers
printed extra editions to keep the public informed about
the progress of the case. Clarence Darrow soon became
the focal point of conversation, and in this excerpt from
his autobiography he tells us about his unwelcome role in
the drama.

IN THE summer of 1924 I was called into the defense of the
Loeb-Leopold case in Chicago. Few cases, if any, ever attracted
such wide discussion and publicity; not only in America, but anywhere in the world. Two boys, named Richard Loeb, who was
seventeen years old, and Nathan Leopold, eighteen years old, were
indicted for murder. Both were sons of wealthy families, well
known and highly respected in Chicago and elsewhere.

A young boy, named Robert Franks, fourteen years old, had
disappeared on his way home from school. He did not return that
night, and the parents were greatly alarmed over his absence. The
next day the father received a letter saying that his son was safe

and would be returned on the payment of a ransom of $10,000. The letter contained explicit directions as to how the money should be delivered. Mr. Franks was to put it in a package, stand on the rear platform of a certain train leaving Chicago about four o'clock that afternoon, and throw the money off at a lonely spot near a grain elevator south of Englewood. Mr. Franks went to the bank for the money and was preparing to go to the train when the afternoon papers printed a story about the discovery of a dead boy lying naked in a culvert under a railroad crossing some twenty miles south of the city. Everything led to the belief that it was Robert Franks. The information was telephoned to the Franks home, and the father felt satisfied that the poor boy was his son, and he really was.

Before going to the place on the prairie where the money was to be delivered, both Loeb and Leopold saw the story in the papers, so, of course, they did not go after the money. The authorities immediately began an investigation. A number of suspects were brought in within a few days and put through strict grillings, as is usual in cases of murder. Two or three of these were seriously injured in their standing, and suffered notoriety and loss of positions from which they have never recovered, although wholly innocent of the charge.

In the inspection of the place and surroundings where the dead boy was discovered, a pair of eyeglasses was found. The oculist who sold them was traced, and he stated that he had never sold but two pairs just like that—one of these purchasers was now in Europe, so obviously he could not have been in any way connected with the crime; the other customer was a young man named Nathan Leopold. The Leopold home was near the Franks residence. These two families and the Loeb family had been neighbors and friends for years. Young Leopold was a graduate of the University of Chicago and was then in his second year of the law course in that university. He was to leave for Europe in a few days. This trip had been planned for some time. His father had given him the money for this summer vacation, and the tickets were purchased.

The eyeglasses having been sold to Nathan Leopold, the State's attorney sent for him and questioned him as to his whereabouts that night. Leopold answered everything that was asked, saying that on that night he and Loeb were automobiling in the parks and the country around Chicago, driving Leopold's car. No one in the State's attorney's office or anywhere else had the slightest idea that Leopold could possibly be involved in the case, but out of prudence it was thought best to hold him a short time for further investigation. The boy, after advising with his father and Mr. Benjamin Bachrach, consented to this, the two older men having not the faintest suspicion that young Leopold had anything whatever to do with the affair.

The next day the officers sent for Richard Loeb and asked him about that evening; he said he did not remember where he was, but thought that he and Leopold went driving, but could not tell where they went. It seemed to have been agreed that if anything happened and they were arrested within a week they should tell their prearranged story, as afterwards told by Leopold; but if arrested after that they were to say that they did not remember where they drove. As fate would have it, Nathan was arrested before the week was over, and Loeb after its expiration. Still, the officers did not lay any stress on the variance in their statements. Both boys were of wealthy families and always had plenty of money; no one could think of any possible motive for committing such a deed. It occurred to one of the officers, however, to send for Leopold's chauffeur and question him. The chauffeur said that Leopold's car was not used that night; that it was in the garage for repairs. This story was easily verified, and the boys were questioned further. In a day or two they broke down and confessed and told their story with all its ghastly details. The clothes were taken off the Franks boy so that identity might not be disclosed; some of them were placed in the lagoon in Jackson Park; some of them were buried; and some were burned. The boys were taken to all the places covered by their route, including the place where the clothes were buried, and their story was fully corroborated by what was found.

It seemed that Loeb had gotten it into his head that he could commit a perfect crime, which should involve kidnapping, murder, and ransom. He had unfolded his scheme to Leopold because he needed someone to help him plan and carry it out. For this plot

Leopold had no liking whatever, but he had an exalted opinion
of Loeb. Leopold was rather undersized; he could not excel in
sports and games. Loeb was strong and athletic. He was good at
baseball and football, and a general favorite with all who knew
him. Both of them always had money. Loeb had $2,000 in cash,
a number of Liberty Bonds whose coupons had not been cashed,
and a standing order to draw money whenever he wanted it by asking the cashier at his father's office.

Several times there was trouble between the boys about going
on with their plan. At one time their correspondence, offered in
evidence, and published by the press, revealed that they nearly
reached the point of open breach, and extreme violence.

When their plans were actually completed they arranged to get
a car from a renting office, and Leopold, under another name, was
to refer to Loeb, also under another name, as reference for the
expense and safe return of the car. Loeb's assumed name was given
as that of a resident of the Hotel Morrison, where he had rented
a room and deposited a valise in which there happened to be a
book drawn by him from the University of Chicago Library.

Before this they had written the ransom letter. This was addressed "Dear Sir," as they had no idea whose boy would be taken
and to whom the letter would be mailed.

Around four o'clock one afternoon they got into the car, drove
within a few squares of Loeb's home, along one of the best residence districts of Chicago, over to a private school that Loeb had
formerly attended, arriving there just as the afternoon session was
over and the boys were coming out. One after another was surveyed by the boys in the car until poor Robert Franks came along.
He was invited into the car for a ride; he got into the front seat
with Leopold, who was driving; and within ten minutes he was
hit on the head by a chisel in the hands of Loeb, was stunned by
the blow, and soon bled to death. All this happened in a thickly
populated section of Chicago and close to the homes of all three
of the boys.

The car was then driven slowly for twenty miles through the
main streets and parts of the South Side of the city, solidly built up
and congested with automobiles going in all directions. It was

summertime; the afternoons were long and evenings late. Leopold was a botanist and a lover of birds. He had often been in that far section gathering flowers and catching birds; he had a rare collection and was creating a museum for himself; he had mounted the birds with great skill, and many of them were very valuable. During these excursions he had become thoroughly familiar with that out-of-the-way locality and remembered the culvert under the railroad tracks, which could be reached only by an unfrequented road. When they got into that vicinity the sun had not yet disappeared, so they drove for an hour or two waiting for the twilight to fade into deeper darkness. Then they placed the boy in the culvert and drove away.

When they got back to town they took out the ransom letter and addressed it to Mr. Jacob Franks, the father of the boy that they had left out in the country. They then went to a restaurant, ate a hearty meal, and drove to Leopold's home. This residence was in a well-settled block next door to a large apartment building. The boy was killed in the rented car and it was soaked with blood, not only inside but also on the outside. They left the car standing in the street in front of the house while they went up to Leopold's room and discussed the events of the day until a late hour, when Loeb went home.

In the morning after the killing Loeb came back to Leopold's home. They took the car into the garage and washed it as best they could, but did not remove all the stains, as the evidence brought out. When the car was dry, Leopold took it back to the agency where he had hired it.

Loeb is a good-natured, friendly boy. I realize that most people will not be able to understand this, and perhaps will not believe it. Some may remember Daniel Webster's address to a jury in a murder case. He pictured the accused: his low brow, his murderous eye, his every feature loudly proclaimed him a fiend incarnate. One would suppose from Daniel Webster's foolish argument that the defendant would be recognized as a murderer wherever he went. A part of this tirade was published in the old school reader, and we used to "speak" it on the last day of the term. We youngsters wondered why the Lord needed to put a mark on Cain's brow, for after reading Daniel Webster's recipe we could go out on the street and pick out killers everywhere, for all seemed to be marked. But Daniel Webster was not a psychologist; he was a politician and an orator, and that was enough for one man.

"Dicky" Loeb was not only a kind-*looking* boy but he *was* and *is* a kindly boy. He was never too busy to personally do a favor for any one that he chanced to know. There was no reason why he should be put into prison for life excepting for the strange and unfortunate circumstances that might not occur again in a thousand years.

Leopold had not the slightest instinct toward what we are pleased to call crime. He had, and has, the most brilliant intellect that I ever met in a boy. At eighteen he had acquired nine or ten languages; he was an advanced botanist; he was an authority on birds; he enjoyed good books. He was often invited to lecture before clubs and other assemblages; he was genial, kindly, and likable. His father was wealthy, and this son was his great pride. Every one prophesied an uncommon career for this gifted lad. He is now in prison for life for the most foolish, most motiveless, act that was ever conceived in a diseased brain by his boon companion.

Leopold had scarcely seen Robert Franks before the fatal day. Loeb had played tennis with him and they were good friends. Why, then, did these two boys commit this rash and horrible deed? I presume they know less about the reason than others who have studied the case and the boys as well. There are many things that human beings cannot understand, and of all the fathomless questions that confront and confuse men, the most baffling is the human mind. No one can tell what will be the outcome of any life. To quote Oscar Wilde:

> For none can tell to what Red Hell
> His sightless soul may stray.

The terrible deed had been committed. The two boys were in the shadow of the gallows; their confession had been made; their families were in the depths of despair, and they came to me to assist the lawyers already employed. My feelings were much upset; I wanted to lend a hand, and I wanted to stay out of the case. The act was a shocking and bizarre performance; the public and press were almost solidly against them.

In a terrible crisis there is only one element more helpless than the poor, and that is the rich. I knew then, and I know now, that except for the wealth of the families a plea of guilty and a life sentence would have been accepted without a contest. I knew this, and I dreaded the fight.

No client of mine had ever been put to death, and I felt that it would almost, if not quite, kill me if it should ever happen. I have never been able to read a story of an execution. I always left town if possible on the day of a hanging. I am strongly—call it morbidly, who will—against killing. I felt that I would get a fair fee if I went into the case, but money never influenced my stand one way or the other. I knew of no good reason for refusing, but I was sixty-eight years old, and very weary. I had grown tired of standing in the lean and lonely front line facing the greatest enemy that ever confronted man—public opinion.

But, I went in, to do what I could for sanity and humanity against the wave of hatred and malice that, as ever, was masquerading under its usual nom de plume: "Justice."

II

We lawyers for Loeb and Leopold knew that it would be impossible to get much time for the preparation of the case. People who know nothing of Criminal Courts are always declaiming against the long delays. Truth is, when there is a public outcry against some defendant, all other business in the court is set aside for a criminal prosecution. The case must be tried at once while the haters are hating and hot on the trail.

Our attention is constantly called to the English and their way; but their newspapers are not permitted to publish details of crimes, or refer to the suspected authors, or otherwise to stir up the mob to anger against the defendant. In America, if the case is one of public interest, a campaign that reeks with venom is at once launched against the accused; columns of interviews and pictures are printed each day; what the defendant is alleged to have said is scattered in bold type all over the pages before the case is tried, and members of the family are followed about and forced to talk; all the neighbors and even casual acquaintances are interviewed, and the stories grow lurid and appalling. Newspaper sales shoot up beyond belief. Day by day efforts are made to get new versions so that the public will not by any means slacken their thoughts and feelings about the matter. Every prospective juror called into the box knows the case, and all its details, as presented by the press. He has all the bias of a partisan, and it is not possible for him to give the defendant a fair trial. Juror after juror is excused because of having an opinion. The lawyers for the defense are roundly criticized for the time they take, as though they should join the State and the mob and help get their clients hanged. Then the law must be changed; members of the legislature are politicians, and to them the voice of the people is the voice of God, so they must pass a new law authorizing a person to sit on a jury even if he already has an opinion but says he can set it aside.

Every one who thinks knows how common it is for men to set aside their views. Most men never have but one or two ideas, any-how, and to these they hang like grim death. How often do people set aside their beliefs on politics, on religion, or any other question if in conflict with something they want to do? To set aside an opin-ion without evidence is not only psychologically impossible, but is physically absurd. Every man realizes that when he happens to be personally interested in some matter in court; whether the case be civil or criminal, on every question and point, he weighs what will be the attitude of the judge, and how it will affect the judge's mind. He feels the same about the jury. It is hard enough for the accused to get a fair hearing no matter how much caution is taken.

We knew that seldom had a case been handled like this one; and everyone, far and near, had made up their minds what should be done. Naturally we wanted delay; all that we could possibly get. We needed it for preparing our case, but we needed it still more so that the passions of men might have a chance to cool. We were aware that there could be no defense except the mental condition of the boys. The statutes of Illinois provide that for murder in the first degree a sentence of death may be imposed, or one of imprison-ment in the penitentiary for not less than fourteen years. And still, to this day the case is discussed as if the penalty was unheard of in the case of murder. From the beginning we never tried to do anything but save the lives of the two defendants; we did not even claim or try to prove that they were insane. We did believe and sought to show that their minds were not normal and never had been normal.

The statutes of Illinois provide that on a plea of guilty the court may hear evidence in mitigation or aggravation of the offense. I doubt if any judge anywhere in any civilized country ever failed to hear evidence or statements in mitigation or aggravation of an offense when he had to use his judgment as to the severity of the sentence to be imposed. With or without the statute, courts always find out what they can about the defendants before passing sentence.

Before any lawyer was employed the State had called into their counsel the best-known alienists in Chicago. This made it necessary for us to go outside the State of Illinois to find alienists to examine the defendants. About that time the National Association of Psychiatrists were holding their convention in Atlantic City. We at once delegated Mr. Walter Bachrach, one of the counsel for the defendants, to go to the convention and secure three or four of those of highest standing in their profession to come and make an investigation of the two boys. This was absolutely necessary. Thereupon we secured Dr. William Alanson White, Dr. William Healy and Dr. Bernard Gluck to come to make the examination.

Dr. White had for many years been superintendent of the United States Hospital for the Insane, in Washington, D. C., and had been long recognized as one of the leading authorities in the country. He has written more books on mental abnormalities, and the human mind in general, than any other man in America. Dr. William Healy was then, and is now, the psychiatrist of the Baker Foundation of Boston, organized by a judge with intelligence and a philanthropic spirit for the purpose of examining and reporting the delinquents that reached the Juvenile Court in Boston. Dr. Healy, years before, had helped in the establishing of the Juvenile Court in Chicago, and for a long time was in charge of the examination

of the delinquents that were brought into its jurisdiction. He had
written extensively on these subjects and was highly regarded and
respected the world over. Dr. Bernard Gluck had for years been the
alienist specialist appointed by the state of New York, having general charge and supervision of examining the inmates of prisons
of the state. He was considered as unquestionably one of the most
brilliant alienists in America.

These three physicians together with Dr. Bowen, of Boston, and
Dr. Hurlburt, an able young alienist of Chicago, met in Chicago.
Dr. Bowen was an expert whose business related to the careful
and specific action of ductless glands, that now universally are believed to have so much of importance to do with human conduct.
From the time of our entry into the case until the matter was called
into court we were able to secure only a week's delay.

Two indictments were returned against each of the boys: one
for murder and one for kidnapping. A few years before this a case
of the kidnapping of a child in Illinois attracted a great deal of attention, indignation, and discussion, at which time, in obedience to
the demand of the crowd, the legislature passed a law providing
the same punishment for kidnapping as for murder. If they had
used a grain of sense people would have foreseen that the statute
would tend to the killing of every one kidnapped in order to destroy the evidence; murder could not add to the penalty if the offenders were caught. But the public and the legislature did not
think so far.

Both the indictments against the boys were returned into court
and were automatically placed on the docket of the chief justice,
who, at the time, was the Honorable John Caverly. We spent considerable time deliberating as to what we should do. The feeling
was so tense and the trial was so near that we felt we could not
save the boys' lives with a jury. It seemed out of the question to
find a single man who had not read all about the case and formed
a definite opinion. Judge Caverly had formerly been a judge of
the Municipal Court and had helped form the Juvenile Court, and
we believed that he was kindly and discerning in his views of life.
After thorough consideration we concluded that the best chance was
on a plea of guilty. Only a few knew what was to be done—the

boys and their parents, two or three relatives, and the attorneys in the case. A large and expectant crowd was eagerly awaiting the opening of the court. I arose, and in very few words that we had most carefully prepared, spoke of our anxiety in the matter, and the difficulty of getting a fair trial, and said that under the circumstances we had decided to plead guilty in both cases.

Of course the State and everyone else were taken by surprise. The pleas were accepted and entered without objection or delay. What we most feared was that if the State had any conception of our plan they would bring up only one case at a time, saving a chance, if given life sentence, to bring up the second case and, as it were, catch us on the rebound. We were conscious of the risk we were taking and determined to take one chance instead of facing two.

When the pleas were entered the reporters made a wild rush for the door to broadcast the news, but it took some time for the audience to comprehend what was happening, and the surprise was very great. Finally the astonishment in the courtroom subsided and the people sat quiet and waited for the next step. As the State had not been expecting our move, a continuance was granted until the next day.

Never did I have a more hectic life in an equal length of time than through the weeks that elapsed during the hearing of the case and the time used by the judge for consideration and preparation of his opinion. There was little rest by day and but little sleep at night. Of course, long accounts were run every day in the press. On the hearing of the case some forty newspaper reporters from all the main cities of America and all the press associations presented themselves. The proceedings became front-page matter in every hamlet of the country, and were closely followed in all parts of the world. I seldom went to my office in those troublous days, and rarely read any of the letters that came in stacks. These were usually abusive and brutal to the highest degree.

The public seemed to think that we were committing a crime in defending two boys, who probably needed it as much as any two defendants ever on trial for their lives. The most senseless and the most unreasonable criticism was indulged in against the defendants and their attorneys because of the lengthy hearing of the case. It was often asserted that no such proceedings could have been possible anywhere else, and yet the whole process was perfectly regular and would have been so in any state or country where the court had any power to fix the degree of punishment. To be sure the time allowed to lawyers and witnesses was more or less in the control of the court, but the procedure was fixed by the law, and was entirely regular and usual.

While the defense protested that the State should not be permitted to show the details of the killing on a plea of guilty, the State contended that they had the right to show it as bearing upon the condition of mind of the defendants, and the aggravation or mitigation of the penalty. Whatever undue length of time was consumed was caused by the State, as we offered no evidence of any kind on the subject. On the other hand, the State put in all the evidence of the killing with the greatest minuteness and detail. None of these witnesses were cross-examined.

Week after week the trial dragged along. The courtroom, the corridors, and the streets outside were always thronged with those curious to get glimpses of what was going on. The court and every one and everything connected with the affair were strictly guarded as we went back and forth. The days were hard and strenuous, the evenings and nights were given over to consultations and discussions.

When the representatives of the State had consumed all the time they wished, we put on ten to fifteen witnesses, mainly schoolmates of the two boys, who testified to their strange actions and their belief that neither of them was normal. In spite of our desires, some of them went so far as to express the opinion that they were insane. We then called our alienists, who told fully about the condition of the boys, as they understood them. Both boys were decidedly deficient in emotions, as shown by physical tests.

The emotions are most important in keeping both young and old from the commission of unusual acts. To one in possession of normal emotional structure, the thought of any act seriously forbidden by custom, law, or normal feelings is automatically immediately revolting. No such revulsion comes to one of a certain defective nervous system. These boys, especially Loeb, had carried the phantasies usual in children into later youth. Loeb had read and studied detective stories since he was very young and had experimented a great deal as an amateur detective since childhood. The detective was always the hero of the stories that he read, and he conceived the idea that a perfect crime could be accomplished that would baffle for all time the real detectives and police. He had lived with this dream for years. When the story of the killing of Robert Franks was first published he went from place to place with the detectives, telling them how he thought it might have happened, and who might be responsible for the deed. His theories came close to the facts, as they were ultimately disclosed. He bought every edition of the newspapers as the story came out and talked of nothing else. He reminded the detectives that the first stories had spoken of a telephone message being sent from somewhere in Englewood the morning after the disappearance and asked why they did not go to every telephone booth in Englewood and thus probably get a clue. The detectives took his advice, and it transpired that he had done the telephoning himself. He talked incessantly to his family about the affair, unfolding his theories as to the way it all came about. Both he and Leopold were incipient paranoiacs. The whole case disclosed no motive that could induce a sane mind and normal person to commit such a deed.

The intelligence of the public is pretty well shown by their attitude toward the defense of insanity. When the populace clamors for a victim it wants no facts, theories, doctors, lawyers, or scientists to stand in the way. What we term "the public" knows just what it wants done. It also feels that "if 'tis to be done, 't were well it were done quickly." There will be time enough to think it over when the turmoil of the trial is over and the victim is dead, and "better so"—for it is a common belief that it doesn't matter whether the one on trial is insane or not—he is of no use and it is just as well to have him put to death.

Perhaps there is truth in this flippant idea. No doubt that it could be said with a degree of reason about nine-tenths of the people of the world. Doubtless there are those who would say it if

any one was submitted to them for their opinion. Is it at all necessary that a person should be of any value to the world? The jus-
tification for living is that you are alive and do not want to die. If
one cannot justify life in that way, then it can not be justified. It
would be very dangerous to be able to declare that a man could
be executed because he was of no value to the world. If a trial of
this sort should be fairly decided, most of the class who advocate
such ideas would be found wanting, and therefore guilty.

Is insanity so rare that men should deride that condition as a defense in a criminal case? There are more people in our institutions
for the insane than in our prisons. And besides the vast and growing colonies of insane inside asylums, there are large numbers who
are kept by families and friends and their condition carefully concealed from the public; and a much larger class that are idiots, mo-
rons, and plain defectives, and upon any theory are entirely irresponsible for their acts. Any given individual is much more apt to
be insane or mentally defective than he is to be a criminal. A large
percentage of this class go through life without ever disclosing
their real condition, and yet the smallest circumstance may reveal
it at any time. Then, too, the criminal and the insane are very
much alike. In all our large prisons, from time to time, many of the
inmates are collected and sent to insane asylums on being expertly
examined and found mentally unbalanced.

One of the most obvious proofs of mental defect is that there
is no adequate consciousness of the relation between cause and effect in the conduct of the individual. In the case of these two boys
every motive that moves ordinary mortals to action was absent.
There was no malice or hatred, or even dislike against the unfortunate boy. There was no motive for getting money connected
with the foolish plot. The whole performance was childish and
silly, and proved of itself a decided abnormal mentality.

Aside from all of this, to have sentenced two boys of their age to
death on a plea of guilty would have violated every precedent in
Illinois in the one hundred and ten years that it has been a state.
Only two of their age were ever put to death in Illinois, up to that
time, and these were offered life sentences if they would plead

guilty. On trial, the jury fixed the sentence at death, and the judge refused to interfere. Very few men, at any age, are sentenced to death on a plea of guilty. Only a small proportion of those who have been found guilty of murder in Illinois have ever been put to death, and the same is true of most states of the Union where the juries fix the punishment.

In view of these facts, to have executed two boys but seventeen and eighteen years old for the commission of a senseless, motiveless act, and on a plea of guilty, would have been without reason or excuse. Such a sentence would have been a direct response to the mob hysteria outside the court. Judge Caverly could have done nothing else but spare their lives without violating every precedent in the state; he could not have given such a sentence unless awed by fear to write a judgment without parallel in Illinois.

Never was the Criminal Court in Chicago so besieged for admission as during the closing days of this case. At times the crowd swept away officers and ran over each other in frantic efforts to get inside the trial room.

Manifestly, I cannot enter into any discussion of the closing arguments. For years I have been a fairly close student of psychology.

I endeavored in my address to make a plain, straightforward statement of the facts in the case, and I meant to apply such knowledge as we now have of the motives that move men. The argument took the largest part of two court days and was printed almost word for word in some of the Chicago papers, and very extensively by the press outside that city, so that people at the time were fairly familiar with the facts in the case, and certainly of the outcome. When I closed I had exhausted all the strength I could summon. From that day I have never gone through so protracted a strain, and could never do it again, even if I should try.

When the arguments were finished, Judge Caverly adjourned court to consider the case and prepare the opinion. At the end of three weeks he notified us all that he was ready. Every one connected with the defense went to the court under police protection. Judge Caverly was on the bench. The room, the corridors, stairs, streets were a solid jam of people clamoring to get somewhere near to the tragic situation inside. Judge Caverly evidently was deeply moved. The crowded room was deathly still, every one eager to hear. Until the closing words no one could predict what the end was to be. When the climax was reached, men and women rushed pell-mell for the doors. Those of us nearest to the ordeal waited until the building was cleared, then hastened to the street, got into our machines and quickly drove away. For us, the long suspense was over. The lives of Loeb and Leopold were saved. But there was nothing before them, to the end, but stark, blank stone walls.

A WOLF HUNT*

Charles Fenno Hoffman

IN TOLSTOI'S *War and Peace* there is a scene that makes you grip the edges of your chair. It is perhaps the greatest piece of sensory writing in all literature. I refer to the famous wolf-hunt scene. As soon as the servants round up the horses and the dogs and the wolf is sighted, you lose yourself in a chase that does not end until the big gray wolf has been brought down and killed.

Many readers will be surprised to learn that wolf hunts of a comparable sporting nature took place—right here in Chicago. In fact the action of the hunt described by Mr. Hoffman, a transient visitor to Chicago in 1834, bears a slight resemblance to that in *War and Peace*.

Mr. Hoffman's wolf hunt took place long before Count Tolstoi began writing. Conversely, Tolstoi of course had never enjoyed a glimpse into Mr. Hoffman's journal.

Chicago, Illinois, January 13, 1834

. . . SEVERAL officers of the garrison, to whom I am indebted for much hospitable attention and many agreeable hours, stopped opposite the door with a train of carioles, in one of which I was offered a seat to witness a pacing match on the ice. There were several ladies with gentlemen in attendance already on the river, all muffled up, after the Canadian fashion, in fur robes, whose gay trimmings presented a rich as well as most comfortable appearance. The horses, from which the most sport was expected, were a black pony bred in the country and a tall roan nag from the lower Mississippi. They paced at the rate of a mile in something less than

* From *A Winter in the West,* by Charles Fenno Hoffman. Chicago, Fergus Printing Co., 1882.

three minutes. I rode behind the winning horse one heat, and the velocity with which he made our cariole fly over the smooth ice was almost startling. The Southern horse won the race; but I was told that in nine cases out of ten, the nags from his part of the country could not stand up against a French pony.

In the middle of the chase, a wolf, probably roused by the sleigh bells from his lair on the river's bank, trotted along the prairie above, within gunshot, calmly surveying the sport. The uninvited presence of this long-haired amateur at once suggested a hunt for the morrow; and the arrangements were accordingly made by the several gentlemen present for that most exciting of sports, a wolf chase on horseback.

It was a fine bracing morning, with the sun shining cheerily through the still cold atmosphere far over the snow-covered prairie, when the party assembled in front of my lodgings, to the number of ten horsemen, all well mounted and eager for the sport. The hunt was divided into two squads; one of which was to follow the windings of the river on the ice, and the other to make circuit on the prairie. A pack of dogs, consisting of a greyhound or two for running the game, with several of a heavier and fiercer breed for pulling it down, accompanied each party. I was attached to that which took the river; and it was a beautiful sight, as our friends trotted off in the prairie, to see their different-colored capotes and gaily equipped horses contrasted with the bright carpet of spotless white over which they rode; while the sound of their voices was soon lost to our ears, as we descended to the channel of the river, and their lessening figures were hid from our view of the low brush which in some places skirted its banks. The brisk trot in which we now broke, brought us rapidly to the place of meeting, where, to the disappointment of each party, it was found that neither had started any game.

We now spread ourselves into a broad line, about gunshot apart from each other, and began thus advancing into the prairie. We had not swept it thus more than a mile, when a shout on the extreme left, with the accelerated pace of the two furthermost riders in that direction, told that they had roused a wolf. "The devil take the hindermost," was now the motto of the company, and each one spurred for the spot with all eagerness. Unhappily, however, the land along the bank of the river, on the right, was so broken by ravines choked up with snow, that it was impossible for us, who were half a mile from the game when started, to come up at all with the two or three horsemen who led the pursuit. Our horses sunk to their cruppers in the deep snowdrift. Some were repeatedly thrown; and one or two breaking their saddle-girths, from the desperate struggles their horses made in snowbanks, were compelled to abandon the chase entirely.

My stout roan carried me bravely through all; but when I emerged from the last ravine on the open plain, the horsemen who led the chase, from some inequality in the surface of the prairie, were not visible; while a fleet rider, whose tall figure and Indian headdress had hitherto guided me, had been just unhorsed, and, abandoning the game afoot, was now wheeling off apparently with some other object in view. Following on the same course, we soon encountered a couple of officers in a train, who were just coming from a mission of charity in visiting the half-starved orphans of a poor woman, who was frozen to death on the prairie a day or two since—the wolves having already picked her bones before her fate became known. One by one the whole squad to which I belonged collected around to make inquiries about the poor children; and then, as our horses generally were yet in good condition, we scattered once more over the prairie, with the hope of rousing more game.

Not ten minutes elapsed before a wolf, breaking from the dead weeds which, shooting eight or ten feet above the level of the snow, indicated the banks of a deep ravine, dashed off into the prairie, pursued by a horseman on the right. He made instantly for the deep banks of the river, one of whose windings was within a few hundred yards. He had a bold rider behind him, however, in the gentleman who led the chase (a young educated half-blood, well connected in Chicago). The precipitous banks of the stream did not retard this hunter for a moment; but, dashing down to the bed of the river, he was hard upon the wolf before he could ascend the elevation on the opposite side.

Our whole squad reached the open prairie beyond in time to take part in the chase. Nothing could be more beautiful. There was not an obstacle to oppose us in the open plain; and all our dogs having followed the other division of our company, nothing remained but to drive the wolf to death on horseback. Away, then, we went, shouting on his track; the hotly pursued beast gaining on us whenever the crust of a deep snowdrift gave him an advantage over the horse, and we in our turn nearly riding over him when we came to ground comparatively bare. The sagacious animal became at last aware that his course would soon be up at this rate, and turning rapidly in his tracks as we were scattered over the prairie, he passed through our line, and made at once again for the river. He was cut off and turned in a moment by a horseman on the left, who happened to be a little behind the rest; and now came the keenest part of the sport. The wolf would double every moment upon his tracks, while each horseman in succession would make a dash at and turn him in a different direction. Twice I was near enough to strike him with a horsewhip, and once he was under my horse's feet; while so furiously did each rider push at him, that as we brushed by each other and confronted horse to horse, while riding from different quarters at full speed, it required one somewhat used "to turn and wind a fiery Pegasus" to maintain his seat at all.

The rascal, who would now and then look over his shoulder and gnash his teeth, seemed at last as if he was about to succumb; when, after running a few hundred yards in an oblique direction from the river, he suddenly veered his course, at a moment when everyone thought his strength was spent, and gaining the bank before he could be turned, he disappeared in an instant. The rider nearest to his heels became entangled in the low boughs of a tree which grew near the spot; while I, who followed next, was thrown out sufficiently to give the wolf time to get out of view by my horse bolting as he reached the sudden edge of the river. The rest of the hunt were consequently at fault when they came up to us; and after trying in vain to track our lost quarry over the smooth ice for half an hour, we were most vexatiously compelled to abandon the pursuit as fruitless, and proceed to join the other squad of our party, who could now be seen at some distance, apparently making for the same point to which our route was leading. A thicket on the bank soon hid them from our view; and we then moved more leisurely along in order to breathe our horses.

But suddenly the distant cry of hounds gave intimation that new game was afoot; and, on topping a slight elevation, we discerned a party of horsemen far away, with three wolves running apparently about a pistol-shot ahead of them. Our squad was dispersed in an instant. Some struck off at once in the prairie, in a direct line for their object, and were soon brought to in the deep snowbanks; others, taking a more circuitous course, proceeded to double the ravines that were filled with the treacherous drift; and some, more fortunate, took to the frozen river, where the clatter of their hoofs on the hard ice seemed to inspirit their horses anew. I chanced to be one of the latter, and was moreover the first to catch sight again of one of the animals we were pursuing, and find myself nearer to him than any of our party.

The wolf was of the large gray kind. But one of the hunters had been able to keep up with him; and him I could distinguish far off in the prairie, turning and winding his foaming horse as the wolf would double every moment upon his tracks, while half a dozen dogs, embarrassed in the deep snow, were slowly coming up. I reached the spot just as the wolf first stood at bay. His bristling back, glaring eyes, and ferociously distended jaws might have appalled the dogs for a moment; when an impetuous greyhound, who had been for some time pushing through the snowdrifts with unabated industry, having now attained a comparatively clear spot of ground, leaped with such force against the flank of the wolf as to upset him in an instant, while the greyhound shot far ahead of the quarry. He recovered himself instantly, but not before a fierce, powerful hound, whose thick neck and broad muzzle indicated a cross of the bulldog blood with that of a nobler strain, had struck him first upon the haunch, and was now trying to grapple him by the throat. Down again he went, rolling over and over in the deep snow, while the *clicking* of his jaws, as he snapped eagerly at each member of the pack that by turns beset him, was distinctly audible.

The powerful dog, already mentioned, secured him at last by

fixing his muzzle deeply into the breast of the prostrate animal. This, however, did not prevent the wolf giving some fearful wounds to the other dogs which beset him; and, accordingly, with the permission of the gentleman who had led the chase, I threw myself from my horse, and gave the game the coup de grâce with a dirk-knife which I had about me. Two of our party soon after joined us, each with a prairie wolf hanging to his saddlebow; and the others gradually collecting, we returned to Chicago, contented at last with the result of our morning sport.

MASSACRE AT CHICAGO*

Mrs. John H. Kinzie of Chicago

> HERE is a vivid, fascinating, true story about a large-scale frontier massacre. It differs from most historical documents because the author happened to be the daughter of the narrator, who must have been a remarkable woman.
>
> One sees here, for the first time, the *complicated* aspects of a massacre—the cross-currents of emotions among the Indians themselves, the divergent loyalties, the short-sightedness of some of the military and the heroism of the settlers.
>
> This is storytelling at its truest and grandest. It puts to shame anything about Indians and settlers that Hollywood has ever done on the screen.

IT WAS the evening of the seventh of April, 1812. The children of Mr. Kinzie were dancing before the fire to the music of their father's violin. The tea table was spread, and they were awaiting the return of their mother, who had gone to visit a sick neighbor about a quarter of a mile up the river.

Suddenly their sports were interrupted. The door was thrown open, and Mrs. Kinzie rushed in, pale with terror and scarcely able to articulate, "The Indians! the Indians!"

"The Indians? What? Where?" eagerly demanded they all.

"Up at Lee's Place, killing and scalping!"

With difficulty Mrs. Kinzie composed herself sufficiently to give the information, that while she was up at Burns', a man and a boy

---

* This narrative is substantially the same as that published in pamphlet form, in 1836. It was transferred with little variation to Brown's *History of Illinois*, and to a work called *Western Annals*. It was likewise made, by Major Richardson, the basis of his two tales, "Hardscrabble" and "Wau-nan-gee."

were seen running down with all speed on the opposite side of the river; that they had called across to give notice to Burns' family to save themselves, for the Indians were at Lee's Place, from which they had just made their escape. Having given this terrifying news, they had made all speed for the fort, which was on the same side of the river that they then were.

All was now consternation and dismay. The family were hurried into two old pirogues, that were moored near the house, and paddled with all possible haste across the river to take refuge in the fort.

All that the man and boy who had made their escape were able to tell, was soon known; but in order to render their story more intelligible, it is necessary to describe the scene of action.

Lee's Place, since known by the name of Hardscrabble, was a farm intersected by the Chicago River, about four miles from its mouth. The farmhouse stood on the western bank of the south branch of this river. On the same side of the main stream, but quite near its junction with Lake Michigan, stood the dwelling house and trading establishment of Mr. Kinzie.

The fort was situated on the southern bank, directly opposite this mansion—the river, and a few rods of sloping green turf on either side, being all that intervened between them.

The fort was differently constructed from the one erected on the same site in 1816. It had two blockhouses on the southern side, and on the northern a sally-port, or subterranean passage from the parade ground to the river. This was designed either to facilitate escape, in case of an emergency, or as a means of supplying the garrison with water during a siege.

The officers in the fort at this period were Capt. Heald, the commanding officer, Lieut. Helm, the son-in-law of Mr. Kinzie, and Ensign Ronan—the two last were very young men—and the surgeon, Dr. Van Voorhees.

The command numbered about seventy-five men; very few of whom were effective.

A constant and friendly intercourse had been maintained between these troops and the Indians. It is true that the principal men of the Potawatamie nation, like those of most other tribes, went yearly to Fort Malden, in Canada, to receive a large amount of presents, with which the British Government had, for many years, been in the habit of purchasing their alliance; and it was well known that many of the Potawatamies, as well as Winnebagoes, had been engaged with the Ottawas and Shawnees at the battle of Tippecanoe, the preceding autumn; yet, as the principal chiefs of all the bands in the neighborhood appeared to be on the most amicable terms with the Americans, no interruption of their harmony was at any time anticipated.

After the fifteenth August, however, many circumstances were recollected that might have opened the eyes of the whites, had they not been lulled in a fatal security. One instance in particular may be mentioned.

In the spring preceding the destruction of the fort, two Indians of the Calumet band came to the fort on a visit to the Commanding Officer. As they passed through the quarters, they saw Mrs. Heald and Mrs. Helm playing at battledore.

Turning to the interpreter, one of them, Nau-non-gee, remarked: "The white chiefs' wives are amusing themselves very much; it will not be long before they are hoeing in our cornfields!"

This was considered at the time an idle threat, or at most, an ebullition of jealous feeling at the contrast between the situation of their own women and that of the "white chiefs' wives." Some months after, how bitterly was it remembered!

The farm at Lee's Place was occupied by a Mr. White, and three persons employed by him in the care of the farm.

In the afternoon of the day on which our narrative commences, a party of ten or twelve Indians, dressed and painted, arrived at the house, and according to the custom among savages, entered and seated themselves without ceremony.

Something in their appearance and manner excited the suspicions of one of the family, a Frenchman, who remarked, "I do not like the appearance of these Indians—they are none of our folks. I know by their dress and paint that they are not Potawatamies."

Another of the family, a discharged soldier, then said to the boy who was present, "If that is the case, we had better get away from them if we can. Say nothing; but do as you see me do."

As the afternoon was far advanced, the soldier walked leisurely towards the canoes, of which there were two tied near the bank. Some of the Indians inquired where he was going. He pointed to the cattle which were standing among the haystacks on the opposite bank; and made signs that they must go and fodder them, and then they should return and get their supper.

He got into one canoe, and the boy into the other. The stream was narrow, and they were soon across. When they had gained the opposite side, they pulled some hay for the cattle—made a show of collecting them—and when they had gradually made a circuit, so that their movements were concealed by the haystacks, they took to the woods, which were close at hand, and made for the fort.

They had run about a quarter of a mile, when they heard the discharge of two guns successively, which they supposed to have been leveled at the companions they had left behind.

They stopped not nor stayed until they arrived opposite Burns',* where, as before related, they called across to advertise the family of their danger, and then hastened on to the fort.

It now occurred to those who had secured their own safety, that the family of Burns was at this moment exposed to the most imminent peril. The question was, who would hazard his own life to bring them to a place of safety? A gallant young officer, Ensign Ronan, volunteered, with a party of five or six soldiers, to go to their rescue.

They ascended the river in a scow, took the mother, with her infant of scarcely a day old, upon her bed to the boat, in which they carefully conveyed her and the other members of the family to the fort.

A party of soldiers, consisting of a corporal and six men, had that afternoon obtained leave to go up the river to fish.

They had not returned when the fugitives from Lee's Place arrived at the fort, and fearing that they might encounter the Indians,

* Burns' house stood near the spot where the Agency building, or "Cobweb Castle," was afterwards erected.

the commanding officer ordered a cannon to be fired, to warn them of danger.

They were at the time about two miles above Lee's Place. Hearing the signal, they took the hint, put out their torches (for it was now night), and dropped down the river toward the garrison, as silently as possible. It will be remembered that the unsettled state of the country since the battle of Tippecanoe, the preceding November, had rendered every man vigilant, and the slightest alarm was an admonition to beware of "the Indians."

When the fishing party reached Lee's Place, it was proposed to stop and warn the inmates to be upon their guard, as the signal from the fort indicated danger of some kind. All was still as death around the house. They groped their way along, and as the corporal jumped over the small enclosure, he placed his hand upon the dead body of a man. By the sense of touch he soon ascertained that the head was without a scalp, and otherwise mutilated. The faithful dog of the murdered man stood guarding the lifeless remains of his master.

The tale was now told. They retreated to their canoes and reached the fort unmolested about eleven o'clock at night. The next morning a party of the citizens and soldiers volunteered to go to Lee's Place, to learn further the fate of its occupants. The body of Mr. White was found pierced by two balls, and with eleven stabs in the breast. The Frenchman, as already described, lay dead, with his dog still beside him. Their bodies were brought to the fort and buried in its immediate vicinity.

It was subsequently ascertained, from traders out in the Indian country, that the perpetrators of this bloody deed were a party of Winnebagoes, who had come into this neighborhood to "take some white scalps." Their plan had been to proceed down the river from Lee's Place, and kill every white man without the walls of the fort. Hearing, however, the report of the cannon, and not knowing what it portended, they thought it best to remain satisfied with this one exploit, and forthwith retreated to their homes on Rock River.

The inhabitants outside the fort, consisting of a few discharged soldiers and some families of half-breeds, now entrenched themselves in the Agency House. This stood on the esplanade west of the fort, between the pickets and the river, and distant about twenty rods from the former.*

It was an old-fashioned log building, with a hall running through the center, and one large room on each side. Piazzas extended the whole length of the building in front and rear. These were planked up, for greater security, portholes were cut, and sentinels posted at night.

As the enemy were believed to be lurking still in the neighborhood, or, emboldened by former success, likely to return at any moment, an order was issued prohibiting any soldier or citizen from leaving the vicinity of the garrison without a guard.

One night a sergeant and private, who were out on a patrol, came suddenly upon a party of Indians in the pasture adjoining the esplanade. The sergeant fired his piece, and both retreated toward the fort. Before they could reach it, an Indian threw his tomahawk, which missed the sergeant and struck a wagon standing near. The sentinel from the blockhouse immediately fired, and with effect, while the men got safely in. The next morning it was ascertained, from traces of blood to a considerable distance into the prairie, and from the appearance of a body having been laid among the long grass, that some execution had been done.

On another occasion the enemy entered the esplanade to steal horses. Not finding them in the stable, as they had expected, they made themselves amends for their disappointment by stabbing all the sheep in the stable, and then letting them loose. The poor animals flocked towards the fort. This gave the alarm—the garrison was aroused—parties were sent out, but the marauders escaped unmolested.

The inmates of the fort experienced no further alarm for many weeks.

On the afternoon of the seventh of August, Winnemeg, or Catfish, a Potawatamie chief, arrived at the post, bringing despatches from Gen. Hull. These announced the declaration of war between

---

* The present site of the lighthouse.

the United States and Great Britain, and that Gen. Hull, at the head of the Northwestern army, had arrived at Detroit; also, that the island of Mackinac had fallen into the hands of the British.

The orders to Captain Heald were "to evacuate the fort, if practicable, and in that event, to distribute all the United States property contained in the fort, and in the United States factory or agency, among the Indians in the neighborhood."

After having delivered his despatches, Winnemeg requested a private interview with Mr. Kinzie, who had taken up his residence in the fort. He stated to Mr. K. that he was acquainted with the purport of the communications he had brought, and begged him to ascertain if it were the intention of Captain Heald to evacuate the post. He advised strongly against such a step, inasmuch as the garrison was well supplied with ammunition, and with provisions for six months. It would, therefore, be far better, he thought, to remain until a reinforcement could be sent to their assistance. If, however, Captain Heald should decide upon leaving the post, it should by all means be done immediately. The Potawatamies, through whose country they must pass, being ignorant of the object of Winnemeg's mission, a forced march might be made, before those who were hostile in their feelings were prepared to interrupt them.

Of this advice, so earnestly given, Captain Heald was immediately informed. He replied that it was his intention to evacuate the post, but that inasmuch as he had received orders to distribute the United States property, he should not feel justified in leaving it until he had collected the Indians of the neighborhood, and made an equitable division among them.

Winnemeg then suggested the expediency of marching out, and leaving all things standing—possibly while the Indians were engaged in the partition of the spoils, the troops might effect their retreat unmolested. This advice was strongly seconded by Mr. Kinzie, but did not meet the approbation of the Commanding Officer.

The order for evacuating the post was read next morning upon parade. It is difficult to understand why Captain Heald, in such an emergency, omitted the usual form of calling a council of war with his officers. It can only be accounted for by the fact of a want of harmonious feeling between himself and one of his junior officers—Ensign Ronan, a high-spirited and somewhat overbearing, but brave and generous young man.

In the course of the day, finding that no council was called, the officers waited on Captain Heald to be informed what course he intended to pursue. When they learned his intentions, they remonstrated with him, on the following grounds:

First—it was highly improbable that the command would be permitted to pass through the country in safety to Fort Wayne. For although it had been said that some of the chiefs had opposed an attack upon the fort planned the preceding autumn, yet it was well known that they had been actuated in that matter by motives of private regard to one family, and not to any general friendly feeling toward the Americans; and that, at any rate, it was hardly to be expected that these few individuals would be able to control the whole tribe, who were thirsting for blood.

In the next place—their march must necessarily be slow, as their movements must be accommodated to the helplessness of the women and children, of whom there were a number with the detachment. That of their small force, some of the soldiers were super-annuated, others invalid; therefore, since the course to be pursued was left discretional, their unanimous advice was, to remain where they were, and fortify themselves as strongly as possible. Succors from the other side of the peninsula might arrive before they could be attacked by the British from Mackinac, and even should there not, it were far better to fall into the hands of the latter than to become the victims of the savages.

Captain Heald argued in reply that a special order had been issued by the War Department, that no post should be surrendered without battle having been given, and his force was totally inadequate to an engagement with the Indians. That he should unquestionably be censured for remaining, when there appeared a prospect of a safe march through; and that upon the whole he deemed it expedient to assemble the Indians, distribute the property among them, and then ask of them an escort to Fort Wayne, with the promise of a considerable reward upon their safe arrival—adding that he had full confidence in the friendly professions of the Indians, from whom, as well as from the soldiers, the capture of Mackinac had been kept a profound secret.

From this time the officers held themselves aloof, and spoke but little upon the subject, though they considered the project of Captain Heald little short of madness. The dissatisfaction among the soldiers hourly increased, until it reached a high pitch of insubordination.

Upon one occasion, as Captain Heald was conversing with Mr. Kinzie upon the parade, he remarked, "I could not remain, even if I thought it best, for I have but a small store of provisions."

"Why, Captain," said a soldier who stood near, forgetting all etiquette in the excitement of the moment, "you have cattle enough to last the troops six months."

"But," replied Captain Heald, "I have no salt to preserve it with."

"Then jerk* it," said the man, "as the Indians do their venison."

The Indians now became daily more unruly. Entering the fort in defiance of the sentinels, they made their way without ceremony into the officers' quarters. On one occasion, an Indian took up a rifle and fired it in the parlor of the Commanding Officer, as an expression of defiance. Some were of opinion that this was intended among the young men as a signal for an attack. The old chiefs passed backwards and forward among the assembled groups, with the appearance of the most lively agitation, while the squaws rushed to and fro, in great excitement, and evidently prepared for some fearful scene.

Any further manifestation of ill-feeling was, however, suppressed for the present, and Captain Heald, strange as it may seem, continued to entertain a conviction of having created so amicable a disposition among the Indians, as would insure the safety of the command on their march to Fort Wayne.

Thus passed the time until the twelfth of August. The feelings

* This is done by cutting the meat in thin slices, placing it upon a scaffold, and making a fire under it, which dries it and smokes it at the same time.

of the inmates of the fort during this time may be better imagined than described. Each morning that dawned seemed to bring them nearer that most appalling fate—butchery by a savage foe—and at night they scarcely dared yield to slumber, lest they should be aroused by the war-whoop and tomahawk. Gloom and mistrust prevailed, and the want of unanimity among the officers, debarred them the consolation they might have found in mutual sympathy and encouragement.

The Indians being assembled from the neighboring villages, a council was held with them on the afternoon of the twelfth. Captain Heald only attended on the part of the military. He requested his officers to accompany him, but they declined. They had been secretly informed that it was the intention of the young chiefs to fall upon the officers and massacre them while in council, but they could not persuade Captain Heald of the truth of their information. They waited therefore only until he had left the garrison, accompanied by Mr. Kinzie, when they took command of the blockhouses which overlooked the esplanade on which the council was held, opened the portholes, and pointed the cannon so as to command the whole assembly. By this means, probably, the lives of the whites who were present in council were preserved.

In council, the Commanding Officer informed the Indians that it was his intention to distribute among them the next day, not only the goods lodged in the United States Factory, but also the ammunition and provisions, with which the garrison was well supplied. He then requested of the Potawatamies an escort to Fort Wayne, promising them a liberal reward on arriving there, in addition to the presents they were now about to receive. With many professions of friendship and good will, the savages assented to all he proposed, and promised all he required.

After the council, Mr. Kinzie, who understood well not only the Indian character but the present tone of feeling among them, had a long interview with Captain Heald, in hopes of opening his eyes to the present posture of affairs.

He reminded him that since the troubles with the Indians upon the Wabash and its vicinity, there had appeared a settled plan of hostilities toward the whites, in consequence of which it had been the policy of the Americans to withhold from them whatever would enable them to carry on their warfare upon the defenseless inhabitants of the frontier.

Mr. Kinzie recalled to Captain Heald how he had himself left home for Detroit the preceding autumn, but, receiving when he had proceeded as far as De Charme's* the intelligence of the battle of Tippecanoe, he had immediately returned to Chicago, that he might dispatch orders to his traders to furnish no ammunition to the Indians; in consequence of which all they had on hand was secreted, and such of the traders as had not already started for their wintering-grounds took neither powder nor shot with them.

Captain Heald was struck with the impolicy of furnishing the enemy (for such they must now consider their old neighbors) with arms against himself, and determined to destroy all the ammunition except what should be necessary for the use of his own troops.

On the thirteenth the goods, consisting of blankets, broadcloths, calicoes, paints, etc., were distributed, as stipulated. The same evening the ammunition and liquor were carried, part into the sallyport, and thrown into a well which had been dug there to supply the garrison with water in case of emergency; the remainder was transported as secretly as possible through the northern gate, the heads of the barrels knocked in, and the contents poured into the river.

The same fate was shared by a large quantity of alcohol belonging to Mr. Kinzie, which had been deposited in a warehouse near his residence opposite the fort.

The Indians suspected what was going on, and crept, serpentlike, as near the scene of action as possible, but a vigilant watch was kept up, and no one was suffered to approach but those engaged in the affair. All the muskets not necessary for the command on the march were broken up and thrown into the well, together with the bags of shot, flints, gunscrews, and, in short, everything relating to weapons of offense.

* A trading establishment—now Ypsilanti.

Some relief to the general feeling of despondency was afforded by the arrival, on the fourteenth of August, of Captain Wells* with fifteen friendly Miamis.

Of this brave man, who forms so conspicuous a figure in our frontier annals, it is unnecessary here to say more than that he had been residing from his boyhood among the Indians, and consequently possessed a perfect knowledge of their character and habits.

He had heard, at Fort Wayne, of the order for evacuating the fort at Chicago, and knowing the hostile determination of the Potawatamies, he had made a rapid march across the country, to prevent the exposure of his relative, Captain Heald, and his troops to certain destruction.

But he came "all too late." When he reached the post he found that the ammunition had been destroyed, and the provisions given to the Indians. There was, therefore, now no alternative, and every preparation was made for the march of the troops on the following morning.

On the afternoon of the same day, a second council was held with the Indians. They expressed great indignation at the destruction of the ammunition and liquor.

Notwithstanding the precautions that had been taken to preserve secrecy, the noise of knocking in the heads of the barrels had betrayed the operations of the preceding night; and, so great was the quantity of liquor thrown into the river, that the taste of the water the next morning was, as one expressed it, "strong grog."

Murmurs and threats were everywhere heard among the savages. It was evident that the first moment of exposure would subject the troops to some manifestation of their disappointment and resentment.

Among the chiefs were several who, although they shared the general hostile feeling of their tribe toward the Americans, yet

---

* Captain Wells when a boy was stolen from his friends, the family of Hon. Nathaniel Pope, in Kentucky. Although recovered by them, he preferred to return and live among his new friends. He married a Miami woman, and became a chief of the nation. He was the father of the late Mrs. Judge Wolcott, of Maumee, O.

retained a personal regard for the troops at this post, and for the few white citizens of the place. These chiefs exerted their utmost influence to allay the revengeful feelings of the young men, and to avert their sanguinary designs, but without effect.

On the evening succeeding the council, Black Partridge, a conspicuous chief, entered the quarters of the Commanding Officer.

"Father," said he, "I come to deliver up to you the medal I wear. It was given me by the Americans, and I have long worn it, in token of our mutual friendship. But our young men are resolved to imbrue their hands in the blood of the whites. I cannot restrain them, and I will not wear a token of peace while I am compelled to act as an enemy."

Had further evidence been wanting, this circumstance would sufficiently have proved to the devoted band the justice of their melancholy anticipations. Nevertheless, they went steadily on with the necessary preparations; and amid the horrors of their situation, there were not wanting one or two gallant hearts, who strove to encourage, in their desponding companions, the hopes of escape they were far from indulging themselves.

Of the ammunition there had been reserved but twenty-five rounds, beside one box of cartridges, contained in the baggage wagons. This must, under any circumstances of danger, have proved an inadequate supply, but the prospect of a fatiguing march, in their present ineffective state, forbade the troops embarrassing themselves with a larger quantity.

The morning of the fifteenth arrived. All things were in readiness, and nine o'clock was the hour named for starting. Mr. Kinzie had volunteered to accompany the troops in their march, and had entrusted his family to the care of some friendly Indians, who had promised to convey them in a boat around the head of Lake Michigan to a point* on the St. Joseph's river; there to be joined by the troops, should the prosecution of their march be permitted them.

Early in the morning Mr. Kinzie received a message from Topee-nee-bee, a chief of the St. Joseph's band, informing him that

---

* The spot now called Bertrand, then known as *Pare aux Vaches,* from its having been a pasture ground to an old French fort in the neighborhood.

mischief was intended by the Potawatamies who had engaged to escort the detachment; and urging him to relinquish his design of accompanying the troops by land, promising him that the boat containing himself and family should be permitted to pass in safety to St. Joseph's.

Mr. Kinzie declined acceding to this proposal, as he believed that his presence might operate as a restraint upon the fury of the savages, so warmly were the greater part of them attached to himself and his family.

The party in the boat consisted of Mrs. Kinzie and her four younger children, their nurse Grutte, a clerk of Mr. Kinzie's, two servants and the boatmen, besides the two Indians who acted as their protectors. The boat started, but had scarcely reached the mouth of the river, which, it will be recollected was here half a mile below the fort, when another messenger from To-pee-nee-bee arrived to detain them where they were.

In breathless expectation sat the wife and mother. She was a woman of uncommon energy and strength of character, yet her heart died within her as she folded her arms about her helpless infants, and gazed upon the march of her husband and eldest child to certain destruction.

As the troops left the fort, the band struck up the Dead March. On they came in military array, but with solemn mien. Captain Wells took the lead at the head of his little band of Miamis. He had blackened his face before leaving the garrison, in token of his impending fate. They took their route along the lake shore. When they reached the point where commenced a range of sand hills intervening between the prairie and the beach, the escort of Potawatamies, in number about five hundred, kept the level of the prairie, instead of continuing along the beach with the Americans and Miamis.

They had marched perhaps a mile and a half, when Captain Wells, who had kept somewhat in advance with his Miamis, came riding furiously back.

"They are about to attack us," shouted he; "form, instantly, and charge upon them."

Scarcely were the words uttered, when a volley was showered

from among the sand hills. The troops were hastily brought into line, and charged up the bank. One man, a veteran of seventy winters, fell as they ascended. The remainder of the scene is best described in the words of an eyewitness and participator in the tragedy, Mrs. Helm, the wife of Captain (then Lieutenant) Helm, and stepdaughter of Mr. Kinzie.

"After we had left the bank the firing became general. The Miamis fled at the outset. Their chief rode up to the Potawatamies and said:

" 'You have deceived the Americans and us. You have done a bad action, and [brandishing his tomahawk] I will be the first to head a party of Americans to return and punish your treachery.' So saying, he galloped after his companions, who were now scouring across the prairies.

"The troops behaved most gallantly. They were but a handful, but they seemed resolved to sell their lives as dearly as possible. Our horses pranced and bounded, and could hardly be restrained as the balls whistled among them. I drew off a little, and gazed upon my husband and father, who were yet unharmed. I felt that my hour was come, and endeavored to forget those I loved, and prepare myself for my approaching fate.

"While I was thus engaged, the surgeon, Dr. Van Voorhees, came up. He was badly wounded. His horse had been shot under him, and he had received a ball in his leg. Every muscle of his face was quivering with the agony of terror. He said to me—'Do you think they will take our lives? I am badly wounded, but I think not mortally. Perhaps we might purchase our lives by promising them a large reward. Do you think there is a chance?'

" 'Dr. Van Voorhees,' said I, 'do not let us waste the few moments that yet remain to us in such vain hopes. Our fate is inevitable. In a few moments we must appear before the bar of God. Let us make what preparation is yet in our power.'

" 'Oh! I cannot die,' exclaimed he, 'I am not fit to die—if I had but a short time to prepare—death is awful!'

"I pointed to Ensign Ronan, who though mortally wounded and nearly down, was still fighting with desperation on one knee.

" 'Look at that man,' said I, 'at least he dies like a soldier.'

" 'Yes,' replied the unfortunate man, with a convulsive gasp, 'but he has no terrors of the future—he is an unbeliever!'

"At this moment a young Indian raised his tomahawk at me. By springing aside, I avoided the blow which was intended for my skull, but which alighted on my shoulder. I seized him around the neck, and while exerting my utmost efforts to get possession of his scalping knife, which hung in a scabbard over his breast, I was dragged from his grasp by another and an older Indian.

"The latter bore me struggling and resisting towards the lake. Notwithstanding the rapidity with which I was hurried along, I recognized as I passed them the lifeless remains of the unfortunate surgeon. Some murderous tomahawk had stretched him upon the very spot where I had last seen him.

"I was immediately plunged into the water and held there with a forcible hand, notwithstanding my resistance. I soon perceived, however, that the object of my captor was not to drown me, for he held me firmly in such a position as to place my head above water. This reassured me, and regarding him attentively, I soon recognized, in spite of the paint with which he was disguised, Black Partridge.

"When the firing had nearly subsided, my preserver bore me from the water and conducted me up the sandbanks. It was a burning August morning, and walking through the sand in my drenched condition was inexpressibly painful and fatiguing. I stooped and took off my shoes to free them from the sand with which they were nearly filled, when a squaw seized and carried them off, and I was obliged to proceed without them.

"When we had gained the prairie, I was met by my father, who told me that my husband was safe and but slightly wounded. They led me gently back towards the Chicago River, along the southern bank of which was the Potawatamie encampment. At one time I was placed upon a horse without a saddle, but finding the motion insupportable, I sprang off. Supported partly by my kind conductor, Black Partridge, and partly by another Indian, Pee-so-tum, who held dangling in his hand a scalp, which by the black ribbon around the queue I recognized as that of Capt. Wells, I dragged my fainting steps to one of the wigwams.

"The wife of Wau-bee-nee-mah, a chief from the Illinois River, was standing near, and seeing my exhausted condition she seized a kettle, dipped up some water from a stream that flowed near,* threw into it some maple sugar, and stirring it up with her hand gave it to me to drink. This act of kindness, in the midst of so many horrors, touched me most sensibly, but my attention was soon diverted to other objects.

"The fort had become a scene of plunder to such as remained after the troops marched out. The cattle had been shot down as they ran at large, and lay dead or dying around. This work of butchery had commenced just as we were leaving the fort. I well remembered a remark of Ensign Ronan, as the firing went on. 'Such,' turning to me, 'is to be our fate—to be shot down like brutes!'

" 'Well sir,' said the Commanding Officer who overheard him, 'are you afraid?'

" 'No,' replied the high-spirited young man, 'I can march up to the enemy where you dare not show your face;' and his subsequent gallant behavior showed this to be no idle boast.

"As the noise of the firing grew gradually less and the stragglers from the victorious party came dropping in, I received confirmation of what my father had hurriedly communicated in our *rencontre* on the lake shore; namely, that the whites had surrendered after the loss of about two-thirds of their number. They had stipulated, through the interpreter, Peresh Leclerc, for the preservation of their lives, and those of the remaining women and children, and for their delivery at some of the British posts, unless ransomed by traders in the Indian country. It appears that the wounded prisoners were not considered as included in the stipulation, and a horrible scene ensued upon their being brought into camp.

"An old squaw infuriated by the loss of friends, or excited by

* Just by the present State Street Market.

the sanguinary scenes around her, seemed possessed by a de-
moniac ferocity. She seized a stable fork and assaulted one miserable victim who lay groaning and writhing in the agony of his
wounds, aggravated by the scorching beams of the sun. With a
delicacy of feeling scarcely to have been expected under such circumstances, Wau-bee-nee-mah stretched a mat across two poles,
between me and this dreadful scene. I was thus spared in some
degree a view of its horrors, although I could not entirely close
my ears to the cries of the sufferer. The following night five more
of the wounded prisoners were tomahawked.

"The Americans after their first attack by the Indians charged
upon those who had concealed themselves in a sort of ravine,
intervening between the sandbanks and the prairie. The latter
gathered themselves into a body, and after some hard fighting, in
which the number of whites had become reduced to twenty-eight,
this little band succeeded in breaking through the enemy, and
gaining a rising ground, not far from the Oak Woods. The contest
now seemed hopeless, and Lt. Helm sent Peresh Leclerc, a half-
breed boy in the service of Mr. Kinzie, who had accompanied
the detachment and fought manfully on their side, to propose
terms of capitulation. It was stipulated that the lives of all the
survivors should be spared, and a ransom permitted as soon as
practicable.

"But, in the meantime, a horrible scene had been enacted. One
young savage, climbing into the baggage wagon containing the
children of the white families, twelve in number, tomahawked
the children of the entire group. This was during the engagement
near the sand hills. When Captain Wells, who was fighting near,
beheld it, he exclaimed:

" 'Is that their game, butchering the women and children? Then
I will kill too!'

"So saying, he turned his horse's head, and started for the Indian camp, near the fort, where had been left their squaws and
children.

"Several Indians pursued him as he galloped along. He laid
himself flat on the neck of his horse, loading and firing in that
position, as he would occasionally turn on his pursuers. At length

their balls took effect, killing his horse, and severely wounding himself. At this moment he was met by Winnemeg and Wau-ban-see, who endeavored to save him from the savages who had now overtaken him. As they supported him along, after having disengaged him from his horse, he received his deathblow from another Indian, Pee-so-tum, who stabbed him in the back.

"The heroic resolution of one of the soldiers' wives deserves to be recorded. She was a Mrs. Corbin, and had, from the first, expressed the determination never to fall into the hands of the savages, believing that their prisoners were always subjected to tortures worse than death.

"When, therefore, a party came upon her, to make her a prisoner, she fought with desperation, refusing to surrender, although assured, by signs, of safety and kind treatment, and literally suffered herself to be cut to pieces, rather than become their captive.

"There was a Sergeant Holt, who, early in the engagement, received a ball in the neck. Finding himself badly wounded, he gave his sword to his wife, who was on horseback near him, telling her to defend herself—he then made for the lake, to keep out of the way of the balls. Mrs. Holt rode a very fine horse, which the Indians were desirous of possessing, and they therefore attacked her, in hopes of dismounting her.

"They fought only with the butt-ends of their guns, for their object was not to kill her. She hacked and hewed at their pieces as they were thrust against her, now on this side, now on that. Finally, she broke loose from them, and dashed out into the prairie. The Indians pursued her, shouting and laughing, and now and then calling out:

" 'The brave woman! do not hurt her!'

"At length they overtook her again, and while she was engaged with two or three in front, one succeeded in seizing her by the neck behind, and dragging her, although a large and powerful woman, from her horse. Notwithstanding that their guns had been so hacked and injured, and even themselves cut severely, they seemed to regard her only with admiration. They took her to a trader on the Illinois River, by whom she was restored to her friends, after having received every kindness during her captivity.

"Those of the family of Mr. Kinzie, who had remained in the boat, near the mouth of the river, were carefully guarded by Kee-po-tah and another Indian. They had seen the smoke—then the blaze—and immediately after the report of the first tremendous discharge sounded in their ears. Then all was confusion. They realized nothing until they saw an Indian come towards them from the battleground, leading a horse on which sat a lady, apparently wounded.

" 'That is Mrs. Heald,' cried Mrs. Kinzie. 'That Indian will kill her. Run, Chandonnai,' to one of Mr. Kinzie's clerks, 'take the mule that is tied there, and offer it to him to release her.'

"Her captor, by this time, was in the act of disengaging her bonnet from her head, in order to scalp her. Chandonnai ran up, offered the mule as a ransom, with the promise of ten bottles of whiskey, as soon as they should reach his village. The latter was a strong temptation.

" 'But,' said the Indian, 'she is badly wounded—she will die. Will you give me the whiskey, at all events?'

"Chandonnai promised that he would, and the bargain was concluded. The savage placed the lady's bonnet on his own head, and after an ineffectual effort on the part of some squaws to rob her of her shoes and stockings, she was brought on board the boat, where she lay moaning with pain from the many bullet wounds she had received in both arms.

"The horse she had ridden was a fine spirited animal, and, being desirous of possessing themselves of it uninjured, the Indians had aimed their shots so as to disable the rider, without injuring her steed.

"She had not lain long in the boat, when a young Indian of savage aspect was seen approaching. A buffalo robe was hastily drawn over Mrs. Heald, and she was admonished to suppress all sound of complaint, as she valued her life.

"The heroic woman remained perfectly silent, while the savage drew near. He had a pistol in his hand, which he rested on the side of the boat, while, with a fearful scowl, he looked pryingly around. Black Jim, one of the servants who stood in the bow of

the boat, seized an ax that lay near, and signed to him that if he
shot, he would cleave his skull; telling him that the boat contained
only the family of Shaw-nee-aw-kee. Upon this, the Indian retired.
It afterward appeared that the object of his search was Mr. Burnett, a trader from St. Joseph's, with whom he had some account
to settle.

"When the boat was at length permitted to return to the mansion of Mr. Kinzie, and Mrs. Heald was removed to the house, it
became necessary to dress her wounds.

"Mr. K. applied to an old chief who stood by, and who, like
most of his tribe, possessed some skill in surgery, to extract a ball
from the arm of the sufferer.

" 'No, father,' replied he. 'I cannot do it—it makes me sick
here'—(placing his hand on his heart).

"Mr. Kinzie then performed the operation himself with his pen-
knife.

"At their own mansion the family of Mr. Kinzie were closely
guarded by their Indian friends, whose intention it was to carry
them to Detroit for security. The rest of the prisoners remained at
the wigwams of their captors.

"The following morning, the work of plunder being completed,
the Indians set fire to the fort. A very equitable distribution of
the finery appeared to have been made, and shawls, ribbons, and
feathers fluttered about in all directions. The ludicrous appearance of one young fellow who had arrayed himself in a muslin
gown, and the bonnet of one of the ladies, would, under other
circumstances, have afforded matter of amusement.

"Black Partridge, Wau-ban-see, and Kee-po-tah, with two other
Indians, having established themselves on the porch of the building as sentinels, to protect the family from any evil that the young
men might be excited to commit, all remained tranquil for a short
space after the conflagration.

"Very soon, however, a party of Indians from the Wabash made
their appearance. These were, decidedly, the most hostile and
implacable of all the tribes of the Potawatamies.

"Being more remote, they had shared less than some of their
brethren in the kindness of Mr. Kinzie and his family, and con-

sequently their sentiments of regard for them were less powerful.

"Runners had been sent to the villages to apprize them of the intended evacuation of the post, as well as of the plan of the Indians assembled to attack the troops.

"Thirsting to participate in such a scene they hurried on, and great was their mortification on arriving at the river Aux Plaines, to meet with a party of their friends having with them their chief Nee-scot-nee-meg, badly wounded, and to learn that the battle was over, the spoils divided, and the scalps all taken.

"On arriving at Chicago they blackened their faces, and proceeded towards the dwelling of Mr. Kinzie.

"From his station on the piazza Black Partridge had watched their approach, and his fears were particularly awakened for the safety of Mrs. Helm (Mr. Kinzie's stepdaughter), who had recently come to the post, and was personally unknown to the more remote Indians. By his advice she was made to assume the ordinary dress of a Frenchwoman of the country; namely, a short gown and petticoat, with a blue cotton handkerchief wrapped around her head. In this disguise she was conducted by Black Partridge himself to the house of Ouilmette, a Frenchman with a half-breed wife, who formed a part of the establishment of Mr. Kinzie, and whose dwelling was close at hand.

"It so happened that the Indians came first to this house, in their search for prisoners. As they approached, the inmates, fearful that the fair complexion and general appearance of Mrs. Helm might betray her for an American, raised a large featherbed and placed her under the edge of it, upon the bedstead, with her face to the wall. Mrs. Bisson, the sister of Ouilmette's wife, then seated herself with her sewing upon the front of the bed.

"It was a hot day in August, and the feverish excitement of fear and agitation, together with her position, which was nearly suffocating, became so intolerable, that Mrs. Helm at length entreated to be released and given up to the Indians.

" 'I can but die,' said she; 'let them put an end to my misery at once.'

"Mrs. Bisson replied, 'Your death would be the destruction of us all, for Black Partridge has resolved that if one drop of the blood

of your family is spilled, he will take the lives of all concerned
in it, even his nearest friends, and if once the work of murder
commences, there will be no end of it, so long as there remains
one white person, or half-breed, in the country.'

"This expostulation nerved Mrs. Helm with fresh resolution.

"The Indians entered, and she could occasionally see them from
her hiding place, gliding about, and stealthily inspecting every part
of the room, though without making any ostensible search, until
apparently satisfied that there was no one concealed, they left the
house.

"All this time Mrs. Bisson had kept her seat upon the side of
the bed, calmly sorting and arranging the patchwork of the quilt
on which she was engaged, and preserving an appearance of the
utmost tranquillity, although she knew not but that the next moment she might receive a tomahawk in her brain. Her self-
command unquestionably saved the lives of all present.

"From Ouilmette's house the party of Indians proceeded to
the dwelling of Mr. Kinzie. They entered the parlor in which the
family were assembled with their faithful protectors, and seated
themselves upon the floor in silence.

"Black Partridge perceived from their moody and revengeful
looks what was passing in their minds, but he dared not remon-
strate with them. He only observed in a low tone to Wau-
ban-see—

" 'We have endeavored to save our friends, but it is in vain—
nothing will save them now.'

"At this moment a friendly whoop was heard from a party of
newcomers on the opposite bank of the river. Black Partridge
sprang to meet their leader, as the canoes in which they had hastily embarked touched the bank near the house.

" 'Who are you?' demanded he.

" 'A man—who are *you?*'

" 'A man like yourself, but tell me *who* you are'—meaning, tell
me your disposition, and which side you are for.

" 'I am the Sau-ga-nash!'

" 'Then make all speed to the house—your friend is in danger,
and you alone can save him.'

"Billy Caldwell,* for it was he, entered the parlor with a calm step, and without a trace of agitation in his manner. He deliberately took off his accouterments and placed them with his rifle behind the door; then saluted the hostile savages.

" 'How now, my friends! A good day to you. I was told there were enemies here, but I am glad to find only friends. Why have you blackened your faces? Is it that you are mourning for the friends you have lost in battle?' (purposely misunderstanding this token of evil designs). 'Or is it that you are fasting? If so, ask your friend here, and he will give you to eat. He is the Indians' friend, and never yet refused them what they had need of.'

"Thus taken by surprise, the savages were ashamed to acknowledge their bloody purpose. They, therefore, said modestly that they came to beg of their friends some white cotton in which to wrap their dead, before interring them. This was given to them with some other presents, and they took their departure peaceably from the premises.

"Along with Mr. Kinzie's party was a noncommissioned officer who had made his escape in a singular manner. As the troops were about leaving the fort it was found that the baggage horses of the surgeon had strayed off. The quartermaster sergeant, Griffith, was sent to collect them and bring them on, it being absolutely necessary to recover them, since their packs contained part of the surgeon's apparatus, and the medicines for the march.

"This man had been for a long time on the sick report, and for this reason was given the charge of the baggage, instead of being placed with the troops. His efforts to recover the horses being unsuccessful, he was hastening to rejoin his party, alarmed at some appearances of disorder and hostile indications among the Indians, when he was met and made prisoner by To-pee-nee-bee.

"Having taken from him his arms and accouterments, the chief put him into a canoe and paddled him across the river, bidding

---

* Billy Caldwell was a half-breed, and a chief of the nation. In his reply, *"I am a Sau-ga-nash,"* or Englishman, he designed to convey, "I am a *white man.*" Had he said, *"I am a Potawatamie,"* it would have been interpreted to mean, "I belong to my nation, and am prepared to go all lengths with them."

him make for the woods and secrete himself. This he did, and the following day, in the afternoon, seeing from his lurking-place that all appeared quiet, he ventured to steal cautiously into the garden of Ouilmette, where he concealed himself for a time behind some currant bushes.

"At length he determined to enter the house, and accordingly climbed up through a small back window, into the room where the family were. This was just as the Wabash Indians left the house of Ouilmette for that of Mr. Kinzie. The danger of the sergeant was now imminent. The family stripped him of his uniform and arrayed him in a suit of deerskin, with belt, moccasins, and pipe, like a French engagé. His dark complexion and large black whiskers favored the disguise. The family were all ordered to address him in French, and although utterly ignorant of the language he continued to pass for a Weem-tee-gosh,* and as such to accompany Mr. Kinzie and his family, undetected by his enemies until they reached a place of safety.

"On the third day after the battle, the family of Mr. Kinzie, with the clerks of the establishment, were put into a boat, under the care of François, a half-breed interpreter, and conveyed to St. Joseph's where they remained until the following November, under the protection of To-pee-nee-bee's band. They were then conducted to Detroit, under the escort of Chandonnai and their trusty Indian friend, Kee-po-tah, and delivered up as prisoners of war, to Col. McKee the British Indian Agent.

"Mr. Kinzie was not allowed to leave St. Joseph's with his family, his Indian friends insisting on his remaining and endeavoring to secure some remnant of his scattered property. During his excursions with them for that purpose, he wore the costume and paint of the tribe, in order to escape capture and perhaps death at the hands of those who were still thirsting for blood. In time, however, his anxiety for his family induced him to follow them to Detroit, where, in the month of January, he was received and paroled by Gen. Proctor.

"Capt. and Mrs. Heald had been sent across the lake to St.

* Frenchman.

Joseph's the day after the battle. The former had received two wounds, the latter seven in the engagement.

"Lieut. Helm, who was likewise wounded, was carried by some friendly Indians to their village on the Au Sable, and thence to Peoria, where he was liberated by the intervention of Mr. Thomas Forsyth, the half-brother of Mr. Kinzie. Mrs. Helm had accompanied her parents to St. Joseph's, where they resided in the family of Alexander Robinson,* receiving from them all possible kindness and hospitality for several months.

"After their arrival in Detroit, Mrs. Helm was joined by her husband, when they were both arrested by order of the British commander, and sent on horseback, in the dead of winter, through Canada to Fort George on the Niagara frontier. When they arrived at that post, there seemed no official appointed to receive them, and notwithstanding their long and fatiguing journey, in weather the most cold and inclement, Mrs. H., a delicate woman of seventeen years, was permitted to sit waiting in her saddle without the gate for more than an hour, before the refreshment of fire and food, or even the shelter of a roof, was offered her. When Col. Sheaffe, who had been absent at the time, was informed of this brutal inhospitality, he expressed the greatest indignation. He waited on Mrs. Helm immediately, apologized in the most courteous manner, and treated both her and Lieut. H. with the most considerate kindness, until, by an exchange of prisoners, they were liberated, and found means to reach their friends in Steuben County, N. Y.

"Capt. Heald had been taken prisoner by an Indian from the Kankakee, who had a strong personal regard for him, and who, when he saw the wounded and enfeebled state of Mrs. H. released her husband that he might accompany his wife to St. Joseph's. To the latter place they were accordingly carried, as has been related, by Chandonnai and his party. In the meantime, the Indian who had so nobly released his prisoner returned to his village on the Kankakee, where he had the mortification of finding that his conduct had excited great dissatisfaction among his

* The Potawatamie chief, so well known to many of the citizens of Chicago, now residing at the Aux Plaines.

band. So great was the displeasure manifested, that he resolved to make a journey to St. Joseph's and reclaim his prisoner.

"News of his intention being brought to To-pee-nee-bee and Kee-po-tah under whose care the prisoners were, they held a private council with Chandonnai, Mr. Kinzie, and the principal men of the village, the result of which was, a determination to send Capt. and Mrs. Heald to the island of Mackinac, and deliver them up to the British.

"They were accordingly put in a bark canoe, and paddled by Robinson and his wife a distance of three hundred miles along the coast of Michigan, and surrendered as prisoners of war to the Commanding Officer at Mackinac.

"As an instance of the procrastinating spirit of Capt. Heald it may be mentioned that even after he had received certain intelligence that his Indian captor was on his way from the Kankakee to St. Joseph's to retake him, he would still have delayed another day at that place, to make preparation for a more comfortable journey to Mackinac.

"The soldiers, with their wives and surviving children, were dispersed among the different villages of the Potawatamies upon the Illinois, Wabash, Rock River, and at Milwaukee, until the following spring, when they were, for the most part, carried to Detroit, and ransomed.

"Mrs. Burns, with her infant, became the prisoner of a chief, who carried her to his village and treated her with great kindness. His wife, from jealousy of the favor shown to 'the white woman' and her child, always treated them with great hostility. On one occasion she struck the infant with a tomahawk, and narrowly missed her aim of putting an end to it altogether.* They were not left long in the power of the old hag, after this demonstration, but on the first opportunity were carried to a place of safety.

"The family of Mr. Lee had resided in a house on the Lake shore, not far from the fort. Mr. Lee was the owner of Lee's Place,

---

* Twenty-two years after this, as I was on a journey to Chicago in the steamer *Uncle Sam,* a young woman, hearing my name, introduced herself to me, and raising the hair from her forehead, showed me the mark of the tomahawk which had so nearly been fatal to her.

which he cultivated as a farm. It was his son who ran down with the discharged soldier to give the alarm of "Indians" at the fort on the afternoon of the seventh of April. The father, the son, and all the other members of the family had fallen victims on the fifteenth of August, except Mrs. Lee and her young infant. These were claimed by Black Partridge, and carried to his village on the Au Sable. He had been particularly attached to a little girl of Mrs. Lee's, about twelve years of age. This child had been placed on horseback for the march, and as she was unaccustomed to the exercise, she was tied fast to the saddle, lest by any accident she should slip off or be thrown.

"She was within reach of the balls at the commencement of the engagement, and was severely wounded. The horse set off on a full gallop, which partly threw her, but she was held fast by the bands which confined her, and hung dangling as the animal ran violently about. In this state she was met by Black Partridge, who caught the horse and disengaged her from the saddle. Finding her so much wounded that she could not recover, and that she was suffering great agony, he put the finishing stroke to her at once with his tomahawk. He afterward said that this was the hardest thing he ever tried to do, but he did it because he could not bear to see her suffer.

"He took the mother and her infant to his village, where he became warmly attached to the former—so much so, that he wished to marry her, but, as she very naturally objected, he treated her with the greatest respect and consideration. He was in no hurry to release her, for he was in hopes of prevailing on her to become his wife. In the course of the winter her child fell ill. Finding that none of the remedies within their reach were effectual, Black Partridge proposed to take the little one to Chicago, where there was now a French trader living in the mansion of Mr. Kinzie, and procure some medical aid from him. Wrapping up his charge with the greatest care, he set out on his journey.

"When he arrived at the residence of M. Du Pin, he entered the room where he was, and carefully placed his burthen on the floor.

" 'What have you there?' asked M. Du Pin.

" 'A young racoon, which I have brought you as a present,' was the reply, and opening the pack, he showed the little sick infant.

"When the trader had prescribed for its complaint, and Black Partridge was about to return to his home, he told his friend his proposal to Mrs. Lee to become his wife and the manner in which it had been received.

"M. Du Pin entertained some fears that the chief's honorable resolution might not hold out, to leave it to the lady herself whether to accept his addresses or not, so he entered at once into a negotiation for her ransom, and so effectually wrought upon the good feelings of Black Partridge that he consented to bring his fair prisoner at once to Chicago, that she might be restored to her friends.

"Whether the kind trader had at the outset any other feeling in the matter than sympathy and brotherly kindness we cannot say—we only know that, in process of time Mrs. Lee became Madame Du Pin, and that they lived together in great happiness for many years after.

"The fate of Nau-non-gee, one of the chiefs of the Calumet village, and who is mentioned in the early part of the narrative, deserves to be recorded.

"During the battle of the fifteenth of August, the chief object of his attack was one Sergeant Hays, a man from whom he had received many acts of kindness.

"After Hays had received a ball through the body, this Indian ran up to him to tomahawk him, when the Sergeant, collecting his remaining strength, pierced him through the body with his bayonet. They fell together. Other Indians running up soon dispatched Hays, and it was not until then, that his bayonet was extracted from the body of his adversary.

"The wounded chief was carried after the battle to his village on the Calumet, where he survived for several days. Finding his end approaching, he called together his young men, and enjoined them in the most solemn manner, to regard the safety of their prisoners after his death, and to take the lives of none of them from respect to his memory, as he deserved his fate from the hands of those whose kindness he had so ill-requited."

WESTSIDE*

Franc B. Wilke

THE early humorous writing of Chicago authors often possessed a frontierlike quality; it was rough and salty. Read today, it reminds one of Americana oils and drawings executed just before and right after the Civil War, full of realistic, sly details and telling brush strokes of color.

Franc B. Wilke was a local journalist working for the *Times*. He was very popular in his day. His paper sent him to Europe in the late 1870's and his dispatches, gathered into a volume, were full of first-class reporting.

In this sketch, by adding detail upon detail, the author executes a vivid portrait of the West Side of his day. With his tongue deep in his cheek, he tells us a great deal about the district's topography, morals, and the social foibles of his fellow citizens.

ANY person who has ever traveled much, or who has studied physical geography, must have visited, or must have seen, a place known as Westside. It is one of the largest places of its size, and the most singular in respect to its singularity, in the world.

To get to Westside, the traveler provides himself with a waterproof suit of clothing, an umbrella, a life preserver, and a box of troches. He then enters an immense hole under ground which leads mainly westward in one direction, and eastward in another.

This subterranean entrance to Westside was constructed for a double purpose. One of these purposes was to prevent anybody who lives on Westside from leaving. The other was because there is a river which nobody can cross, owing to its exhalations. The subterranean entrance runs under this river.

* From *Walks about Chicago*, by F. B. Wilke. Chicago, Press of Church, Goodman & Donnelley, 1869.

Going through this hole is a work of immense difficulty and danger. The best way to get through in winter is to skate through. In summer, for a few days, in dog days, there is good boating. The innumerable cascades, cataracts, pitfalls, and the intense darkness make its navigation a work of great risk. Like the entrance to Rasselas' Happy Valley, it is constructed to keep people in, who are once in, and to discourage the coming in of those who are out.

Once in Westside the traveler finds himself on an enormous plain sparsely covered with houses. Westside extends from the river to a park somewhere on its limits to the westward. Just where this park is, nobody knows. The boundaries of Westside are as limitless and indefinite as the interval from the Gulf of Mexico to the present time.

The architecture of Westside is fine and peculiar. A residence with a marble front always has a butcher's shop on one side, and a beer saloon on the other. The people who live in Westside are as diversified as their architecture.

Westside has streetcars which are sometimes visible when a rain has laid the dust. One conductor on one of these streetcars washed his hands one spring. At least it was said he did. Nobody was ever able to tell when the time was, or which conductor it was that did it.

Whenever a man in Westside builds a house and puts up a fence in front of it, he immediately calls the space in front of his lot an avenue. Almost every Westsider lives on an avenue. Sometimes a Westside avenue is as much as two hundred or three hundred feet long.

Every other shop in Westside is owned by a butcher, who has always a bloody and half-skinned calf hanging up in his door for a cheerful sign. The thing is so agreeable to Westsiders, that on every pleasant afternoon, the ladies take their knitting work and go and sit in front of the butcher's shop.

Westside is the residence of a good many notable, strong-minded women. These strong-minded women all have virtuous and docile husbands, who are further characterized by their sweetness, and their retiring dispositions. Whenever a Westside woman gets to weigh 270 pounds, she immediately starts out in favor of

woman's rights. In this way, she is able to afford great weight
to the cause which she advocates.

Every woman in Westside once lived on The Avenue of a
place known as Southside. Whenever she goes downtown, she goes
to visit a friend on The Avenue. Whenever she has been downtown,
she has been to call on a friend who lives on The Avenue. A good
many ladies who live in Westside carry the idea, in the cars, that
they live in Southside, on The Avenue, and are only in Westside for
a visit. The uncle, aunt, cousin, grandmother, brother-in-law, step-
sister, half-uncle, and godfather of everybody in Westside lives
on The Avenue in Southside. No young lady in Westside will receive permanent attention from a young man unless he lives on The
Avenue in Southside. When a Westsider of the female persuasion
dies, her spirit immediately wings its way to the blissful and
ecstatic realms of The Avenue on Southside.

The railway companies in Westside never water their track.
They do their stock. The result, in both cases, is to throw dirt in the
eyes of the public.

There are no carriages in Westside. It is so dusty there, that a
vehicle which does not run on rails can never find its way from one
point to another. When it is not dusty it is muddy. The dust has no
top, and the mud no bottom. In either case, locomotion, except on
tracks, is impossible.

Westside has no newspapers. It likewise has no opera house
which is used as a circus. Its principal local amusements consist,
among the men, in chewing tobacco, and among the women, in
going to church. Whenever there is a corner in Westside not occupied as a drugstore, it is occupied by a church.

All the churches in Westside have something going on in
them every evening, and seven afternoons in every week, and four
times every Sunday. Whenever there is anything going on in any
church, they toll the bell for an hour and a quarter before it
commences, and at intervals during the performance. The result is,
that every man in Westside hears from one to eleven bells tolling
cheerfully three-fifths of his time.

A stranger in Westside would conclude that the whole town was
dead, or that ten or fifteen melancholy funerals were in progress

in every neighborhood. There is one church, on the corner of Washington Avenue and Robey Avenue, that has been tolling its bell without cessation for two years. When there isn't a prayer meeting, or somebody dead, they toll it for somebody who is going to die. They use up a sexton there every thirteen days. When there is no prayer meeting, or anything else, or anybody dead, or anybody who is going to die, then the bell tolls for the last deceased sexton.

Westside is immensely philanthropic. It has an asylum for inebriates from Southside, and other places. This asylum has often as many as from one to two inebriates who are undergoing treatment. The treatment consists in leaning against the fence, when tight, and in stepping over the way to a saloon and getting tight, when sober. The asylum is a very cheerful building, with enormous windows of four-by-six glass. Some of the rooms are fine and airy, and would answer for dog kennels if enlarged and properly ventilated.

There are a good many other peculiar things in Westside, which can be better understood by being seen than by being heard of. Anybody who dares to face the dangers and darkness of the hole in the ground by which one reaches Westside, will be well repaid for his visit.

HOW I STRUCK CHICAGO, AND
HOW CHICAGO STRUCK ME

OF RELIGION, POLITICS, AND PIG-STICKING, AND
THE INCARNATION OF THE CITY AMONG SHAMBLES*

Rudyard Kipling

NO ANTHOLOGY concerned with an American city
would be complete without an article in it written by a
wrathful visiting Englishman. Chicago sent Mr. Kipling's
blood pressure bounding upward to dangerous heights.
What did he expect to find here, we may well ask. The
quiet of an English hamlet? The staid dignity of Tavistock
Square?

Like many European visitors whose fame has just begun
to slip, Kipling looked at America with a jaundiced eye.
When he struck Chicago, his jaundice oozed out of his
pores like venom.

Upon his return to England, Kipling wrote a book
about his American journey. Unlike most writers, he wrote
at his best sometimes when he was gripped by a choleric
temper; and this piece of angry literature about Chicago
remains one of the best specimens of vitriolic portraits
extant of a city.

I know thy cunning and thy greed,
Thy hard high lust and willful deed,
And all thy glory loves to tell
Of spacious gifts material.

I HAVE struck a city—a real city—and they call it Chicago. The
other places do not count. San Francisco was a pleasure resort as

well as a city, and Salt Lake was a phenomenon. This place is the first American city I have encountered. It holds rather more than a million people with bodies, and stands on the same soil as Calcutta. Having seen it, I urgently desire never to see it again. It is inhabited by savages. Its water is the water of the Hughli, and its air is dirt. Also it says that it is the "boss" town of America.

I do not believe that it has anything to do with this country. They told me to go to the Palmer House which is a gilded and mirrored rabbit warren, and there I found a huge hall of tessellated marble, crammed with people talking about money and spitting about everywhere. Other barbarians charged in and out of this inferno with letters and telegrams in their hands, and yet others shouted at each other. A man who had drunk quite as much as was good for him told me that this was "the finest hotel in the finest city on God Almighty's earth." By the way, when an American wishes to indicate the next county or state he says, "God A'mighty's earth." This prevents discussion and flatters his vanity.

Then I went out into the streets, which are long and flat and without end. And verily it is not a good thing to live in our East for any length of time. Your ideas grow to clash with those held be every right-thinking white man. I looked down interminable vistas flanked with nine-, ten-, and fifteen-storied houses, and crowded with men and women, and the show impressed me with a great horror. Except in London—and I have forgotten what London is like—I had never seen so many white people together, and never such a collection of miserables. There was no color in the streets and no beauty—only a maze of wire ropes overhead and dirty stone flagging underfoot. A cabdriver volunteered to show me the glory of the town for so much an hour, and with him I wandered far. He conceived that all this turmoil and squash was a thing to be reverently admired; that it was good to huddle men together in fifteen layers, one atop of the other, and to dig holes in the ground for offices. He said that Chicago was a live town, and that all the creatures hurrying by me were engaged in business. That is to say, they were trying to make some money, that they might not die through lack of food to put into their bellies. He took me to canals, black as ink, and filled with untold abominations, and bade me watch the stream of traffic across the bridges. He then took me into a saloon, and, while I drank, made me note that the floor was covered with coins sunk into cement. A Hottentot would not have been guilty of this sort of barbarism. The coins made an effect pretty enough, but the man who put them there had no thought to beauty, and therefore he was a savage. Then my cab-driver showed me business blocks, gay with signs and studded with fantastic and absurd advertisements of goods, and looking down the long street so adorned it was as though each vendor stood at his door howling: "For the sake of money, employ, or buy of, *me* and me only!" Have you ever seen a crowd at our famine-relief distributions? You know then how men leap into the air, stretching out their arms above the crowd in the hope of being seen; while the women dolorously slap the stomachs of their children and whim-per. I had sooner watch famine relief than the white man engaged in what he calls legitimate competition. The one I understand. The other makes me ill. And the cab man said that these things were the proof of progress; and by that I knew he had been reading his newspaper, as every intelligent American should. The papers tell their readers in language fitted to their comprehension that the snarling together of telegraph wires, the heaving up of houses, and the making of money is progress.

I spent ten hours in that huge wilderness, wandering through scores of miles of these terrible streets, and jostling some few hun-dred thousand of these terrible people who talked money through their noses. The cabman left me: but after a while I picked up an-other man who was full of figures, and into my ears he poured them as occasion required or the big blank factories suggested. Here they turned out so many hundred thousand dollars' worth of such and such an article; there so many million other things; this house was worth so many million dollars; that one so many million more or less. It was like listening to a child babbling of its hoard of shells. It was like watching a fool playing with buttons. But I was expected to do more than listen or watch. He demanded that I should admire; and the utmost that I could say was: "Are these things so? Then I am very sorry for you." That made him angry, and he said that insular envy made me unresponsive. So you see I could not make him understand.

About four and a half hours after Adam was turned out of the Garden of Eden he felt hungry, and so, bidding Eve take care that her head was not broken by the descending fruit, shinned up a coconut palm. That hurt his legs, cut his breast, made him breathe heavily, and Eve was tormented with a fear lest her lord should miss his footing and so bring the tragedy of this world to an end ere the curtain had fairly risen. Had I met Adam then, I should have been sorry for him. Today I find eleven hundred thousand of his sons just as far advanced as their father in the art of getting food, and immeasurably inferior to him in that they think that their palm trees lead straight to the skies. Consequently I am sorry in rather more than a million different ways. In our East bread comes naturally even to the poorest by a little scratching or the gift of a friend not quite so poor. In less favored countries one is apt to forget. Then I went to bed. And that was on a Saturday night.

Sunday brought me the queerest experience of all—a revelation of barbarism complete. I found a place that was officially described as a church. It was a circus really, but that the worshipers did not know. There were flowers all about the building, which was fitted up with plush and stained oak and much luxury, including twisted brass candlesticks of severest Gothic design. To these things, and a congregation of savages, entered suddenly a wonderful man completely in the confidence of their God, whom he treated colloquially and exploited very much as a newspaper reporter would exploit a foreign potentate. But, unlike the newspaper reporter, he never allowed his listeners to forget that he and not He was the center of attraction. With a voice of silver and with imagery borrowed from the auction room, he built up for his hearers a heaven on the lines of the Palmer House (but with all the gilding real gold and all the plate-glass diamond) and set in the center of it a loud-voiced, argumentative, and very shrewd creation that he called God. One sentence at this point caught my delighted ear. It was apropos of some question of the Judgment Day and ran: "No! I tell you God don't do business that way." He was giving them a deity whom they could comprehend, in a gold and jewel heaven in which they could take a natural interest. He interlarded his performance with the slang of the streets, the counter, and the Exchange, and he said that religion ought to enter into daily life. Consequently I presume he introduced it *as* daily life—his own and the life of his friends.

Then I escaped before the blessing, desiring no benediction at such hands. But the persons who listened seemed to enjoy themselves, and I understand that I had met with a popular preacher. Later on, when I had perused the sermons of a gentleman called Talmage and some others, I perceived that I had been listening to a very mild specimen. Yet that man, with his brutal gold and silver idols, his hands-in-pocket, cigar-in-mouth, and hat-on-the-back-of-the-head style of dealing with the sacred vessels, would count himself spiritually quite competent to send a mission to convert the Indians. All that Sunday I listened to people who said that the mere fact of spiking down strips of iron to wood and getting a steam and iron thing to run along them was progress. That the telephone was progress, and the network of wires overhead was progress. They repeated their statements again and again. One of them took me to their city hall and board of trade works and pointed it out with pride. It was very ugly, but very big, and the streets in front of it were narrow and unclean. When I saw the face of the men who did business in that building I felt that there had been a mistake in their billeting.

By the way, 'tis a consolation to feel that I am not writing to an English audience. Then should I have to fall into feigned ecstasies over the marvelous progress of Chicago since the days of the great fire, to allude casually to the raising of the entire city so many feet above the level of the lake which it faces, and generally to grovel before the golden calf. But you, who are desperately poor, and therefore by these standards of no account, know things, and will understand when I write that they have managed to get a million of men together on flat land, and that the bulk of these men together appear to be lower than *mahajans* and not so companionable as a Punjabi *jat* after harvest. But I don't think it was the blind hurry of the people, their argot, and their grand ignorance of things beyond their immediate interests that displeased me so much as a study of the daily papers of Chicago. Imprimis, there was some sort of dispute between New York and Chicago as to which town should give an exhibition of products to be hereafter holden, and through the medium of their more dignified journals the two cities were ya-hooing and hi-yi-ing at each other like opposition newsboys. They called it humor, but it sounded like something quite different. That was only the first trouble. The second lay in the tone of the productions. Leading articles which include gems such as: "Back of such and such a place," or "We noticed, Tuesday, such an event," or "don't" for "does not" are things to be accepted with thankfulness. All that made me weep was that, in these papers, were faithfully reproduced all the war cries and "back talk" of the Palmer House bar, the slang of the barbers' shops, the mental elevation and integrity of the Pullman-car porter, the dignity of the Dime Museum, and the accuracy of the excited fishwife. I am sternly forbidden to believe that the paper educates the public. Then I am compelled to believe that the public educates the paper?

Just when the sense of unreality and oppression was strongest upon me, and when I most wanted help, a man sat at my side and began to talk what he called politics. I had chanced to pay about six shillings for a traveling cap worth eighteen pence, and he made of the fact a text for a sermon. He said that this was a rich country and that the people liked to pay two hundred per cent on the value of a thing. They could afford it. He said that the Government imposed a protective duty of from ten to seventy per cent on foreign-made articles, and that the American manufacturer consequently could sell his goods for a healthy sum. Thus an imported hat would, with duty, cost two guineas. The American manufacturer would make a hat for seventeen shillings and sell it for one pound fifteen. In these things, he said, lay the greatness of America and the effeteness of England. Competition between factory and factory kept the prices down to decent limits, but I was never to forget that this people were a rich people, not like the pauper Continentals, and that they enjoyed paying duties. To my weak intellect this seemed like juggling with counters. Everything that I have yet purchased costs about twice as much as it would in England, and when native-made is of inferior quality. Moreover, since these lines were first thought of I have visited a gentleman who owned a factory which used to produce things. He owned the factory still. Not a man was in it, but he was drawing a handsome income from a syndicate of firms for keeping it closed in order that it might not produce things. This man said that if protection were abandoned, a tide of pauper labor would flood the country, and as I looked at his factory I thought how entirely better it was to have no labor of any kind whatever, rather than face so horrible a future. Meantime, do you remember that this peculiar country enjoys paying money for value not received. I am an alien, and for the life of me cannot see why six shillings should be paid for eighteen-penny caps, or eight shillings for half-crown cigar cases. When the country fills up to a decently populated level a few million people who are not aliens will be smitten with the same sort of blindness.

But my friend's assertion somehow thoroughly suited the grotesque ferocity of Chicago. See now and judge! In the village of Isser Jang on the road to Montgomery there be four *changar* women who winnow corn—some seventy bushels a year. Beyond their hut lives Puran Dass, the moneylender, who on good security lends as much as five thousand rupees in a year. Jowala Singh, the *lohar,* mends the village plows—some thirty, broken at the share, in 365 days; and Hukm Chund, who is letterwriter and head of the little club under the travelers' tree, generally keeps the village posted in such gossip as the barber and the midwife have not yet made public property. Chicago husks and winnows her wheat by the million bushels, a hundred banks lend hundreds of millions of dollars in the year, and scores of factories turn out plow gear and machinery by steam. Scores of daily papers do work which Hukm Chund and the barber and the midwife perform, with due regard for public opinion, in the village of Isser Jang. So far as manufactures go, the difference between Chicago on the lake and Isser Jang on the Montgomery road is one of degree only, and not of kind. So far as the understanding of the uses of life goes Isser Jang, for all its seasonal cholera, has the advantage over Chicago.

Jowala Singh knows and takes care to avoid the three or four ghoul-haunted fields on the outskirts of the village; but he is not urged by millions of devils to run about all day in the sun and swear that his plowshares are the best in the Punjab; nor does Puran Dass fly forth in a cart more than once or twice a year, and he knows, on a pinch, how to use the railway and the telegraph as well as any son of Israel in Chicago. But this is absurd. The East is not the West, and these men must continue to deal with the machinery of life, and to call it progress. Their very preachers dare not rebuke them. They gloss over the hunting for money and the twice-sharpened bitterness of Adam's curse by saying that such things dower a man with a larger range of thoughts and higher aspirations. They do not say: "Free yourself from your own slavery," but rather, "If you can possibly manage it, do not set quite so much store on the things of this world." And they do not know what the things of this world are.

I went off to see cattle killed by way of clearing my head, which, as you will perceive, was getting muddled. They say every Englishman goes to the Chicago stockyards. You shall find them about six miles from the city; and once having seen them you will never forget the sight. As far as the eye can reach stretches a township of cattlepens, cunningly divided into blocks so that the animals of any pen can be speedily driven out close to an inclined timber path which leads to an elevated covered way straddling high above the pens. These viaducts are two stories. On the upper story tramp the doomed cattle, stolidly for the most part. On the lower, with a scuffling of sharp hoofs and multitudinous yells, run the pigs. The same end is appointed for both. Thus you will see the gangs of cattle waiting their turn—as they wait sometimes for days; and they need not be distressed by the sight of their fellows running about in fear of death. All they know is that a man on horseback causes their next-door neighbors to move by means of a whip. Certain bars and fences are unshipped, and, behold, that crowd have gone up the mouth of a sloping tunnel and return no more. It is different with the pigs. They shriek back the news of the exodus to their friends, and a hundred pens skirl responsive. It was to the pigs I first addressed myself. Selecting a viaduct which was full of them,

I could hear though I could not see, I marked a somber building whereto it ran, and went there, not unalarmed by stray cattle who had managed to escape from their proper quarters. A pleasant smell of brine warned me of what was coming. I entered the factory and found it full of pork in barrels, and on another story more pork unbarreled, and in a huge room the halves of swine, for whose use great lumps of ice were being pitched in at the window. That room was the mortuary chamber where the pigs lie for a little while in state ere they begin their progress through such passages as kings may sometimes travel. Turning a corner and not noting an overhead arrangement of greased rail, wheel, and pulley, I ran into the arms of four eviscerated carcasses, all pure white and of a human aspect, being pushed by a man clad in vehement red. When I leaped aside, the floor was slippery under me. There was a flavor of farmyard in my nostrils and the shouting of a multitude in my ears. But there was no joy in that shouting. Twelve men stood in two lines—six a side. Between them and overhead ran the railway of death that had nearly shunted me through the window. Each man carried a knife, the sleeves of his shirt were cut off at the elbows, and from bosom to heel he was blood-red. The atmosphere was stifling as a night in the Rains, by reason of the steam and the crowd. I climbed to the beginning of things and, perched upon a narrow beam, overlooked very nearly all the pigs ever bred in Wisconsin. They had just been shot out of the mouth of the viaduct and huddled together in a large pen. Then they were flicked persuasively, a few at a time, into a smaller chamber, and there a man fixed tackle on their hinder legs so that they rose in the air suspended from the railway of death. Oh! it was then they shrieked and called on their mothers and made promise of amendment, till the tackle-man punted them in their backs, and they slid head down into brick-floored passage, very like a big kitchen sink that was blood-red. There awaited them a red man with a knife which he passed jauntily through their throats, and the full-voiced shriek became a sputter, and then a fall as of heavily tropical rain. The red man who was backed up against the passage wall stood clear of the wildly kicking hoofs and passed his hand over his eyes, not from any feeling of compassion, but because the spurted blood was in his eyes, and he had barely time to stick the next arrival. Then that first stuck swine dropped, still kicking, into a great vat of boiling water, and spoke no more words, but wallowed in obedience to some unseen machinery, and presently came forth at the lower end of the vat and was heaved on the blades of a blunt paddle-wheel-thing which said, "Hough! Hough! Hough!" and skelped all the hair off him except what little a couple of men with knives could remove. Then he was again hitched by the heels to that said railway and passed down the line of the twelve men—each man with a knife—leaving with each man a certain amount of his individuality which was taken away in a wheelbarrow, and when he reached the last man he was very beautiful to behold, but immensely unstuffed and limp. Preponderance of individuality was ever a bar to foreign travel. That pig could have been in no case to visit you in India had he not parted with some of his most cherished notions.

The dissecting part impressed me not so much as the slaying. They were so excessively alive, these pigs. And then they were so excessively dead, and the man in the dripping, clammy, hot passage did not seem to care, and ere the blood of such an one had ceased to foam on the floor, such another, and four friends with him, had shrieked and died. But a pig is only the Unclean animal—forbidden by the Prophet.

I was destined to make rather a queer discovery when I went over to the cattle slaughter. All the buildings were on a much larger scale, and there was no sound of trouble, but I could smell the salt reek of blood before I set foot in the place. The cattle did not come directly through the viaduct as the pigs had done. They debouched into a yard by the hundred, and they were big red brutes carrying much flesh. In the center of that yard stood a red Texan steer with a head-stall on his wicked head. No man controlled him. He was, so to speak, picking his teeth and whistling in an open byre of his own when the cattle arrived. As soon as the first one had fearfully quitted the viaduct, this red devil put his hands in his pockets and slouched across the yard, no man guiding him. Then he lowed something to the effect that he was the regularly appointed guide of the establishment and would show them round. They were country folk, but they knew how to behave; and so followed Judas some hundred strong, patiently, and with a look of bland wonder in their faces. I saw his broad back jogging in advance of them, up a lime-washed incline where I was forbidden to follow. Then a door shut, and in a minute back came Judas with the air of a virtuous plough-bullock and took up his place in his byre. Somebody laughed across the yard, but I heard no sound of cattle from the big brick building into which the mob had disappeared. Only Judas chewed the cud with a malignant satisfaction, and so I knew there was trouble, and ran round to the front of the factory and so entered and stood aghast.

Who takes count of the prejudices which we absorb through the skin by way of our surroundings? It was not the spectacle that impressed me. The first thought that almost spoke itself aloud was: "They are killing kine"; and it was a shock. The pigs were nobody's concern, but cattle—the brothers of the Cow, the Sacred Cow—were quite otherwise. The next time an M.P. tells me that India either Sultanizes or Brahminizes a man, I shall believe about half what he says. It is unpleasant to watch the slaughter of cattle when one has laughed at the notion for a few years. I could not see actually what was done in the first instance, because the row of stalls in which they lay was separated from me by fifty impassable feet of butchers and slung carcasses. All I know is that men swung open the doors of a stall as occasion required, and there lay two steers already stunned, and breathing heavily. These two they pole-axed, and half raising them by tackle they cut their throats. Two men skinned each carcass, somebody cut off the head, and in half a minute more the overhead rail carried two sides of beef to their appointed place. There was clamor enough in the operating room, but from the waiting cattle, invisible on the other side of the line of pens, never a sound. They went to their death, trusting Judas, without a word. They were slain at the rate of five a minute, and if the pig men were spattered with blood, the cow butchers were bathed in it. The blood ran in muttering gutters. There was no place for hand or foot that was not coated with thicknesses of dried blood, and the stench of it in the nostrils bred fear.

And then the same merciful Providence that has showered good things on my path throughout sent me an embodiment of the City of Chicago, so that I might remember it for ever. Women come sometimes to see the slaughter, as they would come to see the slaughter of men. And there entered that vermilion hall a young woman of large mold, with brilliantly scarlet lips, and heavy eyebrows, and dark hair that came in a "widow's peak" on the forehead. She was well and healthy and alive, and she was dressed in flaming red and black, and her feet (know you that the feet of American women are like unto the feet of fairies?)—her feet, I say, were cased in red leather shoes. She stood in a patch of sunlight, the red blood under her shoes, the vivid carcasses tacked round her, a bullock bleeding its life away not six feet away from her, and the death factory roaring all round her. She looked curiously, with hard, bold eyes, and was not ashamed.

Then said I: "This is a special Sending. I have seen the City of Chicago!" And I went away to get peace and rest.

CHICAGO*

Carl Sandburg

Hog Butcher for the World,
Tool Maker, Stacker of Wheat,
Player with Railroads and the Nation's Freight Handler;
Stormy, husky, brawling,
City of the Big Shoulders:

They tell me you are wicked, and I believe them; for I have seen
    your painted women under the gas lamps luring the farm boys.
And they tell me you are crooked, and I answer: Yes, it is true
    I have seen the gunman kill and go free to kill again.
And they tell me you are brutal, and my reply is: On the faces of
    women and children I have seen the marks of wanton hunger.
And having answered so I turn once more to those who sneer at
    this my city, and I give them back the sneer and say to them:
Come and show me another city with lifted head singing so proud
    to be alive and coarse and strong and cunning.
Flinging magnetic curses amid the toil of piling job on job, here is
    a tall bold slugger set vivid against the little soft cities;
Fierce as a dog with tongue lapping for action, cunning as a savage
    pitted against the wilderness,
                Bareheaded,
                Shoveling,
                Wrecking,
                Planning,
                Building, breaking, rebuilding,
Under the smoke, dust all over his mouth, laughing with white
    teeth,

* From *Chicago Poems.*

Under the terrible burden of destiny laughing as a young man
laughs,
Laughing even as an ignorant fighter laughs who has never lost a
battle,
Bragging and laughing that under his wrist is the pulse, and under
his ribs the heart of the people,
Laughing!
Laughing the stormy, husky, brawling laughter of Youth, half-
naked, sweating, proud to be Hog Butcher, Tool Maker, Stacker
of Wheat, Player with Railroads and Freight Handler to the
Nation.